Theory of
structure and mechanics
of fibrous assemblies

Theory of structure and mechanics of fibrous assemblies

Bohuslav Neckář
and
Dipayan Das

WOODHEAD PUBLISHING INDIA PVT LTD
New Delhi ● Cambridge ● Oxford ● Philadelphia

Published by Woodhead Publishing India Pvt. Ltd.
Woodhead Publishing India Pvt. Ltd., G-2, Vardaan House, 7/28, Ansari Road
Daryaganj, New Delhi – 110002, India
www.woodheadpublishingindia.com

Woodhead Publishing Limited, 80 High Street, Sawston, Cambridge,
CB22 3HJ UK

Woodhead Publishing USA 1518 Walnut Street, Suite1100, Philadelphia

www.woodheadpublishing.com

First published 2012, Woodhead Publishing India Pvt. Ltd.
© Woodhead Publishing India Pvt. Ltd., 2012

Woodhead Publishing India Pvt. Ltd. ISBN: 978-81-90800-17-4
Woodhead Publishing Ltd. U.K. ISBN: 978-1-84569-791-4

Typeset by Sunshine Graphics, New Delhi
Printed and bound by Replika Press Pvt. Ltd.

Preface

"The imagination is more important than the knowledge."

—*Albert Einstein*

It is known that the textile fibrous assembly has accompanied human civilization since its inception. It is claimed by the archeological discoveries in the Czech Republic that textiles were existing before the 27th century BC[1]. It is obvious that during this extremely long period, people have gained a wide range of empirical knowledge and experience about the manufacturing of textile materials and their behaviors.

One can say that along this extremely long period, empiricism has been the main and might be the only source of development of textile materials and manufacturing technologies. In fact, during the industrial revolution in the 19th century the handwork was replaced by the machines, but textiles – material, structure, and end-use characteristics – have not been changed significantly. The other engineering branches began to develop exact concepts on the basis of knowledge of natural science, but the textile fibrous assemblies did not deeply follow this way of thinking as it was found to be very difficult at that time. (Before 100 years ago, Marschik, in one of his earlier work, tried to establish a mathematical model for yarn and fabric and wrote "….theoretical investigation and clarifying of phenomenon occur during spinning and weaving processes and determinations of end product properties are almost impossible"[2]). Firstly, during the second half of the 20th century, the textile researchers applied exact methods such as mathematical modeling of textile fibrous assemblies. Gradually, it was recognized that the routine application of results gained from the other technical branches would not be a too much successful way; namely, textiles have their specific structure, which is manifested in a unique way.

---

1. Adovasio, J. M., Hyland, D. C., and Soffer, O. (1997). Textiles and Cordage: A Preliminary Assessment, In: Svoboda, J. (ed.), Pavlov I – Northwest. The Dolní Vì stonice Studies, Volume 4, Brno, pp. 403–424.
2. "…eine rechnungsmßige Verfolgung oder Erklärung der Vorgänge beim Spinen und Weben sowohl, als auch der Eigenschaften der Endprodukte fast unmöglich ist. " Marschik, S., Physicalish-technische Untersuchungen von Gespinsten und Geweben, Wien, 1904 (German).

(Therefore, the textile fibrous assemblies are used also as specific technical materials). To understand the structure of textile fibrous assemblies, it needs specific methods such as mathematical modeling. At the present time, it appears that the exact knowledge about textile structure is widely spreaded, thanks to the computer application and computer-aided design.

A lot of textbooks have dealt with the methods of manufacturing of textile materials, but there are only a few books available on the exact formulation of the internal structure of textile materials and the mathematical modeling on the behavior of textiles. The main aim of this book is to introduce the theory of structure and mechanics of fibrous assemblies in order to partially fulfill the shortage of literature in this field. It includes mainly the original results of the theoretical researches carried out on the structure and mechanics of fibrous assemblies. We hope that this book will be used as a textbook in universities and as a special study material for scientific researchers. Each topic is therefore started with very basic and simple discussions and gradually continued to the more sophisticated formulations for specialists only. We have tried to keep the continuity of logical way of thinking in deriving the relationships needed for explanation without any discontinuation. The derivation of the mathematical expressions is provided relatively in a detailed manner so that the reader, who has less experience in formulation and manipulation of mathematical expressions, can easily follow the text. (The authors do not like the idiom "The reader can himself easily derive....," the so-called "easy derivation" may represent a work of one month!). This results in relatively large number of equations which may cause a "repulsive" view. The dimensionless equations are valid in any coherent unit system (for example, international SI system). To keep the logical continuity of the text, some special mathematical formulations are given separately in appendices.

This book should be useful for the university students as well as the experienced researches. A few topics mentioned in this book can be used for teaching of the undergraduate and postgraduate students and the other special and sophisticated topics can be studied by the doctoral students and the scientific researchers. We would like to remind our dear readers that any topic of this book cannot be automatically studied and mechanically processed. The topics of this book should be understood as a "road map" only, which would guide us to create our own ideas and own understanding of the structure and mechanics of fibrous assemblies using our own mind. We hope that this book will prove to be very useful by the readers.

We gratefully acknowledge the support received from the Grant Agency of Czech Republic GAÈR under project number 106/09/1916 for carrying out some of the research themes reported in this book and processing of the manuscript of this book. We are also thankful to our universities Technical University of Liberec and Indian Institute of Technology Delhi for supporting our research work.

Bohuslav Neckáø
Dipayan Das

Contents

Introduction to fibers and fibrous assemblies

A fiber is a coherent and slender entity with sufficiently high "length-to-diameter" ratio, often known as aspect ratio or slenderness ratio. The high aspect ratio is intrinsically associated with high specific surface area (ratio of surface area to mass). The high aspect ratio and the associated high specific surface area impart a unique advantage to the fibers over other materials in many critical applications.

The fibers are generally procured in the form of large ensembles such as bales, tows, etc. They are mechanically processed and arranged to create fibrous assemblies of the first hierarchical level such as sliver, roving, yarn, nonwoven, etc. and, when necessary, followed by more complex hierarchical levels such as woven fabric, knitted fabric, braided fabric, etc. The fibrous assemblies of the first hierarchical level are called as simple or "primary" fibrous assemblies; they are produced directly from fibers. The fibrous assemblies of the second hierarchical level are known as composed or "secondary" fibrous assemblies; they are produced from "primary" fibrous assemblies. Sometimes, from geometrical point of view, the fibrous assemblies are divided into three categories: one-dimensional or linear fibrous assembly, two-dimensional or planar fibrous assembly and three-dimensional or spatial fibrous assembly.

This book is dealt with the fibrous assemblies of the first hierarchical level, otherwise known as simple or primary fibrous assemblies. Each simple or primary fibrous assembly has its own specific characteristics as mentioned below.

(1) *Constituents of fibrous assembly*. The simple or primary fibrous assembly consists of fibers, and the fibers are either of same type or of different types.
(2) *Geometrical arrangement of fibers*. The geometrical arrangement of fibers in the simple or primary fibrous assembly is characterized by
   (a) Packing arrangement of fibers, i.e., how the fibers are packed inside the fibrous assembly
   (b) Directional arrangement of fibers, i.e., how the fibers are oriented in the fibrous assembly

(3) *Mutual interaction of fibers*. The mutual interaction among fibers in
     the simple or primary fibrous assembly is characterized by
     (a)   Type of interaction, i.e., the type of force (mechanical, thermal,
           chemical, etc.) exerted onto the fibers to realize fiber-to-fiber
           contacts.
     (b)   Characteristics of fiber-to-fiber contacts, i.e., number of fiber-
           to-fiber contacts and distance between neighboring contacts.

Basic properties of single fibers and fibrous assemblies

The basic structural element of the fibrous assemblies considered here is fiber. It is sufficiently long and thin. It is characterized by many properties such as length, fineness, diameter, aspect ratio, cross-sectional shape, surface area, specific surface area, strength, breaking elongation, etc. Numerous fibers constitute the fibrous assembly. Like fibers, the fibrous assembly is also characterized by its properties such as total length of fibers in the assembly, total surface area occupied by fibers in the assembly, etc. In this chapter, the basic characteristics of individual fibers are described and their relations to those of the fibrous assembly are derived. The fibrous assembly is considered to be made up of homogeneous or heterogeneous fibers.

1.1   Fiber characteristics: definitions and relations

Starting parameters. Figure 1.1 illustrates a fiber of length l, mass m_f, volume V_f, and surface area A_f. Let us assume a homogenous fibrous assembly contains N number of such identical fibers. If L, m, V, A represent length, mass, volume, and surface area of all fibers in the assembly, respectively; then we can write

$$L = N\,l, \ m = N\,m_f, \ V = N\,V_f, \ A = N\,A_f. \dots (1.1)$$

Fiber density (ρ). Using Eq. (1.1), the fiber density can be expressed as follows

$$\rho = m_f / V_f = m/V. \qquad \dots (1.2)$$

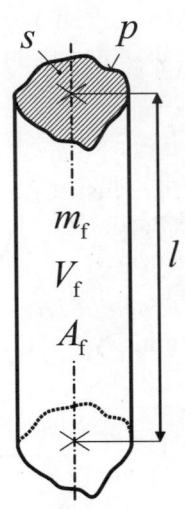

1.1 Scheme of a fiber.

Table 1.1 shows the density values of some commonly used fibers.

Table 1.1 Fiber density values (according to Goswami et al. [1]).

Fiber	ρ[kgm^3]
Cotton	1520
Linen, jute	1520
Wool	1310
Natural silk	1340
Viscose	1500
Acetate	1320
Polyester	1360
Polyamide	1140
Polyacrylonitrile	1300
Polypropylene	910

Fiber fineness (*t*). In practice, it is often necessary to specify the fineness characteristic of fibers. The fiber fineness is usually defined by fiber mass per unit length; in other words, it is called "linear density," or "titre." Using Eq. (1.1), the fiber fineness can be expressed as follows

$$t = \frac{m_{\mathrm{f}}}{l} = \frac{m}{L}. \qquad \qquad \dots (1.3)$$

According to the international standard unit system ("SI" system), the dimension for mass is [kg] and for length is [m]. Accordingly, the dimension for fiber fineness expressed by Eq. (1.3) is [kg m^{-1}] ≡ [Mtex]"megatex" (1Mtex = 10^{6}tex), which is an impractical unit to express fiber fineness. In practice, the dimensions "tex," [tex] = [g/km], or "decitex", [dtex] = [g/10 km] are used as shown below

$$t_{[\mathrm{tex}]} = m_{[\mathrm{g}]} / L_{[\mathrm{km}]} = m_{[\mathrm{mg}]} / L_{[\mathrm{m}]} \,, \qquad t_{[\mathrm{dtex}]} = 10\, m_{[\mathrm{g}]} / L_{[\mathrm{km}]} = 10\, m_{[\mathrm{mg}]} / L_{[\mathrm{m}]} \,.$$

In industry, fibers such as cotton, wool, manufactured, and micro fibers are used. The fiber fineness values of some commonly used fibers are given in Table 1.2.

Example 1.1: Consider a cotton fiber of 1.7 dtex fineness and 28 mm length. By Eq. (1.3), the fiber mass is obtained as m_f = 0.00476 mg, that

Table 1.2 Fineness of different types of fibers

Fibers	Fineness
Micro-fibers	< 1 dtex
Cotton and compatible manufactured fibers	about 1.6 dtex
Wool and compatible manufactured fibers	about 3.5 dtex
Carpet fibers, industrial fibers	> 7 dtex

is, 1 kg of this fiber has a total length $L = 5852$ km. A normal shirt of 200 g contains a total fiber length $L = 1176$ km.

The fineness of cotton fibers is usually determined by "air flow" method. Using the well-known micronaire instrument, the rate of airflow through a porous plug of cotton fibers is measured. The measurements from this instrument are designated as micronaire values t_{mic} in the unit of microgram per inch. The fineness of cotton fibers typically ranges from 3 micronaire to 5 micronaire (fine to coarse). The system in which the fineness of fibers is expressed in terms of mass for a specified unit of length is called direct system. The most commonly used unit for fiber fineness in direct system is "denier," where the mass is measured in gram and the specified length is 9000 m. Thus, $t_{[tex]} = 0.111 t_{[den]}$.

Notes: Wool is the only fiber whose fineness, in practice, is specified by its diameter in the unit of micrometer as shown in Table 1.3.

By applying Eqs. (1.2) and (1.3), we get

$$t = \frac{V_f}{l}\rho = \frac{V}{L}\rho, \quad V_f = \frac{tl}{\rho}, \quad V = \frac{tL}{\rho}, \quad \frac{V_f}{l} = \frac{V}{L} = \frac{t}{\rho}. \qquad \dots (1.4)$$

Example 1.2: We consider a cotton fiber of 1.7 dtex fineness, 28 mm length and 1520 kgm^{-3} density. By applying Eq. (1.4), we find the value of fiber volume is $V_f = 0.00313$ mm^3.

Equation (1.4) points out a limitation for the use of t as a measure of fiber fineness. In the fiber-based product industry, we think about "fineness" in terms of fiber geometry, particularly "area of cross-section" or "diameter." As such, the use of fiber volume per unit length (the ratio V_f/l or V/L) would be more logical to express the fineness of fibers. In contrast, the standard value of fiber fineness t must be divided by the value of fiber density ρ in order to obtain the value of fiber volume per unit length. Otherwise, if we compare the values of fineness t of two fibers having different densities, we may find that the "heavier" fiber (higher value of ρ) is thinner than the "lighter" one (smaller value of ρ).

Example 1.3: Consider the case where viscose fibers of 1.7 dtex fineness in a product are substituted by polypropylene fibers of the same fineness (1.7 dtex). By applying the values of fiber density as mentioned in Table 1.1 into Eq. (1.4), we find that $V/L = 0.000113$ mm^2 for viscose fibers and $V/L = 0.000187$ mm^2 for polypropylene fibers. We realize that polypropylene fibers have 65% higher volume than that of viscose fibers. To obtain $V/L = 0.000113$ mm^2 for polypropylene fibers, the fineness of polypropylene fibers, according to Eq. (1.4), would have been $t = 1.03$ dtex.

It is thus more logical to use the value V/L to express fiber fineness than the value t. However, in industrial practice, the latter is preferred to the former, because the laboratory methods for measurement of t are easier than those for measurement of V/L.

Fiber cross-sectional area (s). The shaded area shown in Fig. 1.1 represents fiber cross-sectional area, which is formed by intersecting a plane perpendicular to the axis of the fiber. Assuming that fiber cross-sectional area s is constant throughout its length (or generally speaking we consider the expression s as the mean fiber cross-sectional area), the volume of individual fibers is expressed as $V_f = sl$, and the volume of all fibers in the fibrous assembly is expressed by $V = sL$. By substituting this expression into Eq. (1.4), we get the expression for fiber cross-sectional area as follows

$$t = s\rho, \quad s = \frac{V_f}{l} = \frac{V}{L} = \frac{t}{\rho}. \qquad \ldots (1.5)$$

The expression for fiber cross-sectional area is identical to the expression for fiber volume per unit length. Hence we realize that fiber cross-sectional area is an important measure of fiber geometry, i.e., the "size" of a fiber.

Example 1.4: We consider a wool fiber of 3.5 dtex fineness and 1310 kg m^{-3} density (found from Table 1.1). According to Eq. (1.5), we find the cross-sectional area of wool fiber is $s = 0.0002672$ mm^2.

Equivalent fiber diameter (d). Let us consider a cylindrical fiber as shown in Fig. 1.2a. The fiber cross-sectional shape is circular and the fiber cross-sectional area is given by $s = \pi d^2/4$, where d is fiber diameter. By applying Eq. (1.5), we find the following expression for fiber diameter

$$d = \sqrt{\frac{4s}{\pi}} = \sqrt{\frac{4t}{\pi\rho}}, \quad t = \frac{\pi d^2}{4}\rho. \ \ldots (1.6)$$

Let us now consider a fiber with non-circular cross-sectional shape, such a fiber is presented in a classical geometrical way without any defined diameter (Fig. 1.2b). The variable d calculated from Eq. (1.6) expresses the diameter of an equivalent circular cross-sectional area, which is shown also in Fig. 1.2b, and this diameter is known as equivalent fiber diameter. The correct value of fiber cross-sectional area can be calculated without considering the

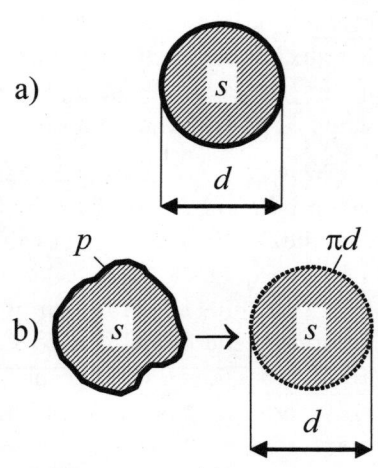

1.2 Fiber cross-section.

real shape of the fiber. The area of a circular cross-section is

$$s = \frac{\pi d^2}{4}.$$ ... (1.7)

By applying Eqs. (1.5) and (1.7), the fiber volume is expressed as follows

$$V_f = sl = \frac{\pi d^2}{4} l.$$ ... (1.8)

Analogously, the volume of a fibrous assembly is given by

$$V = sL = \frac{\pi d^2}{4} L.$$ ... (1.9)

Example 1.5: Referring to the values of fiber density given in Table 1.1 and by applying Eq. (1.6), we calculate the diameter of a polyester micro-fiber of 0.7 dtex fineness is $d = 0.0081$ mm, the diameter of a cotton fiber of 1.7 dtex fineness is $d = 0.0119$ mm, the diameter of a wool fiber of 3.5 dtex fineness is $d = 0.0184$ mm, and the diameter of a polyester fiber of 7 dtex fineness is $d = 0.0256$ mm. Generally, the diameter of textile fibers ranges from 0.005 mm to 0.035 mm.

The fineness of wool fibers is often expressed by the so-called Bradford fiber fineness scale (for example 60's, 80's, etc.). Hladík [2] reported the Bradford fiber fineness values and the corresponding equivalent fiber diameter values and these are shown in Table 1.3. The relationship between the Bradford fiber fineness value B_{Brad}[1] and the equivalent fiber diameter d is obtained from Table 1.3, and is expressed by

Table 1.3 Bradford fiber fineness scale

B_{Brad}	Equivalent diameter d [µm]		
	Average value	Minimum value	Maximum value
80's	18.8	–	19.25
70's	19.7	19.25	20.20
64's	20.7	20.20	22.00
60's	23.3	22.00	24.12
58's	24.9	24.12	25.65
56's	26.4	25.65	28.45
50's	30.5	28.45	31.55
48's	32.6	31.55	33.30
46's	34.0	33.30	35.10
44's	36.2	35.10	37.45
40's	38.7	37.45	39.20
36's	39.7	39.20	–

1. The numerical count grade implies that a yarn can be spun using the indicated grade fiber and has a weight of 453.69 (one pound) for a length of 512m (560 yd) times the numerical count.

$$d_{[\mu m]} = \frac{\left(18.8 - \dfrac{1.544u}{1-e^u}\right)\left(39.86 - \dfrac{0.722v}{1-e^{-v}}\right)}{69.66 - 0.772 B_{Brad}},$$

$$u = \left(B_{Brad} - 65.88\right)/2, \quad v = B_{Brad} - 38.6.$$

After calculating the value of d, Eq. (1.6) can be used to estimate fiber fineness.

Fiber aspect ratio (Λ). The fiber length and fiber diameter are frequently used to characterize the geometry of the fibers. It is then reasonable to introduce the expression of fiber aspect ratio, which is defined by the ratio of fiber length l and fiber diameter d as shown below

$$\Lambda = l/d. \qquad \qquad \text{... (1.10)}$$

Typical values of fiber aspect ratio are given in Table 1.4.

Table 1.4 Fiber aspect ratio

Fiber	Aspect ratio (Λ)
Cotton	1500
Wool	3000
Flax	1250
Ramie	3000

The values of aspect ratio of fibers are in the order of thousands. We introduce one interesting example here in connection with fiber aspect ratio. If we enlarge our model of fiber, we may get a pipe of 1 cm diameter (such a pipe is used for supplying gas in chemical laboratories), and if we consider the aspect ratio of that pipe same as that of a fiber for example, $\Lambda = 2000$, then the length of that pipe is about 20 m. We may recognize from this example that the application of mechanical force at one end of a fiber may not affect the other end.

Perimeter (p) *and shape factor* (q) *of fiber cross-section.* The real perimeter p encloses the real cross-section of a fiber as shown in Fig. 1.2b. The perimeter of an imaginary equivalent circle of sectional area s is πd. It is well known from geometry that a circle is the shortest possible curve enclosing a given area, therefore, $p \geq \pi d$. Then $p/(\pi d) \geq 1$, and

$$q = \frac{p}{\pi d} - 1 \geq 0, \quad p = \pi d(1+q). \qquad \qquad \text{... (1.11)}$$

The values of q, given by Malinowska [3], depend on fiber cross-sectional shape, in other words, on shape factor ($q = 0$ for cylindrical fibers only). The value of shape factor q becomes higher when the shape of fiber cross-section is irregular, i.e., far away from circular shape. Some typical shape factor values are given in Table 1.5. Note that Morton and Hearle [4] used another definition of shape factor and the fiber with circular cross-section showed the shape factor of zero.

Table 1.5 Cross-sectional shape and shape factor

Shape of fiber cross-section	q [1]
Circle – ideal (O)	0
Circle – real fiber	0 to 0.07
Triangle – ideal (△)	0.29
Triangle – real fiber	0.09 to 0.12
Mature cotton	0.20 to 0.35
Irregular saw	> 0.60

A lot of useful information can be obtained by enlarging the images of fiber cross-section using microscopy technique. Nowadays computers are used for evaluation of fiber perimeter and fiber cross-section (image processing technique). By applying the value q from Table 1.5 into Eq. (1.11), the perimeter p of fiber cross-section can be calculated.

Fiber specific surface area (a). The fiber surface area is expressed by $A_f = pl$ (Figure 1.1). The exact fiber surface area should include the areas of cross-sections of the two ends. Usually, these areas are negligibly small as compared to that of the cylindrical surface, and are ignored; the resulting error is negligibly small. Thus, by rearranging Eq. (1.11), we find the following expression for fiber surface area

$$A_f = pl = \pi d(1+q)l. \qquad \qquad ...(1.12)$$

Analogously, by using Eqs. (1.11) and (1.12), the surface area of fibers in a fibrous assembly A can be expressed as follows

$$A = NA_f = \pi d(1+q)Nl = \pi d(1+q)L. \qquad ...(1.13)$$

According to the definition of fiber density expressed in Eq. (1.2) and by applying Eq. (1.8) or (1.9), we get the following expressions for mass of a single fiber and also for a fibrous assembly

$$m_f = V_f \rho = \left(\pi d^2/4\right)l\rho. \qquad \qquad ...(1.14)$$

$$m = V\rho = \left(\pi d^2/4\right)L\rho. \qquad \qquad ...(1.15)$$

Fiber specific surface area is expressed by surface area per unit mass of fiber. By applying Eqs. (1.12) and (1.14) or (1.13) and (1.15), we get the following expression for fiber specific surface area

$$a = \frac{A_f}{m_f} = \frac{A}{m} = \frac{\pi d(1+q)l}{(\pi d^2/4)l\rho} = \frac{\pi d(1+q)L}{(\pi d^2/4)L\rho} = \frac{4(1+q)}{\rho d}. \qquad \dots (1.16)$$

An alternative expression for a is obtained by substituting Eq. (1.16) into Eq. (1.16) as follows

$$a = \frac{4(1+q)}{\rho}\sqrt{\frac{\pi\rho}{4t}} = 2\sqrt{\pi}\frac{1+q}{\sqrt{\rho t}}. \qquad \dots (1.17)$$

The fiber surface characteristics strongly affect the end-use properties (sorption, hand, etc.) of fibrous assemblies, which are very important from the consumer point of view. In particular, they strongly influence the physiological and comfort properties of apparel.

Example 1.6: An ordinary shirt is produced from cotton fibers of 1.5 dtex fineness, shape factor of 0.28 and fiber density of 1520 kgm^{-3}. We calculate the fiber specific surface area $a = 300.5$ m^{2}kg^{-1} from Eq. (1.17). The weight of such a cotton shirt is about 0.2 kg and the total surface area of the fibers in the shirt is 60.1 m^2.

The dimension of fiber specific surface area derived from Eq. (1.16) or eventually from Eq. (1.17) is m^{2}kg^{-1} and its magnitude, typically, is in the range of a few hundreds. But, the value of fiber specific surface area measured by the B.E.T. method (surface adsorption of gas molecules) is found to be substantially higher than that calculated on the basis of Eqs. (1.16) and (1.17)[2]. The principle of B.E.T. method is based on the absorption of gas molecules by the fiber surface, which may pass through "micro cracks" and "micro voids" of the fiber surface, whereas the specific surface area calculated from Eqs. (1.16) and (1.17) considers only the shape factor of fiber cross-section obtained from microscopy.

Fiber surface area per unit volume (γ). The ratio between fiber surface area and fiber volume is a useful measure to characterize the geometrical structure of fibers. This is expressed by $\gamma = A_f / V_f = A/V$. By applying Eqs. (1.12) and (1.8), or (1.13) and (1.9), we get the following expression for fiber surface area per unit volume

$$\gamma = \frac{A_f}{V_f} = \frac{A}{V} = \frac{\pi d(1+q)l}{(\pi d^2/4)l} = \frac{\pi d(1+q)L}{(\pi d^2/4)L} = \frac{4(1+q)}{d}. \qquad \dots (1.18)$$

By substituting Eq. (1.6) into Eq. (1.18), we get an alternative expression for γ as shown below

$$\gamma = 4(1+q)\sqrt{\frac{\pi\rho}{4t}} = 2\sqrt{\pi}(1+q)\sqrt{\frac{\rho}{t}}. \qquad \dots (1.19)$$

---

2.   For example, on the basis of B.E.T. method, the specific surface area of bleached cotton fiber ranges from 6000 m^{2}kg^{-1} to 8000 m^{2}kg^{-1}.

By rearranging Eqs. (1.16) and (1.18), we can also find that

$$\gamma = a\rho. \qquad \qquad \dots (1.20)$$

Example 1.7: Let us refer the previous example, where cotton fibers are of 1.5 dtex fineness, shape factor of 0.28, and density of 1520 kg m^{-3}. By applying Eq. (1.19), we find the fiber surface area per unit volume is $\gamma = 456.8$ mm^{-1}.

The fiber surface area per unit volume γ is a general geometrical variable and does not depend on fiber density and is more useful than the fiber specific surface area a.

According to Eq. (1.18), the inverse of fiber surface area per unit volume is directly proportional to the equivalent fiber diameter. The value $1/\gamma$ has the dimension of fiber length and to some extent, it is a measure of fiber "thickness." Later we show that this is a very useful variable for calculating the size of pores among fibers.

Notes: Sometimes it is very useful to write the expressions describing an object or a process without any dimension. Here we introduce a useful new dimensionless variable $A_f^{3/2}/V_f$. According to Eqs. (1.12), (1.8), and (1.10), it is true that $A_f^{3/2}/V_f = \left[\pi d(1+q)l \right]^{3/2} / \left[\left(\pi d^2/4 \right)l \right] = \pi^{1/2}(1+q)^{3/2}(l/d)^{1/2} = \pi^{1/2}(1+q)^{3/2}\Lambda^{1/2}$. While this expression does not provide any new information, it is another useful dimensionless expression of the two variables q and Λ.

Tensile stress (σ). In engineering physics, the ratio of the applied force F and the cross-sectional area defines mechanical (or engineering) stress σ^* (In SI system, it is measured in 1 Nm^{-2} = 1 Pa units). In fiber/textile technology, traditionally the term stress is used to denote specific stress σ; it is expressed by the ratio of the applied force and the linear density of fiber (or yarn) (In SI system, its unit is 1 NMtex^{-1}). By using Eq. (1.5) the relationship between the two is expressed as follows

$$\sigma = \frac{F}{t} = \frac{F}{s\rho} = \frac{\sigma^*}{\rho}. \qquad \qquad \dots (1.21)$$

The value of stress at which the fiber (or yarn) breaks is called tenacity.

Earlier, the so-called "breaking length" $L = R$ was defined by the length required to break the fiber under its own weight. According to Eq. (1.3), the mass of a fiber of length R is Rt. By using the acceleration due to gravity $g = 9.81$ m s^{-2}, the weight (gravitation force) is $F = Rtg$. According to Eq. (1.21), it is valid that $\sigma = F/t = Rg$, where $\sigma_{[cN\,tex^{-1}]} = 0.981\,R_{[km]}$. Thus, the tenacity in cNtex^{-1} is approximately equal to the breaking length in kilometers. Also, the unit of force F was earlier expressed by the so-called "pond" [p], which was known as "gram force." It is valid that $F_{[\mathrm{p}]} = F_{[\mathrm{N}]}/0.00981 = F_{[\mathrm{cN}]}/0.981$.

"Denier" $T_{[\mathrm{den}]} = 9\,t_{[\mathrm{tex}]} = 0,9\,t_{[\mathrm{dtex}]}$ frequently expresses fiber fineness. Accordingly, fiber tenacity in "pond per denier" is expressed by $\sigma_{[\mathrm{p/den}]} = F_{[\mathrm{p}]}/T_{[\mathrm{den}]} = \sigma_{[\mathrm{cN\,dtex}^{-1}]}/0.8829$.

The expression of specific tensile stress is not a reasonable expression for fibers having different densities; because the value of fiber fineness is dependent on the value of fiber density. In such case, it is recommended to consider the stress as mechanical (engineering) stress $\sigma^* = \sigma\rho$. The reason for standardizing the specific stress is the same for standardizing the fineness.

Example 1.8: We consider a polyester fiber, tenacity of $\sigma = 0.43$ Ntex^{-1} and density of $\rho = 1360$ kgm^{-3}. The calculated value of mechanical (engineering) strength, according to Eq. (1.21), is $\sigma^* = 585$ MPa. Similarly, for a cotton fiber of tenacity $\sigma = 0.32$ Ntex^{-1} and fiber density $\rho = 1520$ kgm^{-3}, the mechanical (engineering) strength is $\sigma^* = 487$ MPa. In case of using units of specific stress, we find that the polyester fiber has 33% higher tenacity than the cotton fiber. In fact, if we apply the unit of mechanical stress, we find that the polyester fiber has only 20% higher specific (engineering) strength value than the cotton fiber. Here we may remind that ordinary steel has mechanical (engineering) strength of $\sigma^* = 500$ MPa. This means that the strength of both fibers is almost compatible with that of ordinary steel.

1.2   Characteristics of fibrous assemblies

Packing density (μ) – *definition*. The cotton wool is so fine and soft product that it is used for surgical dressings, while during the middle age the wooden stakes were used as an execution tool. Interestingly both of these materials are composed of cellulose. This peculiar example is given to show that the behavior of an ultimate material depends not only on the constituent material, but also on the compactness of the final product.

Figure 1.3 illustrates a three-dimensional section of a fibrous assembly of total volume V_c. The volume of the fibers occupied by this section is V, thus $V \le V_c$. The difference between the volumes $V_c - V$ expresses the volume of air present in the three-dimensional plane, i.e., the empty spaces between fibers.

The fiber compactness is measured by the ratio of the volume occupied by the fibers to the total volume of the fiber assembly as shown below.

$$\mu = \frac{V}{V_c}, \qquad \mu \in \langle 0, 1 \rangle. \qquad\qquad \dots (1.22)$$

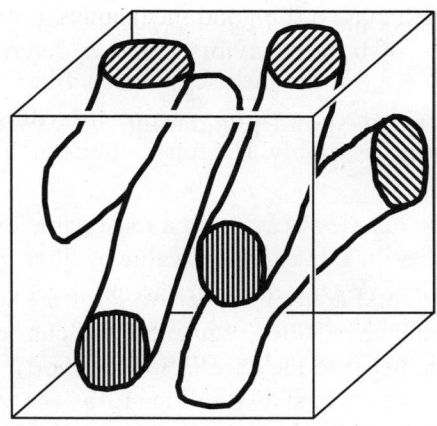

1.3 Section of a fibrous assembly in a three-dimensional plane.

In textile literature, the variable μ is defined as packing density (In chemical technology, the same definition is known as "volume fraction"). Some typical values for packing densities of different fibrous assemblies are listed in Table 1.6.

It is important to observe that the textile materials contain relatively high volume of air between the fibers. This imparts softness, porosity, pleasant hand, and good drapability, etc. (If we buy a package of ordinary cotton wool from a shop, we pay actually 97% of our money for air and only 3% for cotton wool). At the same time, textiles are strong and relatively

Table 1.6 Typical packing density values

Group	Fibrous assemblies	μ [1]
Linear textiles	Monofilament	1
	Limit structure(*)	0.907
	Hard twisted silk	0.75 to 0.85
	Wet spun linen yarn	about 0.65
	Combed cotton yarn	0.5 to 0.6
	Carded cotton yarn	0.38 to 0.55
	Worsted yarn	0.38 to 0.50
	Woolen yarn	0.35 to 0.45
	Cotton roving	0.10 to 0.20
	Sliver	about 0.03
Other textiles	Woven fabric	0.15 to 0.30
	Knitted fabric	0.10 to 0.20
	Cotton wool(**)	0.02 to 0.04
	Leather (textiles)(**)	0.005 to 0.02
Other materials	Earthenware(**)	0.20 to 0.23
	Wood(**)	0.3 to 0.7
	Animal leather(**)	0.33 to 0.66

(*) See later. (**) Piller and Trávníček [5] and Piller [6].

mechanical stress resistant (thanks to the good mechanical properties of textile fibers). The presence of both behaviors together determines the typical end use of textiles.

Packing density (μ) – *areal interpretation.* Figure 1.4a illustrates an infinitly thin section of a fibrous assembly. The total volume of this section is given by

$$dV_c = ab\,dh = S_c\,dh, \qquad \ldots (1.23)$$

where $ab = S_c$ denotes the total area of "upper wall" of the section. In this section, there are N number of fiber segments (We can ignore the curvatures of these segments because they are infinitely short). A typical j-th fiber segment ($j = 1, 2, \ldots, N$) is shown in Fig. 1.4b. The volume of this elementary section is expressed as a product of the projected area and the perpendicular height, i.e. $s^*_j\,dh$. The total volume of all fiber segments is given below

$$dV = \sum_{j=1}^{N}\left(s^*_j\,dh\right) = dh\sum_{j=1}^{N}s^*_j = S\,dh, \qquad \ldots (1.24)$$

where $\sum_{j=1}^{N}s^*_j = S$ is the total sectional area of all fibers that are present in the "upper wall" section. Now we can express the sectional area packing density using the general definition given in Eq. (1.22) as follows

$$\mu = \frac{dV}{dV_c} = \frac{S\,dh}{S_c\,dh} = \frac{S}{S_c}. \qquad \ldots (1.25)$$

It is obvious from the above expression that the packing density can be expressed as a ratio of the sectional area of all fibers to the total area of

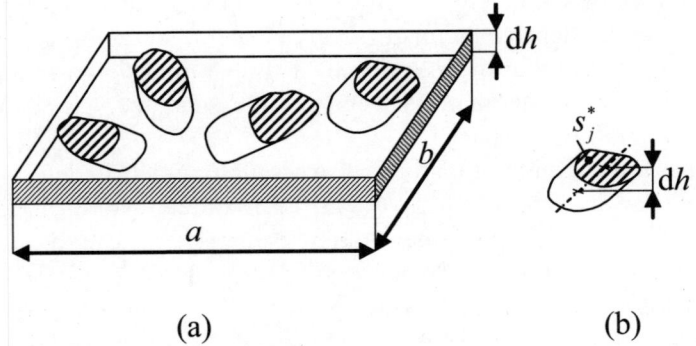

(a)   (b)

1.4 Fiber segments in an elementary section of a fibrous assembly.

the fibrous assembly including "the empty spaces" and fibers. The expression stated in Eq. (1.25) can be considered as the areal interpretation of packing density.

Such expression is called local packing density and may be used as a measure of compactness of small areas around the sectional plane ("the upper wall" section) of the fibrous assembly. If we assume that the observed fibrous assembly has the same packing density in all sections, then we can use Eq. (1.25) as the packing density of the whole assembly. This assumption is very useful to express the packing density of linear textiles (for example, yarns, etc.) as the ratio of sectional areas.

Packing density (μ) – *mass density interpretation.* The fibrous assembly shown in Fig. 1.3 has mass m and total volume V_c. The mass density ρ^* of the fibrous assembly is then given by the fraction m/V_c as shown below

$$\rho^* = m/V_c \qquad \left(V_c = m/\rho^*\right). \qquad\qquad \text{... (1.26)}$$

The mass m refers to the mass of fiber only (The mass of air and the mass of adhesives imparted during finishing are not considered). The volume of these fibers is V. According to Eq. (1.2), fiber mass density is $\rho = m/V$, $V = m/\rho$. Applying Eqs. (1.26) and (1.2) into Eq. (1.22), we find

$$\mu = \frac{m/\rho}{m/\rho^*} = \frac{\rho^*}{\rho}. \qquad\qquad \text{... (1.27)}$$

The above expression gives another expression of packing density where it is defined as a ratio between the density of the fibrous assembly and the density of fibers. This expression is known as the mass density interpretation of packing density.

This interpretation of packing density is applicable for formulating the media-continuum models (continuum models utilize mass element idea). The density ρ^* of such element can be divided by an "arbitrary" constant ρ to get packing density factor μ of this element. Actually, the packing density factor at any arbitrary point of a three-dimensional space takes either 1 if only fibrous material occupies the space or 0 if there is no fibrous material in the space.

The mass density interpretation is also useful for practical determination of packing density. It is difficult to use Eq. (1.22) directly for the calculation of packing density, because fiber volume cannot be measured directly in ordinary textile laboratories. The mass of the assembly can be simply found by weighing the assembly and its total volume can also be easily calculated from its macro-dimensions. Hence, the density of the fibrous assembly can be estimated from Eq. (1.26). The fiber density can be obtained, for example, from Table 1.1. By applying these two density values in Eq. (1.27), we can estimate the packing density (Earlier authors, e.g. Marschik [7], used directly ρ^* in lieu of packing density).

Example 1.9: An American cotton bale of dimensions 1.6m×0.8m×0.6m has a weight of 230 kg. Accordingly, the bale volume is $V_c = 0.768$ m³, and the bale density is calculated from Eq. (1.26) as $\rho^* = 299.5$ kgm⁻³. By applying the estimated bale density value and the given cotton fiber density value according to Table 1.1 into Eq. (1.27), we find the packing density of the bale is $\mu = 0.197$.

Porosity (permeability) (ψ). The measure of fiber compactness in a fibrous assembly can also be characterized by the presence of relative amount of air in the fibrous assembly. For example, the fibrous assembly shown in Fig. 1.3 has a total volume of V_c including fiber volume V. Then the volume of air (volume of pores) between fibers in that assembly is

$$V_p = V_c - V. \qquad \ldots (1.28)$$

The relative volume of air is expressed by *porosity* $\psi = V_p/V_c$. By applying Eqs. (1.22) and (1.28) into the expression of porosity, we find the following expression

$$\psi = \frac{V_p}{V_c} = \frac{V_c - V}{V_c} = 1 - \frac{V}{V_c} = 1 - \mu. \qquad \ldots (1.29)$$

Idealized fibrous assembly. The textile fibrous assemblies are usually composed of fibers, i.e., group of fibers arranged in the "longitudinal" direction of the assembly. In an idealized fibrous assembly, the circular fibers are parallelly and uniformly distributed along the axis of the assembly. In such a fibrous assembly, the fibers are arranged in a configuration around a single core fiber as shown in Fig. 1.5a. The repeat of the unit structure gives an equilateral triangle as shown in Fig. 1.5b.

Packing density of fibrous assembly. The packing density of the triangular section of the fibrous assembly shown in Fig. 1.5b can be

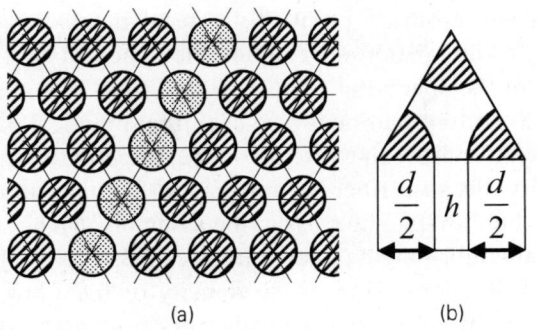

(a)   (b)

Figure 1.5 Hexagonal structure.

considered equal to the packing density of the whole structure. The length of each side of the triangle is $d+h$ and the height of the triangle is $(d+h)\cos30°$. Hence, the area of the triangle is obtained as follows

$$S_c = \frac{(d+h)(d+h)\cos30°}{2} = \frac{\sqrt{3}}{4}(d+h)^2. \qquad \ldots (1.30)$$

The area occupied by the fibers in the triangular section of the assembly is equal to the summation of the areas of three equal sectors (shown by the shaded color in Fig. 1.5b), each is making an angle of 60° to the vertex of the triangle. This area is given by the following expression

$$S = \frac{\pi d^2}{8}. \qquad \ldots (1.31)$$

By substituting Eqs. (1.30) and (1.31) into Eq. (1.25), we get the packing density of the triangle and thus for the whole structure as shown below

$$\mu = \frac{\dfrac{\pi d^2}{8}}{\dfrac{\sqrt{3}}{4}(d+h)^2} = \frac{\pi}{2\sqrt{3}}\frac{1}{\left(1+\dfrac{h}{d}\right)^2}. \qquad \ldots (1.32)$$

Limit structure. In the most compact type of fiber arrangement, all fibers are in contact with each other. This structure is called limit structure. Theoretically no more fibers can penetrate further into it. In such a limit structure, the distance between fibers is $h = 0$ and by applying this into Eq. (1.32), we obtain the limit of packing density as shown below

$$\mu_{lim} = \frac{\pi}{2\sqrt{3}} \cong 0,907. \qquad \ldots (1.33)$$

Compact (tight) structure. Figure 1.6a illustrates a column of dotted fibers taken from the hexagonal structure (a similar column is shown in Fig. 1.5a). At the same time, due to the applied forces, the shaded fiber (shown in Fig. 1.6a) from a neighboring column tries to penetrate into the empty space between fibers (in the direction marked by an arrow).

Now considering the space between fibers ($h < d/2$), the shaded fiber cannot pass through the empty space due to the unavailability of sufficient space. Therefore, some surrounding fibers must be displaced, as shown in Fig. 1.6b, where the lower fiber is shifted till it contacts the other fiber in the same column. The resultant space $2h < d$ is still not sufficient to allow the shaded fiber to pass through the empty space. The shaded fiber may get enough space to pass though the empty space when at least two fibers

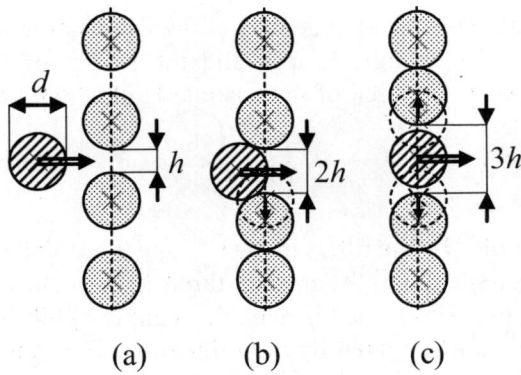

(a)   (b)   (c)

1.6 Compact structure.

are displaced as shown in Fig. 1.6c and as a result of this, a space of 3*h* occurs. If the space *h* between fibers is very small, three or more fibers should be shifted to allow the shaded fiber to pass through the empty space. In short, the shaded fiber may pass through the empty space of the column of dotted fibers when at least 2 (dotted) fibers are shifted.

There are two or more dotted fibers standing against each shaded fiber and "resisting to allow" one shaded fiber to pass through the empty space of the dotted fibers. This reminds us about "the protecting wall" in football game. In such a structure, the movement of individual fibers is limited and it behaves as a strong, compact, and hard one.

The structure, where *h* < *d*/2, is called compact or tight structure. The packing density of this structure is obtained from Eq. (1.32) by the following manner

$$\mu > \frac{\pi}{2\sqrt{3}} \frac{1}{\left(1 + \dfrac{d/2}{d}\right)^2} = \frac{\pi}{2\sqrt{3}} \frac{1}{(1.5)^2} \cong 0.403 . \qquad \ldots (1.34)$$

Intermediate structure. Figure 1.7a resembles same as Fig. 1.6a, where a column of fibers is taken from the hexagonal structure. Here we assume that the space between fibers is $h \in \langle d/2, d \rangle$. In this case also the shaded fiber cannot pass through the empty space between the dotted fibers without shifting other neighboring dotted fibers. It is clear that the displacement of one dotted fiber is sufficient to allow the shaded fiber to pass through the empty space and it is shown in Fig. 1.7b.

In this case it is difficult to guess whether the shaded fiber will surely pass through the column of dotted fibers. There is an equal "fight" between the shaded and dotted fibers. Probably, some shaded fibers will pass through the empty space while some other shaded fibers will fail. The movement of individual fibers is partially limited. Such a structure behaves somehow

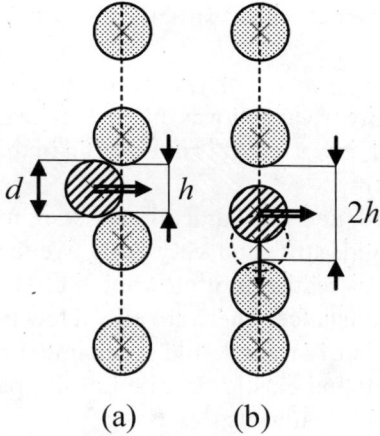

1.7 Intermediate structure.

uncertainly and imperfectly. It has less mechanical resistance and is less soft and drapable compared to the compact (tight) structure.

The structure, where $h \in \langle d/2, d \rangle$, is called intermediate structure. The highest packing density of this kind of structure is equal to the lower limit of packing density of compact structure, i.e., $\mu \cong 0.403$ and the lowest packing density of this kind of structure is obtained from Eq. (1.32) as follows

$$\mu = \frac{\pi}{2\sqrt{3}} \frac{1}{\left(1 + \dfrac{d}{d}\right)^2} = \frac{\pi}{2\sqrt{3}} \frac{1}{2^2} \cong 0.227. \qquad \ldots (1.35)$$

Loose structure. Figure 1.8 illustrates the same as Fig. 1.6a, where a column of fibers is taken from the hexagonal structure. In this case, we assume that the space between the dotted fibers is more than fiber diameter d. The shaded fiber can pass through the empty space of the column of dotted fibers without any special resistance because there is sufficient space between the dotted fibers available to allow the shaded fiber to pass through. Such a structure enables the individual fibers to move freely through the structure. Each fiber is "on its own" and is not "supported" by other fibers, i.e., not obstructed by other fibers. This structure has very low mechanical resistance and is significantly soft, porous, and drapable. The structure, where $h > d$, is called loose structure. The packing density of such a structure is less than the lower limit of the packing density of intermediate structure, i.e., $\mu < 0.227$.

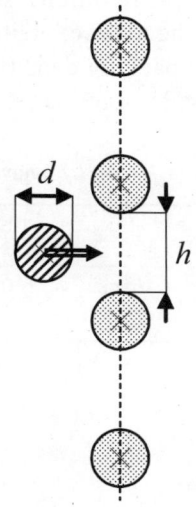

1.8 Loose structure.

An overview of different type of structures on the basis of fiber packing is given in Table 1.7.

Remarks on packing density of yarns and roving. The most popular type of fibrous assembly is yarn. It was created at the earlier time of human civilization and is still now used. It is interesting to think about this genius invention of ancient time.

We use high strength and mechanically resistant materials, viz. stones, iron, etc. They are rigid, stiff, and very hard. We also use very soft and elastic materials such as feather, cotton wool, etc. They have low strength and low mechanical resistance. There are only a few materials, which have both satisfactory levels of strength and mechanical resistance and at the same time they are soft and elastic. Textile fabrics, particularly garments, are the example of such materials.

However, a tight structure imparts sufficient strength and mechanical resistance to the material, but a loose structure gives pleasant and soft hand to the material. The structure, which gives sufficient strength and mechanical resistance as well as pleasant and soft hand to the material, must have a packing density in the range of $\mu = 0.403$ and a little bit higher. If we compare this with the values mentioned for the packing density of yarn in Table 1.6, we find that the packing density for all yarns lie almost within this range. Practically, yarns are the particular type of fibrous assemblies, which have such level of packing density, and therefore they are called optimum fibrous assemblies and they have all the properties mentioned for both type of structures. Some advanced technological processes of manufacturing textiles are bypassing yarns [8], thus neglecting the role of fiber packing on the product characteristics.

The traditional semi-product in yarn production is roving, and according to the ideas explained in this chapter, it should have a loose structure, i.e., the packing density of it should be about $\mu < 0.227$, which is respected in textile practice.

Table 1.7 An overview of different types of structures on the basis of fiber packing

Type of structures	Limit	Compact or tight	Intermediate	Loose
Packing density	0.907	from 0.403 to 0.907	from 0.227 to 0.403	less than 0.227
Images of border structures		$h = 0$ $\mu_{lim} = 0.907$	$h = d/2$ $\mu = 0.403$	$h = d$ $\mu = 0.227$

1.3   Characteristics of fiber blend

In the previous discussions, all fibers were considered identical although, in reality, the individual parameters of a fibrous assembly vary within one type of fiber material. The values and derived equations given in the previous discussions actually correspond to "the average" values of a real fibrous assembly. However, in textile mills different types of fibers are blended together to produce textile materials. The fiber parameters in the blend differ to such an extent that it is essential to consider the mean characteristic values of the blend from the corresponding average values of individual components.

Starting parameters. We are now considering a multi-fiber blend of n components (different types of fibers). The blend has total mass m and the mass of i-th component of the blend is m_i, where $i = 1, 2, ..., n$ then it is valid to write that

$$\sum_{i=1}^{n} m_i = m, \quad m_i \leq m. \qquad \ldots (1.36)$$

We consider the (mean) fiber parameters of i-th component, which are density ρ_i, fineness t_i, fiber length l_i, and specific area a_i, or surface area per unit volume γ_i. Analogously, the characteristics of the whole blend will be expressed without any subscript.

Mass fraction (g_i). The mass fraction g_i of i-th component is defined by

$$g_i = \frac{m_i}{m}, \quad \left(m_i = mg_i\right). \qquad \ldots (1.37)$$

From Eqs. (1.36) and (1.37), it is valid to write

$$\sum_{i=1}^{n} g_i = 1. \qquad \ldots (1.38)$$

· In textile practice, the blend composition is characterized either by the mass fraction ("weight fraction") or by the mass percentage of components. In textile mills, the mass fraction (mass percentage of components) is preferred, because it is easy to weigh the different components of the blend.

Mean fiber density (ρ). The volume of i-th component of the blend is V_i and the total volume of the blend is V, then from the definition of fiber density given by Eq. (1.2) and applying Eq. (1.37), we can write that

$$V_i = \frac{m_i}{\rho_i} = m\frac{g_i}{\rho_i}, \qquad \ldots (1.39)$$

$$V = \sum_{i=1}^{n} V_i = m \sum_{i=1}^{n} \frac{g_i}{\rho_i}. \qquad \qquad ...(1.40)$$

The mean fiber density of the blend is obtained from Eqs. (1.2) and (1.40), and it is expressed by

$$\rho = \frac{m}{V} = \frac{1}{\sum_{i=1}^{n} \frac{g_i}{\rho_i}} \quad \left(\frac{1}{\rho} = \sum_{i=1}^{n} \frac{g_i}{\rho_i} \right). \qquad ... (1.41)$$

It is obvious from Eq. (1.41) that the mean value of fiber density of the blend is the weighted harmonic (not arithmetic!) mean value of the fiber density values of the individual components of the blend (Remember that the harmonic mean value is lower than the arithmetic mean value).

Volume fraction (v_i). The volume fraction v_i of i-th component of the blend is defined by the ratio between the volume of i-th component of the blend and the total volume of the blend V. From Eqs. (1.39) to (1.41), we get

$$v_i = \frac{V_i}{V} = \frac{m \frac{g_i}{\rho_i}}{m \sum_{i=1}^{n} \frac{g_i}{\rho_i}} = g_i \frac{\rho}{\rho_i} \quad \left(\sum_{i=1}^{n} v_i = 1 \right). \qquad ... (1.42)$$

The mass fraction of the individual components of the blend g_i is not a very important variable when studying the structure of the blend. This value is frequently used in textile practice, because it is easy to determine during blending process; on the contrary the volume fraction v_i determines the relative space, i.e., the "size" occupied by the individual component, and it is an essential characteristic for predicting the behavior of the blend.

Mean fiber fineness (t). From Eqs. (1.3) and (1.37), the fiber length L_i of i-th component in the blend is expressed as follows

$$L_i = \frac{m_i}{t_i} = m \frac{g_i}{t_i}. \qquad ... (1.43)$$

It is evident that the total length L of all fibers in the blend is

$$L = \sum_{i=1}^{n} L_i = m \sum_{i=1}^{n} \frac{g_i}{t_i}. \qquad ... (1.44)$$

By substituting Eq. (1.44) into (1.3), we get the following expression for mean fiber fineness of the blend

$$t = \frac{m}{m \sum\limits_{i=1}^{n} \dfrac{g_i}{t_i}} = \frac{1}{\sum\limits_{i=1}^{n} \dfrac{g_i}{t_i}}. \qquad \ldots (1.45)$$

It is important to remember that the mean value of fiber fineness of the blend is also a weighted harmonic mean of the fineness values of individual components of the blend.

Mean fiber cross-sectional area (s). The mean fiber cross-sectional area of the blend can be directly estimated from Eq. (1.5) by using the values of mean fiber fineness and mean fiber density of the blend. This can also be found from the mean fiber cross-sectional area of the individual components of the blend. Equation (1.5) expresses the fineness of i-th component of the blend as $t_i = s_i \rho_i$. Equation (1.42) can also be expressed by $v_i/\rho = g_i/\rho_i$. By substituting both equations into Eq. (1.45), we get an alternative expression for the mean fineness of the blend

$$t = \frac{1}{\sum\limits_{i=1}^{n} \dfrac{g_i}{s_i \rho_i}} = \frac{1}{\sum\limits_{i=1}^{n} \dfrac{v_i}{s_i \rho}} = \frac{\rho}{\sum\limits_{i=1}^{n} \dfrac{v_i}{s_i}}. \qquad \ldots (1.46)$$

The mean fiber cross-sectional area of the blend is obtained by applying Eqs. (1.5) and (1.46) and rearranging them as follows

$$s = \frac{t}{\rho} = \frac{1}{\sum\limits_{i=1}^{n} \dfrac{v_i}{s_i}}. \qquad \ldots (1.47)$$

The mean fiber cross-sectional area of the blend is the weighted harmonic mean of the mean fiber cross-sectional area of the individual components of the blend.

Mean equivalent fiber diameter (d). The mean equivalent fiber diameter of the blend is obtained directly from Eq. (1.6) by applying the expressions for mean fiber fineness and mean fiber density of the blend. It is also possible to calculate this value from the equivalent fiber diameter of the individual components of the blend. From Eq. (1.7), we find the mean fiber cross-sectional area of the blend is $s = \pi d^2/4$, and the cross-sectional area of the individual component of the blend is $s_i = \pi d_i^2/4$. By applying both equations into Eq. (1.47) and rearranging, we get the following expression for the mean equivalent fiber diameter of the blend

$$\frac{\pi d^2}{4} = \frac{1}{\sum\limits_{i=1}^{n} \frac{4v_i}{\pi d_i^2}}, \quad d = \frac{1}{\sqrt{\sum\limits_{i=1}^{n} \frac{v_i}{d_i^2}}}. \qquad \ldots (1.48)$$

It is evident that the mean equivalent fiber diameter of the blend d is neither the arithmetic nor the harmonic mean of the mean equivalent fiber diameter of the individual components of the blend d_i, but the square value of mean equivalent fiber diameter d of the blend is the weighted harmonic mean of the square value of equivalent fiber diameter of the individual components of the blend d_i. However, there are many empirical expressions available for the arithmetic mean of the mean equivalent fiber diameter [9–11].

Fiber length fraction (λ_i). The fiber length fraction of i-th component of the blend is denoted by λ_i and it is defined by the ratio of the fiber length of i-th component of the blend L_i and the total fiber length of the whole blend L. By applying Eqs. (1.43), (1.44) and (1.45), we find the following expression for the fiber length fraction of i-th component

$$\lambda_i = \frac{L_i}{L} = \frac{m \dfrac{g_i}{t_i}}{m \sum\limits_{i=1}^{n} \dfrac{g_i}{t_i}} = g_i \frac{t}{t_i} \quad \left(\sum\limits_{i=1}^{n} \lambda_i = 1\right). \qquad \ldots (1.49)$$

Remark: The fiber length fraction of a parallel fibrous assembly (for example, continuous filament yarn) is also the relative frequency of the number of fibers of the individual component.

Mean fiber length (l). The (mean) length of fibers of i-th component is denoted by l_i (considering a staple fibrous assembly) and the number of fibers in i-th component of the blend is estimated from Eq. (1.1) as $N_i = L_i/l_i$. By applying Eqs. (1.43) and (1.49), we find the following expression for the number of fibers in i-th component of the blend

$$N_i = \frac{L_i}{l_i} = m \frac{g_i}{l_i t_i} = \frac{m}{l_i} \frac{\lambda_i}{t}. \qquad \ldots (1.50)$$

From the above expression, we can express the total number of fibers in the blend as follows

$$N = \sum\limits_{i=1}^{n} N_i = \frac{m}{t} \sum\limits_{i=1}^{n} \frac{\lambda_i}{l_i}. \qquad \ldots (1.51)$$

The mean fiber length of the blend is obtained from Eqs. (1.1), (1.3) and (1.51) as shown below

$$l = \frac{L}{N} = \frac{\dfrac{m}{t}}{\dfrac{m}{t}\displaystyle\sum_{i=1}^{n}\dfrac{\lambda_i}{l_i}} = \frac{1}{\displaystyle\sum_{i=1}^{n}\dfrac{\lambda_i}{l_i}}. \qquad \dots (1.52)$$

Here again we recognize that the mean fiber length of the blend is a weighted harmonic mean of the mean fiber length of the individual components.

Relative frequency (υ_i). The ratio between the number of fibers in *i*-th component and the total number of fibers in the blend is known as the relative frequency υ_i. By applying Eq. (1.50) into Eq. (1.52), we find the following expression for the relative frequency of number of fibers of *i*-th component of the blend

$$\upsilon_i = \frac{N_i}{N} = \frac{\dfrac{m\,\lambda_i}{l_i}\,t}{\dfrac{m}{t}\displaystyle\sum_{i=1}^{n}\dfrac{\lambda_i}{l_i}} = \lambda_i\frac{l}{l_i} \quad \left(\sum_{i=1}^{n}\upsilon_i = 1\right). \qquad \dots (1.53)$$

Mean fiber aspect ratio (Λ). The mean fiber aspect ratio of the blend is found directly from Eq. (1.10) by applying the mean fiber length and the mean equivalent fiber diameter of the blend. It can also be derived from the fiber aspect ratio of the individual components of the blend. According to Eq. (1.10), fiber aspect ratio of *i*-th component of the blend is expressed by $\Lambda_i = l_i/d_i$ and from Eq. (1.53) we find $l_i = \lambda_i l/\upsilon_i$. By combining both of these expressions, we find the following expression for the fiber diameter of *i*-th component of the blend

$$d_i = \frac{l_i}{\Lambda_i} = \frac{\lambda_i l}{\upsilon_i \Lambda_i}. \qquad \dots (1.54)$$

The mean fiber aspect ratio of the blend is found from Eq. (1.10) where $\Lambda = l/d$. By rearranging Eqs. (1.48) and (1.54), we find the following expression for the mean fiber aspect ratio of the blend

$$\Lambda = \frac{l}{d} = l\sqrt{\sum_{i=1}^{n}\frac{v_i}{d_i^2}} = l\sqrt{\sum_{i=1}^{n}\frac{v_i\upsilon_i^2\Lambda_i^2}{\lambda_i^2 l^2}} = \sqrt{\sum_{i=1}^{n}\left(\frac{v_i\upsilon_i^2}{\lambda_i^2}\Lambda_i^2\right)}. \qquad \dots (1.55)$$

Mean specific surface area (*a*). From Eq. (1.16), it is valid that the surface area of *i*-th component of the blend is $A_i = m_i a_i$. By substituting this expression into Eq. (1.37), we find the surface area of *i*-th component of the blend as follows

$$A_i = m_i a_i = m g_i a_i. \qquad \ldots (1.56)$$

Accordingly, the surface area of all fibers *A* in the blend is obtained as follows

$$A = \sum_{i=1}^{n} A_i = m \sum_{i=1}^{n} (g_i a_i). \qquad \ldots (1.57)$$

The mean specific surface area of the blend can be obtained by comparing Eqs. (1.16) and (1.57) as follows

$$a = \frac{A}{m} = \sum_{i=1}^{n} (g_i a_i). \qquad \ldots (1.58)$$

The mean specific surface area of the blend is the summation of the product of mass fraction and the mean specific surface area of the individual components of the blend.

Mean specific surface area per unit volume (γ). The relationship between the volume and the specific surface area of *i*-th component of the blend is given by Eq. (1.20) as $a_i = \gamma_i / \rho_i$. Similarly, for the blend it is valid that $\gamma = a\rho$. Furthermore, according to Eq. (1.42), it is valid that $g_i = v_i \rho_i / \rho$. By substituting these expressions into Eq. (1.58), we find

$$a = \sum_{i=1}^{n} \left(\frac{v_i \rho_i}{\rho} \frac{\gamma_i}{\rho_i} \right) = \sum_{i=1}^{n} \frac{v_i \gamma_i}{\rho}, \quad a\rho = \sum_{i=1}^{n} (v_i \gamma_i), \quad \gamma = \sum_{i=1}^{n} (v_i \gamma_i). \qquad \ldots (1.59)$$

The mean surface area per unit volume of the blend is the arithmetic mean of the fiber surface area per unit volume of the blend components.

Mean shape factor of fiber cross-section (*q*). The mean shape factor of fiber cross-section of the blend can be found directly from Eq. (1.18) by applying the expressions for mean specific surface area per unit volume and the mean equivalent fiber diameter of the blend. Of course, it is also possible to derive this expression from the mean shape factor of fiber cross-section of the individual components of the blend. From Eq. (1.6), the fineness of the blend is $t = (\pi d^2 / 4)\rho$ and the fineness of *i*-th component of the blend is $t_i = \left(\pi d_i^2 / 4 \right) \rho_i$. The ratio between these two expressions is obtained as follows

$$\frac{t}{t_i} = \frac{d^2 \rho}{d_i^2 \rho_i}.$$ ... (1.60)

From Eq. (1.49), we find $t/t_i = \lambda_i/g_i$ and from Eq. (1.42), we find $\rho/\rho_i = v_i/g_i$. By substituting both of these expressions into Eq. (1.60) and rearranging, we get the following expression for the equivalent fiber diameter of i-th component of the blend

$$\frac{\lambda_i}{g_i} = \frac{d^2}{d_i^2} \frac{v_i}{g_i}, \quad d_i^2 = \frac{v_i}{\lambda_i} d^2, \quad d_i = \sqrt{\frac{v_i}{\lambda_i}} d.$$ ... (1.61)

From Eq. (1.18), we obtain $1+q = \gamma d/4$ for the blend and $\gamma_i = 4(1+q_i)/d_i$ for the i-th component of the blend. By substituting the above expression for the equivalent fiber diameter of i-th component of the blend into Eq. (1.59), we find the following expression for the mean shape factor of fiber cross-section of the blend

$$1+q = \frac{\gamma d}{4} = \frac{d}{4} \sum_{i=1}^{n} (v_i \gamma_i) = \frac{d}{4} \sum_{i=1}^{n} \left[v_i \frac{4(1+q_i)}{d_i} \right]$$

$$= \frac{d}{4} \sum_{i=1}^{n} \left[v_i \frac{4(1+q_i)}{\sqrt{(v_i/\lambda_i)}d} \right] = \sum_{i=1}^{n} \left[\sqrt{v_i \lambda_i} (1+q_i) \right],$$

$$q = \sum_{i=1}^{n} \left[\sqrt{v_i \lambda_i} (1+q_i) \right] - 1.$$ ... (1.62)

Fiber surface area fraction (α_i). The fiber surface area fraction of i-th component of the blend α_i is defined by the ratio between the mean surface area of the i-th component of the blend A_i and the surface area of all fibers of the blend A. This is obtained by applying Eqs. (1.56), (1.57), and (1.58) as follows

$$\alpha_i = \frac{A_i}{A} = \frac{mg_i a_i}{m \sum_{i=1}^{n} (g_i a_i)} = g_i \frac{a_i}{a}.$$ ... (1.63)

Mass fraction (g_i). Sometimes, it is required to find out the mass fraction of i-th component of the blend from the other known parameters.

If the volume fraction of v_i of i-th component of the blend is known, we can use Eqs. (1.42) and (1.38) to estimate the mass fraction of i-th component of the blend in the following manner

$$v_i \rho_i = g_i \rho, \quad \sum_{i=1}^{n} v_i \rho_i = \rho \sum_{i=1}^{n} g_i = \rho, \quad g_i = \frac{v_i \rho_i}{\sum_{i=1}^{n} v_i \rho_i}. \qquad \dots (1.64)$$

If the length fraction of i-th component of the blend λ_i is given, we find an expression for the mass fraction of i-th component of the blend by applying Eqs. (1.49) and (1.38) as shown below

$$\lambda_i t_i = g_i t, \quad \sum_{i=1}^{n} \lambda_i t_i = t \sum_{i=1}^{n} g_i = t, \quad g_i = \frac{\lambda_i t_i}{\sum_{i=1}^{n} \lambda_i t_i}. \qquad \dots (1.65)$$

If the frequency fraction of i-th component of the blend υ_i is known, then by applying and rearranging Eqs. (1.53), (1.49) and (1.38), we find another expression for the mass fraction of i-th component of the blend as follows

$$\upsilon_i l_i = \lambda_i l = \frac{g_i}{t_i} tl, \quad \upsilon_i l_i t_i = g_i tl, \quad \sum_{i=1}^{n} \upsilon_i l_i t_i = tl \sum_{i=1}^{n} g_i = tl,$$

$$g_i = \frac{\upsilon_i l_i t_i}{\sum_{i=1}^{n} \upsilon_i l_i t_i}. \qquad \dots (1.66)$$

If the surface fraction of i-th component of the blend α_i is given, we can apply Eqs. (1.63) and (1.38) to get one more expression for the mass fraction of i-th component of the blend as follows

$$\frac{\alpha_i}{a_i} = \frac{g_i}{a}, \quad \sum_{i=1}^{n} \frac{\alpha_i}{a_i} = \frac{1}{a} \sum_{i=1}^{n} g_i = \frac{1}{a}, \quad g_i = \frac{\dfrac{\alpha_i}{a_i}}{\sum_{i=1}^{n} \dfrac{\alpha_i}{a_i}}. \qquad \dots (1.67)$$

Example 1.10: We consider a binary blend of 40% cotton and 60% polyester. The bold numbers in Table 1.8 indicate the known fiber parameters. In the other boxes of the table, we find the calculated parameters for the individual components of the blend and also for the whole blend. The number of equations used to calculate these parameters is also mentioned in Table 1.8.

Table 1.8 Given and calculated values of the parameters for the individual components and for the blend.

Parameters	Dimension	Components		Blend	
		Cotton	Polyester	Value	Equation number
Fineness t	[dtex]	**1.5**	**1.7**	1.614	(1.45)
Length l	[mm]	**28**	**40**	33.77	(1.52)
Density ρ	[kg m^{-3}]	**1520**	**1360**	1420	(1.41)
Fiber shape factor q	[1]	**0.30**	**0.04**	0.143	(1.17), or (1.62)
Cross-sectional area $s - (1.5)$	[μm^2]	**98.7**	**125**	114	(1.5), or (1.47)
Equivalent diameter $d - (1.6)$	[μm]	11.2	12.6	12.0	(1.6), or (1.48)
Aspect ratio $\Lambda - (1.10)$	[1]	2500	3175	2814	(1.10), or (1.55)
Specific surface area $a - (1.17)$	[m^{2}kg^{-1}]	305.2	242.5	267.6	(1.58)
Surface area/unit volume $\gamma - (1.20)$	[mm^{-1}]	463.9	329.7	379.9	(1.59)
Mass fraction g	[%]	**40**	**60**	–	–
Volume fraction v	[%]	37.4	62.6	–	(1.42)
Length fraction λ	[%]	43.0	57.0	–	(1.49)
Frequency fraction υ	[%]	51.9	48.1	–	(1.53)
Surface area fraction α	[%]	45.6	54.4	–	(1.63)

Example 1.11: In the above example we would like to replace polyester fibers by polypropylene fibers keeping the same fineness of 1.7 dtex and the same fiber cross-section shape factor of 0.04. From physiological and hygienic point of view, it is needed to keep same surface area fraction of fibers i.e., $\alpha_{COTTON} = 45.6\%$ and $\alpha_{POLYPROPYLENE} = 54.4\%$. By applying the values of fiber density given in Table 1.1 into Eq. (1.17), we find that the specific fiber surface area of polypropylene is $a = 296.4$ m^{2}kg^{-1}. The calculated value of the specific surface area for cotton fibers is $a = 305.2$ m^{2}kg^{-1}. According to Eq. (1.67), we find the mass fraction of cotton fibers is $g_{COTTON} = 44.9\%$ (instead of 40%) and for polypropylene is $g_{POLYPROPYLEN} = 55.1\%$ (instead of 60%). This means that increasing cotton fiber percentage by 5% more in the new blend, the same surface area can be maintained for both of the blends.

References

1. Goswami, B. C., Martindale, J. G., and Scardino, F. L. (1977). *Textile Yarns: Technology, Structure, and Applications*, John Wiley & Sons, New York.
2. Hladik, V. (1970). *Textilní vlákna (Textile Fibers)*, Prague.
3. Malinowska, K. (1979). *Prace Inst. Wlok (Research Report)*, 29.
4. Morton, W. E., and Hearle, J. W. S. (1962). *Physical Properties of Textile Fibers*, The Textile Institute and Butterworth and Company, London.
5. Piller, B., and Trávniček, Z. (1956). *Syntetická vlákna díl 1* (Synthetic Fibers, Part I), SNTL, Prague.

6. Piller, B. (1967). *Synthetická vlákna – výroba a zpracování tvarovaných přízí* (Synthetic Fibers – Manufacturing and Processing of Textured Yarns, Part I), SNTL, Prague.
7. Marschik, S. (1904). *Physicalisch-technische Untersuchungen von Gespinsten und Geweben* (Physical and Technical Investigation of Yarns and Fabrics), Wien.
8. Pikovskij, G. J. (1977). *Textil Buduschcego* (Textile in Future).
9. Clague, D. S., and Phillips, R. J. (1997). A numerical calculation of the hydraulic permeability of three-dimensional disordered fibrous media, *Physics of Fluids*, **9**(6), 1562–1572.
10. Mattern, K. J., and Deen, W. M. (2008). Mixing rules for estimating the hydraulic permeability of fiber mixtures, *Journal of American Institute of Chemical Engineers*, **54**(1), 32–41.
11. Tafreshi, H. V., Rahman, M. S. A., Jaganathan, S., Wang, Q., and Pourdeyhimi, B. (2009) Analytical expressions for predicting permeability of bimodal fibrous porous media, *Chemical Engineering Science*, **64**, 1154–1159.

Pores in fibrous assemblies

2.1 Pores and their general characteristics

Pores between fibers. The porosity ψ expresses the relative volume of air present in a fibrous assembly. It is determined as one minus packing density of the fibrous assembly – see Eq. (29). Nevertheless, a given volume of air can be concentrated in a few relatively big spaces or the same volume of air can be distributed in a relatively higher number of very small channels. (One can imagine a homogenous block of polyester bored with some big holes, although its porosity can be comparable with a polyester fabric but its fluid flow behavior would be definitely different). The porosity and the size of air gaps in a fibrous assembly are very important factors to decide the fluid flow and filtration behaviors of the fibrous assembly.

It is not an easy task to determine the size and shape of pores experimentally. It is possible to analyze pore characteristics using some direct experimental methods. These methods are generally based on the evaluation of microscopic sections of the fibrous assembly using the image analysis technique. Some indirect methods are also frequently used. The principle of these methods is based on capillarity and fluid flow phenomena of fibrous porous materials. The so-called mercury porosimetry or liquid porosimetry works on the principle of capillarity [1–3]. Other methods are based on the application of Kozeny-Carman's flow equation [4–6]. (The well-known fiber micronaire measuring apparatus is based on the principle of "air-flow" method and this apparatus is calibrated to directly give fiber fineness expressed in $\mu g/in$). The pore size can also be evaluated indirectly from the size of particles passed through the fibrous porous material. The experimental method of aerosol filtration is given in ISO 12956 [7]. In textile practice, it is easier to estimate the pore characteristics from theoretical models rather than from experimental methods. A few theoretical models [8–11] based on Poissionian polyhedra theory was developed to estimate the pore characteristics in nonwoven fibrous materials, however, a more generalized theory [12] to predict the pore characteristics of fibrous materials was also reported.

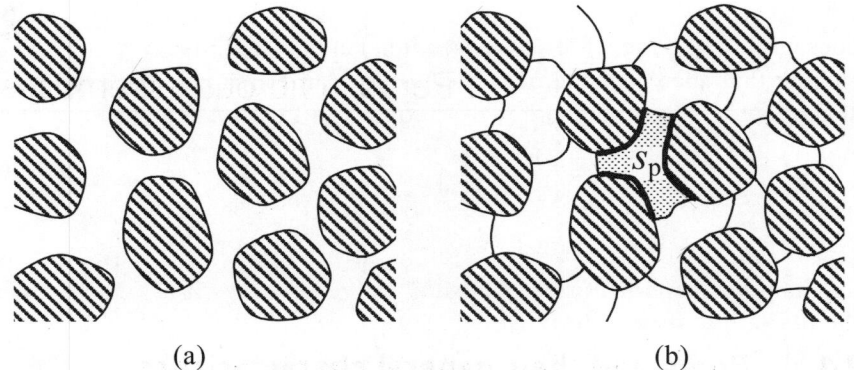

(a)   (b)

2.1 Scheme of a section of fibrous assembly and definition of pores.

Definition of pores. Figure 2.1a displays the scheme of a general section of a fibrous assembly with (shaded) fibers. There are gaps among fibers shown in the section of the assembly. Let us imaginatively divide the space of the gaps by means of "fictive borders" which are represented by thin lines in Fig. 2.1b. In this way, we divide the entire space of gaps into many "channels" or "capillaries" or "tubes", which are called pores.

Note: Here the pores are created with the help of fictive borders that are placed quite arbitrarily. It appears that such pores are determined objectively by the structure of the fibrous assembly as well as subjectively by our "feeling".

It is obvious that a pore, such as the dotted pore shown in Fig. 2.1b, is in contact with the fiber body as shown by thick lines, i.e., "real borders" and by thin lines, i.e., "fictive borders" that distinguish one pore from the other pores. This pore has a capillary shape and it can be considered as an "air fiber". Therefore, the expressions mentioned in Chapter 1 for fibers are also valid in a similar way for pores.

Note: The variables related to the pores are displayed with the subscripted character "p".

Characteristics of pores. Let us denote the pore cross-sectional area by s_p. This is shown in Fig. 2.1b. The equivalent pore diameter can be expressed with analogy to Eq. (1.6) or (1.7) as follows

$$d_p = \sqrt{\frac{4s_p}{\pi}} \qquad \left(s_p = \frac{\pi d_p^2}{4} \right). \qquad \qquad \text{... (2.1)}$$

The total perimeter of pore is composed of two parts: the real part, i.e., the common border between pore and real fiber, and the fictive part i.e., the distinguishing lines between pores. Let us now introduce a variable called the perimeter of pore p_p, which is defined – in contrast to fiber – by the total length of real borders only, because the fictive borders do not exist in reality. It should be emphasized that the perimeter p_p generally does not enclose the whole cross-sectional area s_p, and therefore it can be smaller than the perimeter of a circle of the same area πd_p. Then the pore shape factor q_p can be expressed analogous to Eq. (1.11) as follows

$$q_p = \left(\frac{p_p}{\pi d_p} - 1\right) > (-1), \qquad p_p = \pi d_p \left(1 + q_p\right). \qquad \text{... (2.2)}$$

The pore shape factor can take a negative value, as it is evident from the definition of pore perimeter.

Although in a real fibrous assembly, the pore characteristics vary widely, but the variability of pore characteristics is not considered in the following discussion. We assume that all pores have the same characteristics. The variables and expressions corresponding to all fibers in a fibrous assembly as mentioned in Chapter 1 are valid in a similar way for all pores in a fibrous assembly. These characteristics can be regarded as the average of all pores in a fibrous assembly.

Using the expressions derived earlier for fibers we can obtain the corresponding expressions for pores (air fibers). If we denote the total pore length in a fibrous assembly by L_p, then with an analogy to Eq. (1.9), we can find the following expression for the total pore volume in a fibrous assembly

$$V_p = s_p L_p = \frac{\pi d_p^2}{4} L_p. \qquad \text{... (2.3)}$$

Similarly, using Eq. (1.13), the total pore surface area A_p can be expressed as follows

$$A_p = p_p L_p = \pi d_p \left(1 + q_p\right) L_p. \qquad \text{... (2.4)}$$

The pore surface area per unit volume γ_p can be expressed with analogy to Eq. (1.18) as follows

$$\gamma_p = \frac{A_p}{V_p} = \frac{4\left(1 + q_p\right)}{d_p}. \qquad \text{... (2.5)}$$

(The same expression can also be obtained by applying Eqs. (2.3) and (2.4) into Eq. (2.5) that defines the pore surface area per unit volume as $\gamma = A_p / V_p$).

Relationship between fiber and pore characteristics. The area of "real borders" in a fibrous assembly defines the surface area of pores. A major part of fiber surface area shares with that of pore, but in some places fibers contact with other fibers, and these contacts create very small junction as shown in Fig. 2.2. These junctions are a part of fiber surface area A, but they are not a part of pore surface area A_p; therefore, it is valid to write that $A > A_p$. The majority of these junctions occupy very small, so they can be approximated to point contacts. In this case, the difference between the values A and A_p is negligible, and we can consider that the surface areas of pores and fibers are more or less equal. Let us assume that

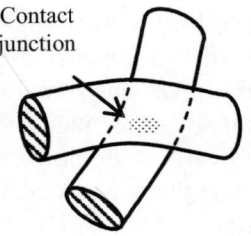

Contact junction

2.2 Scheme of fiber-to-fiber contact.

$$A_p = A. \qquad \ldots (2.6)$$

The pore surface area per unit volume expressed in Eq. (2.5) can be rearranged using Eqs. (2.6), (1.18), (1.22) and (1.29) as shown below

$$\gamma_p = \frac{A_p}{V_p} = \frac{A}{V_p} = \frac{A}{V}\frac{V}{V_c}\frac{V_c}{V_p} = \gamma\,\mu\frac{1}{\psi} = \gamma\frac{\mu}{1-\mu}. \qquad \ldots (2.7)$$

Substituting Eqs. (2.5) and (1.18) into Eq. (2.7), we can obtain the following expression for equivalent pore diameter d_p

$$\frac{4\left(1+q_p\right)}{d_p} = \frac{4\left(1+q\right)}{d}\frac{\mu}{1-\mu}, d_p = \frac{1+q_p}{1+q}\frac{1-\mu}{\mu}d,\left(\frac{d_p}{d} = \frac{1+q_p}{1+q}\frac{1-\mu}{\mu}\right). \quad \ldots (2.8)$$

Further, substituting Eqs. (1.13) and (1.18) into Eq. (2.6) and using Eq. (2.8) we can find the following expression for the total pore length L_p

$$\pi d_p\left(1+q_p\right)L_p = \pi d\left(1+q\right)L, \quad \pi\frac{1+q_p}{1+q}\frac{1-\mu}{\mu}d\left(1+q_p\right)L_p = \pi d\left(1+q\right)L,$$

$$L_p = \left(\frac{1+q}{1+q_p}\right)^2\frac{\mu}{1-\mu}L, \quad \left(\frac{L_p}{L} = \left(\frac{1+q}{1+q_p}\right)^2\frac{\mu}{1-\mu}\right). \qquad \ldots (2.9)$$

The equivalent pore diameter represents the (mean) size of air gaps among fibers and the total length of pores represents the quantity of pores ("air tubes") in a fibrous assembly. Eqs. (2.8) and (2.9) express these quantities as functions of parameters q, μ and d or L. Nevertheless, there is also an unknown quantity, i.e., pore shape factor q_p whose value depends upon 1) the structure of fibrous assembly and 2) the way of determination of fictive borders as discussed earlier with reference to Fig. 2.1. Therefore, the derived expressions as stated in Eqs. (2.8) and (2.9) are not possible to use at this moment for numerical calculation.

As noted earlier, the pores are imaginatively created with the help of fictive borders that are placed quite arbitrarily. In fact, we have not got the chance to determine the fictive borders subjectively. The fibrous assembly has always taken a part of certain physical process (wicking, fluid flow, filtration, etc.) and this process can determine the "fictive borders" indirectly. So, the same fibrous assembly can take different types of pores in different physical processes. Therefore, the quantity q_p depends in reality on the structure of the fibrous assembly, i.e., the geometry including packing density of the fibrous assembly and the type of physical process used. (It can be simply stated that an identical fibrous assembly has different types of pores suitable for different physical processes).

Nevertheless, the total pore surface area, the total volume of pores, and the pore surface area per unit volume are independent to the pore shape factor q_p. According to Eq. (2.6), it is valid to write that $A_p = A$, where the total fiber surface area, according to Eq. (1.13), is $A = \pi d(1+q)L$. So, the total pore surface area depends on the fiber quantities only. The total volume of pores V_p is given by Eq. (2.3), where d_p can be determined from Eq. (2.8) and L_p can be determined form Eq. (2.9). Using these equations we obtain the following expression

$$V_p = \frac{\pi d_p^2}{4} L_p = \frac{\pi}{4}\left(\frac{1+q_p}{1+q}\right)^2\left(\frac{1-\mu}{\mu}\right)^2 d^2 \cdot \left(\frac{1+q}{1+q_p}\right)^2 \frac{\mu}{1-\mu} L = \frac{\pi}{4}\frac{1-\mu}{\mu}d^2 L.$$

This expression shows that the total volume of pores V_p also depends only on the fiber characteristics. Further, substituting Eq. (2.8) into Eq. (2.5) and then applying Eq. (1.18) we obtain

$$\gamma_p = \frac{4(1+q_p)}{d_p} = 4(1+q_p)\frac{1+q}{1+q_p}\frac{\mu}{1-\mu}\frac{1}{d} = \frac{\mu}{1-\mu}\frac{4(1+q)}{d}$$

$$= \frac{\mu}{1-\mu}\gamma, \quad \left(\frac{\gamma_p}{\gamma} = \frac{\mu}{1-\mu}\right). \qquad \ldots (2.10)$$

It shows that the pore surface area per unit volume γ_p too is a function of the fiber quantities only.

2.2   Some special variants of pores

Some special variants of pores can be originated from a prior hypothesis of the conventional value of pore shape factor q_p. Such a hypothesis can be formulated without any knowledge of the physical process that uses the fibrous assembly.

Conventional pores. We often would like to have standardized information about the size of air gaps among fibers. For this purpose, let us introduce an idea of conventional pore, which is based on the conventional value of pore shape factor shown below

$$q_p = q_p^* = 0. \qquad \qquad \qquad ...(2.11)$$

Note: The quantities related to the conventional pore are displayed with the superscripted character *.

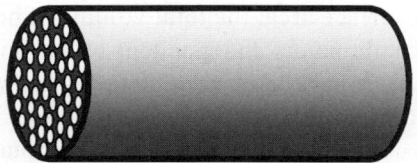

2.3 Scheme of a structure corresponding to conventional pores.

Figure 2.3 shows the scheme of a structure that corresponds precisely to the assumption stated in Eq. (2.11), that is, a set of cylindrical pores lies inside a compact cylinder. Evidently, this does not correspond to a fibrous structure. Nevertheless, the volume of pores and the pore surface area as well as the pore surface area per unit volume remain the same as that of a real fibrous assembly.

Using Eqs. (2.8), (2.9), and (2.11) the conventional pore diameter can be expressed as follows

$$d_p^* = \frac{1}{1+q}\frac{1-\mu}{\mu}d, \quad \left(\frac{d_p^*}{d} = \frac{1}{1+q}\frac{1-\mu}{\mu}\right) \qquad ...(2.12)$$

and the total length of conventional pores is expressed as follows

$$L_p^* = (1+q)^2 \frac{\mu}{1-\mu}L, \quad \left(\frac{L_p^*}{L} = (1+q)^2 \frac{\mu}{1-\mu}\right). \qquad ...(2.13)$$

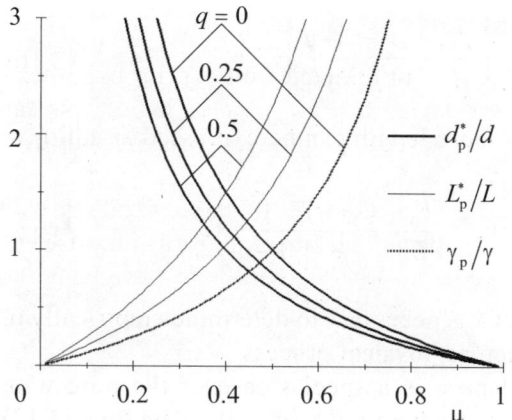

2.4 Graph of conventional pore diameter, conventional pore length, and pore surface area per unit volume as a function of packing density μ.

Note: Comparing the general expression of equivalent pore diameter shown in Eq. (2.8) with the expression of conventional pore diameter shown in Eq. (2.12), we obtain the following relation between the conventional pore diameter and the equivalent pore diameter

$$d_p^* = d_p / (1 + q_p).$$
   ... (2.14)

The behavior of Eqs. (2.12), (2.13) and (2.10), are graphically shown in Fig. 2.4 for different values of q. (The dotted curve of γ_p/γ is identical to the curve of L_p^*/L when $q = 0$. This can also be obtained from Eqs. (2.13) and (2.10)).

The conventional pore diameter (and/or ratio d_p^*/d), i.e., a measure of "size of gaps", is decreasing with the increase in packing density. On the other hand, the total length of conventional pores (and/or ratio L_p^*/L) is increasing with the increase in packing density. (The earlier big spaces are converted into many small pores with the increase of packing density).

Pores with constant shape factor (variant I). Sometimes it is reasonable to consider that the pore shape factor q_p is independent of packing density of fibrous assembly, i.e., it is a constant. Then we can write

$$1 + q_p = k \ldots \text{constant.}$$
   ... (2.15)

Substituting Eq. (2.15) into Eq. (2.8), the equivalent pore diameter can be obtained as follows

$$d_p = \frac{k}{1+q}\frac{1-\mu}{\mu}d, \quad \left(\frac{d_p}{d} = \frac{k}{1+q}\frac{1-\mu}{\mu}\right), \qquad (2.16)$$

and from Eq. (2.9), the total pore length can be expressed as follows

$$L_p = \frac{(1+q)^2}{k^2}\frac{\mu}{1-\mu}L, \quad \left(\frac{L_p}{L} = \frac{(1+q)^2}{k^2}\frac{\mu}{1-\mu}\right). \qquad ...(2.17)$$

Notes: 1. A suitable value of k is necessary to determine empirically in relation to a particular physical process.

     2. The conventional pore is a special case of the pore with constant shape factor, where $k = 1$ ($q_p = 0$) – see Eqs. (2.12) and (2.13).

Pores with constant total length (variant II). In other cases, it is useful to assume that the total pore length L_p is independent of packing density of fibrous assembly, i.e., it is a constant. Then it is possible to rearrange Eq. (2.9) as follows

$$1+q_p = k\sqrt{\frac{\mu}{1-\mu}}, \text{ where } k = \sqrt{\frac{L}{L_p}}(1+q)...\text{constant.} \qquad ... (2.18)$$

Note: According to the last expression the pore shape factor q_p is not a constant now, but it increases with the increase in packing density. That means the shape of pore cross-section is more deviating from circularity.

Substituting Eq. (2.18) into Eq. (2.9), the total pore length is obtained as follows

$$L_p = \frac{(1+q)^2}{k^2}L, \quad \left(\frac{L_p}{L} = \frac{(1+q)^2}{k^2}\right),...\text{constant.} \qquad ... (2.19)$$

Substituting Eq. (2.18) into Eq. (2.8), the equivalent pore diameter is obtained as follows

$$d_p = \frac{k}{1+q}\sqrt{\frac{\mu}{1-\mu}}\frac{1-\mu}{\mu}d = \frac{k}{1+q}\sqrt{\frac{1-\mu}{\mu}}d, \quad \left(\frac{d_p}{d} = \frac{k}{1+q}\sqrt{\frac{1-\mu}{\mu}}\right). \qquad ... (2.20)$$

Note: Here also a suitable value of k is necessary to determine empirically in relation to a particular physical process.

Generalized pores (variant III). Equations (2.16) and (2.20) express the equivalent pore diameter, and Eqs. (2.17) and (2.19) express the total pore length. The difference between these expressions is due to the exponent of the fraction $(1 - \mu)/\mu$. This facilitates to generalize the previous expressions and introduce the following empirical relation to calculate the equivalent pore diameter

$$d_p = \frac{k}{1+q}\left(\frac{1-\mu}{\mu}\right)^a d, \quad \left(\frac{d_p}{d} = \frac{k}{1+q}\left(\frac{1-\mu}{\mu}\right)^a\right). \qquad \dots (2.21)$$

The value of parameter a lies probably in the interval $\langle 0.5; 1\rangle$.

From Eqs. (2.8) and (2.21), the pore shape factor can be expressed as follows

$$\frac{1+q_p}{1+q}\frac{1-\mu}{\mu}d = \frac{k}{1+q}\left(\frac{1-\mu}{\mu}\right)^a d, \quad \left(1+q_p\right)\frac{1-\mu}{\mu} = k\left(\frac{1-\mu}{\mu}\right)^a,$$

$$q_p = k\left(\frac{\mu}{1-\mu}\right)^{1-a} - 1. \qquad \dots (2.22)$$

By applying Eq. (2.22) into Eq. (2.9), the following expression for the total pore length is obtained

$$L_p = \frac{(1+q)^2}{\left\{k\left[\mu/(1-\mu)\right]^{1-a}\right\}^2}\frac{\mu}{1-\mu}L = \frac{(1+q)^2}{k^2}\left(\frac{\mu}{1-\mu}\right)^{2a-1}L,$$

$$\left(L_p/L = \left[(1+q)^2/k^2\right]\left[\mu/(1-\mu)\right]^{2a-1}\right). \qquad \dots (2.23)$$

Figure 2.5 plots the values proportional to d_p, q_p, L_p as functions of packing density μ and parameter a.

Experimental results. Three samples of layered webs of 70 g/m² made up of polyester fibers of 6.7 dtex (cylindrical, $d = 0.025$ mm, $q = 0$) were prepared by compressing a nonwoven material to constant thickness of 7 mm as shown in Fig. 2.6. The (average) pore diameter of these samples was measured by *POROMETER* ("Porous Material Inc."). The experimental values of μ and d_p are shown by three black circles in Fig. 2.7. The thick line denotes the behavior of Eq. (2.21) corresponding to the equivalent pore diameter of variant III. The dotted line indicates the behavior of Eq. (2.20) corresponding to the equivalent pore diameter of variant II. It is shown that both curves are very similar and they correspond to the experimental results very well. It can be said that the measuring instrument probably considers pores of variant II.

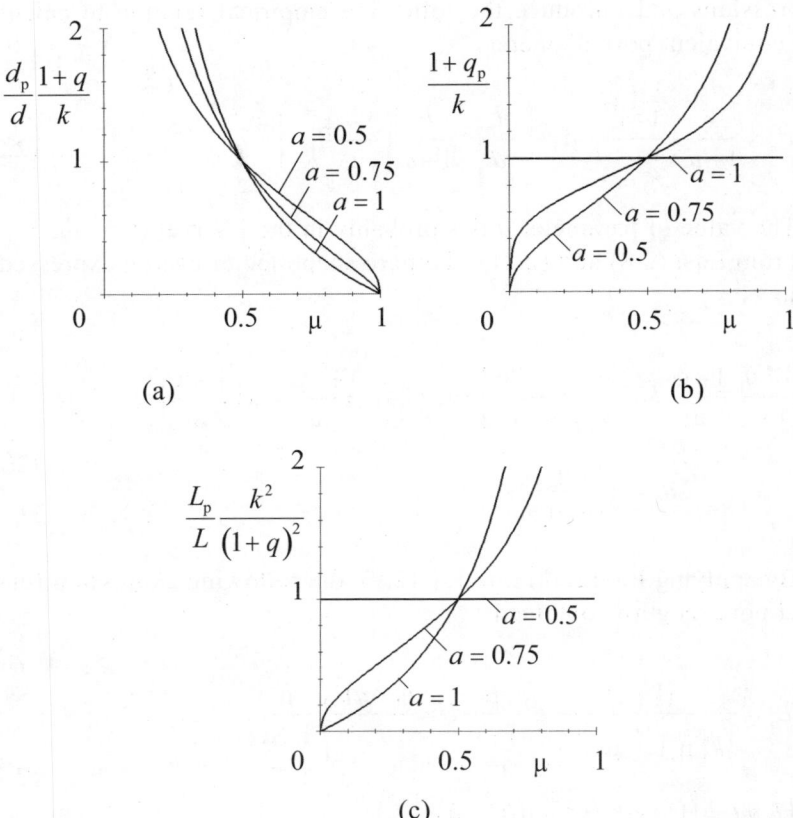

2.5 Plots of the effect of packing density on the values of d_p, q_p, and L_p for different values of parameter a. (a) Equation (2.21), (b) Equation (2.22), (c) Equation (2.23).

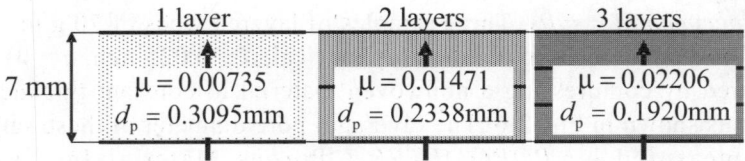

2.6 Scheme of samples prepared.

2.3   Some possible applications

Pores influence many physical processes; nevertheless, each physical process uses "its own" type of pores in the same fibrous structure. (Let us imagine it so that each physical process chooses "its own" fictive borders adequate to its physical principle).

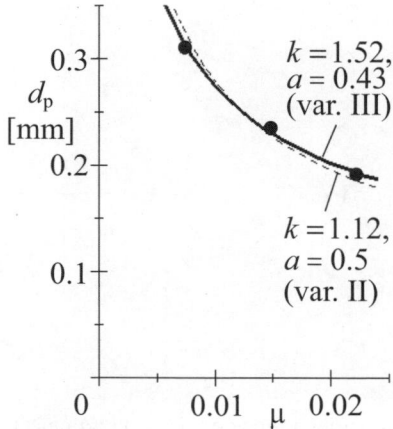

$$0.3$$
$$d_p$$
$$[mm]$$
$$0.2$$

$k = 1.52,$
$a = 0.43$
(var. III)

$k = 1.12,$
$a = 0.5$
(var. II)

$$0.1$$

$$0 \qquad 0.01 \quad \mu \quad 0.02$$

2.7 Comparison of experimental results (●) and curves derived.

Independent pore characteristics. Let us consider a fibrous assembly with equivalent fiber diameter d, fiber shape factor q, total fiber length L, and packing density μ. On the basis of these parameters, we can estimate the following pore characteristics independent of the physical process used:

1. Porosity ψ, given by Eq. (1.29)
2. Pore surface area per unit volume γ_p, given by Eq. (2.10)
3. Conventional pore diameter d_p^*, given by Eq. (2.12)
4. Conventional pore length L_p^*, given by Eq. (2.13)

Example 2.1: A shirt of mass 180 g is produced by using cotton yarn. The fiber fineness is 1.5 dtex, the fiber shape factor is $q = 0.32$, and the fiber density according to Table 1.1 is $\rho = 1520$ kg m^{-3}. According to Eq. (1.3), the total fiber length in the shirt $L = 1200$ km, and the equivalent fiber diameter according to Eq. (1.6) is $d = 0.0112$ mm. The packing density of yarn is $\mu = 0.42$. The yarn porosity according to Eq. (1.29) is found to be $\psi = 0.58$, the pore surface area per unit volume calculated from Eq. (2.10) is $\gamma_p = 341$ mm^{-1}, the conventional pore diameter given by Eq. (2.12) is $d_p^* = 0.0117$ mm, and the conventional pore length according to Eq. (2.13) is $L_p^* = 1514$ km.

Absorbency (wetting). Sometimes absorbency (wetting) of fibrous porous materials is evaluated. The fundamental idea of this process is governed by the capillarity phenomenon. Figure 2.8 shows the surface tension vectors[1] between the perpendicular immersed wall (i.e., fiber) and air σ_{12}, between the wall and liquid σ_{13}, and between the air and liquid σ_{23}

---

1. Surface tension vector represents a force per length unit.

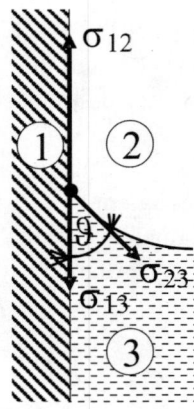

2.8 Scheme of capillary phenomenon: surface tensions ①...wall, ②...air ③...liquid.

at the common point of all these three media. A liquid column will be "pulled up" by the surface tension $\sigma_{12} - \sigma_{13}$, which is in equilibrium with the vertical component of the surface tension σ_{23} at the common point, i.e., $\sigma_{12} - \sigma_{13} = \sigma_{23} \cos \vartheta$. The value of all these surface tensions and the magnitude of angle ϑ are constant for the given three media. The entire (real) pore perimeter p_p (see Equation (2.2)) pulls up the liquid column due to the force

$p_p (\sigma_{12} - \sigma_{13}) = p_p \sigma_{23} \cos \vartheta = \pi d_p (1 + q_p) \sigma_{23} \cos \vartheta$. This force must be in equilibrium with the pressure of the pulled up liquid column. If we consider a liquid of density ρ_3, acceleration due to gravity g, and capillary column height h, then by applying Eq. (2.1), which defines the pore cross-sectional area s_p, we can estimate the volume of "pulled up" liquid column $s_p h = (\pi d_p^2 / 4) h$; the mass of the liquid column is $(\pi d_p^2 / 4) h \rho_3$. From the conditions of equilibrium, and by applying Eqs. (2.14) and (2.12), we can derive the following expression for the height of liquid column

$$\pi d_p (1 + q_p) \sigma_{23} \cos \vartheta = \frac{\pi d_p^2}{4} h \rho_3 g,$$

... (2.24)

$$h = \frac{4 \sigma_{23} \cos \vartheta (1 + q_p)}{g \rho_3} = \frac{4 \sigma_{23} \cos \vartheta}{g \rho_3} \frac{1}{d_p^*}, \quad h = \frac{4 \sigma_{23} \cos \vartheta}{g \rho_3} \frac{\mu}{1 - \mu} \frac{1 + q}{d}.$$

According to the above expression, we can state that the height of liquid column is indirectly proportional to the magnitude of the conventional pore diameter.

Example 2.2: We consider a shirt of 180g mass prepared by using cotton fibers of 1.5 dtex fineness, 0.32 shape factor, and 1520 kg m⁻³ density. The equivalent fiber diameter according to Eq. (1.6) is $d = 0.112$ mm. Let the packing density of yarn is $\mu = 0.42$. The conventional pore diameter, according to Eq. (2.12), is $d_p^* = 0.0117 \text{ mm}$. Let the surface tension between air and water be $\sigma_{23} = 0.072 \text{ N m}^{-1}$, the angle of contact be $\vartheta = 0°$, and the density of water be $\rho_3 = 1000 \text{ kg m}^{-3}$. Then the height of water column, according to Eq. (2.24), is calculated as $h = 24.50 \text{ cm}$.

The above simplified expression is obtained due to neglecting the curvature of the wall and the skewness of the pores. It is convenient to use the generalized pore diameter, i.e., the equivalent pore diameter d_p with constant shape factor (variant I) instead of conventional pore diameter d_p^*. By comparing Eqs. (2.20) and (2.12), we find the following expression for estimating the height of liquid column in case of $d_p = kd_p^*$

$$h = \frac{4\sigma_{23}\cos\vartheta}{g\rho_3}\frac{1}{kd_p^*}, \quad h = \frac{4\sigma_{23}\cos\vartheta}{g\rho_3}\frac{\mu}{1-\mu}\frac{1+q}{kd}. \qquad \ldots (2.25)$$

Generally, it is possible to use the equivalent diameter of the generalized pore d_p (variant III) instead of the conventional pore diameter d_p^*. In this case, by comparing Eqs. (2.21) and (2.12), we find $d_p = kd_p^*\left[\mu/(1-\mu)\right]^{1-a}$. Then, we obtain the following expression for estimating the height of liquid column

$$h = \frac{4\sigma_{23}\cos\vartheta}{g\rho_3}\left(\frac{1-\mu}{\mu}\right)^{1-a}\frac{1}{kd_p^*}, \quad h = \frac{4\sigma_{23}\cos\vartheta}{g\rho_3}\left(\frac{\mu}{1-\mu}\right)^{a}\frac{1+q}{kd}. \qquad \ldots (2.26)$$

In this case, the parameters k and a are required to be found out experimentally.

Laminar flow. The way of thinking, which was used to formulate the expressions related to absorbency (wetting), can be extended to the laminar flow through porous fibrous assemblies. (Such flow is applied also in "air flow meters" to estimate fiber finesses – Micronaire, W.I.R.A. apparatus, etc.).

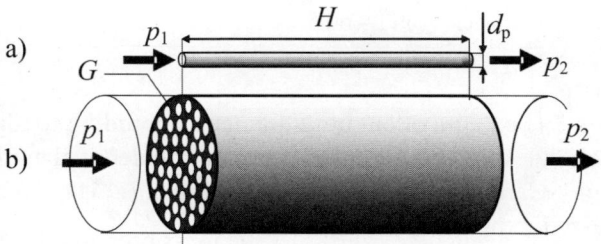

2.9 Scheme of fluid flow through a porous material.

Figure 2.9a shows one idealized pore in a form of a thin cylindrical tube of diameter d_p and length H. Due to the pressure drop $\Delta p = p_1 - p_2$, fluid of volume Q_1 will flow per unit time through the tube. According to the well-known Hagen-Poiseuille's law, the fluid volume is

$$Q_1 = \frac{\pi d_p^4}{128\eta} \frac{\Delta p}{H} \qquad \qquad \dots (2.27)$$

where η is the dynamic viscosity of fluid.

The flow of fluid through the porous fibrous material is shown in Fig. 2.9b. The total cross-sectional area of the material is G. Then pore area is $G(1-\mu)$. We assume that the pores are formed from a lot of such thin tubes as shown in Fig. 2.9a. The number of such tubes n_p found in the porous fibrous material is obtained by applying Eq. (2.1) as follows

$$n_p = G(1-\mu)/s_p = 4G(1-\mu)/(\pi d_p^2). \qquad \dots (2.28)$$

The volume of fluid flowing through the porous material per unit time is

$$Q = Q_1 n_p = \frac{G(1-\mu)d_p^2}{32\eta} \frac{\Delta p}{H}. \qquad \dots (2.29)$$

By substituting the expression for fiber surface area per unit volume γ and applying Eq. (1.18) into Eq. (2.21) for equivalent pore diameter (variant III), we obtain

$$d_p = \frac{4k}{\gamma}\left(\frac{1-\mu}{\mu}\right)^a. \qquad \dots (2.30)$$

By applying Eq. (2.30) into Eq. (2.29) and rearranging, we find the following expression for Q

$$Q = \frac{k^2}{2} \frac{A}{\gamma^2\eta} \frac{\Delta p}{H} \frac{(1-\mu)^{2a+1}}{\mu^{2a}}. \qquad \dots (2.31)$$

In case $a = 1$ (i.e., equivalent pore diameter according to alternative I), we can recognize that the above expression is identical with the well-known Kozeny-Carman's equation. For $a \neq 1$, Eq. (2.31) can be regarded as a generalized expression.

Example 2.3: Let us consider that a shirt of 150 g m^{-2} areal density and 0.5 mm thickness, made up of cotton fibers of 1.5 dtex fineness, 0.32 shape factor, and 1520 kg m⁻³ density, is tested for its air flow behavior. The pressure drop across the fabric is maintained at 125 Pa and the cross-sectional area of the fabric under the test is 38.30 cm². The equivalent fiber diameter according to Eq. (1.6) is $d = 0.112$ mm. The packing density of the fabric, according to Eq. (1.27), is $\mu = 0.1974$. The conventional pore diameter, according to Eq. (2.12), is $d_p^* = 0.0370$ mm. Let the dynamic viscosity of air be $\eta = 1.78 \times 10^{-5}$ Pa s. Then, the volumetric rate of air flow through the fabric is calculated by using Eq. (2.29) as $Q = 0.001847$ m³ s⁻¹.

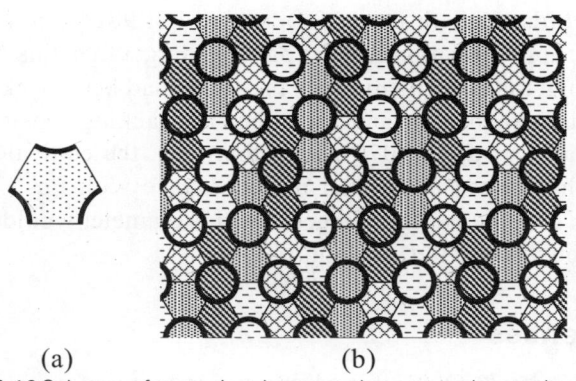

(a)   (b)

2.10 Scheme of pores in a hexagonal structure (example of variant II).

Filtration of particles. We now consider the problem of filtration of particles by using an assembly of almost parallel fibers (In a real assembly, the fibers are randomly oriented). These fibers are oriented in the fibrous assembly in a similar manner as they are oriented in a regular hexagonal structure as shown earlier in Fig. 2.5. The cross-section of the fibers is assumed to be circular with equivalent fiber diameter d (The fiber shape factor q equals to zero). The distance joining the fiber surfaces h is considered as the pore fictive borders and the sections of such pores have similar shape as shown in Fig. 2.10a. The pores create imaginary pipes of length equal to the fiber length.

The number of such pores is twice the number of fibers. It is shown in Fig. 2.10b that the fibers of the same design (shading) have one pore "over" and another one "under" fiber. It is valid that $L_p/L = 2$. This means that we are dealing with pores of constant length (alternative II). According to Eq. (2.19), $k/(1+q) = 1/\sqrt{2}$, i.e., equivalent pore diameter, according to Eq. (2.20), is

$$d_p = \frac{1}{\sqrt{2}}\sqrt{\frac{1-\mu}{\mu}}d. \qquad\qquad \dots (2.32)$$

Probably, as a first approximation, this value corresponds to the commensurable size of the particles, which passes through the filter. The most general solution can be established if we consider variant III to calculate the equivalent pore diameter from Eq. (2.20) or (2.21) after estimating the parameter k or the two parameters k and a based on experimental data.

Example 2.4: Let us consider that the circular polyester fibers of 20 micron diameter are packed according to a regular hexagonal structure in a fibrous filter medium such that the packing density of such a structure is $\mu = 0.2270$. The equivalent pore diameter of such a structure can be calculated in accordance with Eq. (2.32) as $d_p = 114.9824$ μm. It can be then said as a first approximation that the particles larger than this diameter cannot pass through the filter medium. If the fibers had been packed most tightly in a regular hexagonal arrangement then the packing density would have been calculated as $\mu = 0.9070$ and in that case, the equivalent pore diameter would have been calculated in accordance with Eq. (2.32) as $d_p = 4.9936$ μm. Then, the particles larger than this diameter wouldn't have been passing through the filter medium.

2.4   References

1. Jena, A., and Gupta, K. (2003). Liquid extrusion techniques for pore structure evaluation of nonwovens, *International Nonwovens Journal*, 45–53.
2. Jena, A., and Gupta, K. (2002). Measurement of pore volume and flow through porous materials, *Materialprüfung*, **44**, 243.
3. Miller, B., and Tyomkin, I. (1994). Liquid porosimetry: New methodology and applications, *Journal of Colloid and Interface Science*, **162**, 163–170.
4. Kozeny, J. (1927). Ueber kapillare Leitung des Wassers im Boden, Sitzungsber Akad. Wiss., *Wien*, **136**, 271–306 (German).
5. Carman, P. C. (1937) Fluid flow through granular beds, *Transactions*, Institute of Chemical Engineers, London, **15**, 150–166.
6. Carman, P. C. (2010) Flow of gasses through porous media, Butterworths, London.
7. International Organization for Standardization (2010). Geotextiles and geotextile-related products – determination of the characteristic opening size, ISO 12956.
8. Faure, Y. H., Gourc, J. P., Millot, F., and Sunjoto, S. (1986). Theoretical and experimental determination of the filtration opening size, *Proceedings of the Third International Conference on Geotextiles*, Vienna, 1275–1280.
9. Faure, Y. H., Gourc, J. P., and Gendrin, P. (1990). Structural study of porometry and filtration opening size of geotextiles, In *Geosynthetics: Microstructure and Performance* (ed. Peggs, I. D.), **1076**, 102–119.
10. Lombard, G., Rollin A., and Wolff, C. (1989). Theoretical and experimental opening sizes of heat-bonded geotextiles, *Textile Research Journal*, **59**, 208–217.

11. Simmonds, G. E., Bomberger, J. D., and Bryner, M. A. (2007). Designing nonwovens to meet pore size specifications, *Journal of Engineered Fibres and Fabrics*, **2**(1), 1–15.
12. Neckář, B., and Ibrahim, S. (2003). Theoretical approach for determining pore characteristics between fibers, *Textile Research Journal*, **73**, 611–619..

Arrangement of fibers – fiber orientation

3.1   Fiber orientation and its general description

Empirical meaning of orientation. The arrangement of fibers in a fibrous assembly should be described not only by their packing characteristics, but also by their directional arrangement. The directional arrangement of fibers is often referred to fiber orientation. The orientation of fibers in a fibrous assembly primarily determines its geometrical and mechanical properties.

It is well known that the cotton-carded ring spun yarns are stronger than the rotor yarns spun from the same material. The friction spun yarns are weaker than those spun by the ring or rotor spinning technology. The higher strength of combed yarns is achieved not only due to the removal of short fibers, but also due to almost perfect fiber orientation. The differences in yarn properties are obtained mainly due to different degrees of "fiber parallelization" or fiber orientation [1]. (It ranges from almost parallel fiber structure to the so-called "sauerkraut" structure).

The orientation of fibers also determines the anisotropy in mechanical properties of fibrous webs which are used to prepare nonwoven or composite structures. The fibrous composites are known to be stronger and stiffer in the direction at which most of the fibres are oriented and weaker and more compliant in the direction of least orientation [2]. The orientation of fibres also determines the fluid permeability and fluid absorption behaviours. It is known that a fibrous porous material exhibits higher permeability when its constituent fibres are aligned with the flow of a fluid as compared to when the fibres are oriented across the flow of the fluid [3]. The anisotropy in fluid absorption of a fibrous material can also be explained by the orientation of fibres [4]. The orientation of fibres is considered to be one of the very important characteristics of a tissue engineering scaffold as it greatly influences the orientation of cells, growth of tissues, and other related functions of the tissues [5]. Sometimes a variety of fiber arrangement is required in a fibrous assembly to meet a set of pre-defined mechanical properties. There are several sophisticated and expensive technologies available today that are being used for layering of textile layers in defined directions (for example, tri-axial fabric manufacturing technology, which was developed during Apollo shuttle program). Recent advances in electrospinning especially in the design of web collection devices made it possible to create nano-fibrous scaffolds with controlled fibre orientation [5].

The natural vegetable and animal tissues also "utilize" the advantage of fiber orientation. The longitudinal orientation of grass or straw imparts more mechanical resistance against the stresses created by wind. The structure of bone is oriented in the most frequent stressing direction. From mechanical point of view, the spider web is found to have almost optimum "network" structure.

Concept of orientation vector. Figure 3.1 illustrates the curvature of a single fiber, which varies widely in a fibrous assembly; thus the term "orientation" is not clear, but it can be intuitively thought. Therefore, the term "orientation" is required to be exactly defined.

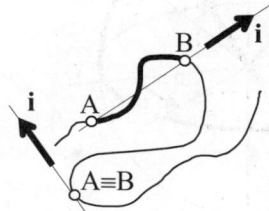

3.1 Orientation vector of a fiber segment.

Let us consider a fiber segment of finite length (e.g., the segment AB shown by thick black line in Fig. 3.1), which can be designated by a suitable orientation vector **i**. Conventionally, this is implemented according to the following considerations:

1. The orientation vector has a direction of joining the end points (A and B) of the fiber segment.
2. The orientation vector is unitary.

At any arbitrary point on a fiber, a very short length (infinitely short segment) can be defined. (The curvature of fibers is considered as a smooth curve). Then, the end points A≡B of such segments coincide. Accordingly, the orientation vector follows the direction of the tangent to the fiber curvature as shown in Fig. 3.1.

Note: It is obvious that the orientation vector depends on the pre-defined length and pre-defined direction of the selected fiber segment.

Spatial coordinates of orientation vectors. The unit vector **i** shown in Fig. 3.2 can be defined in a three-dimensional space by three Cartesian

·coordinates x_1, x_2, x_3, or by spherical coordinates r (radius), ϑ (angle of inclination to x_3-axis) and φ (angle of inclination to x_1-axis). In this case, it is always valid that $r = 1$ (unit vector) and the angles can generally lie in the intervals $\vartheta \in \langle 0, \pi \rangle$, and $\varphi \in \langle 0, 2\pi \rangle$. The two vectors **i** and $-$**i** shown in Fig. 3.2, however, represent the same direction. (In reality, a fiber segment is not identical to an arrow). Let us therefore accept a convention that the angle ϑ of the directional vector lies in the interval $\vartheta \in (0, \pi/2)$. (We use the upper hemisphere only, shown in Fig. 3.2). So, each orientation vector is given by a couple of angles $\vartheta \in \langle 0, \pi/2 \rangle$ and $\varphi \in \langle 0, 2\pi \rangle$.

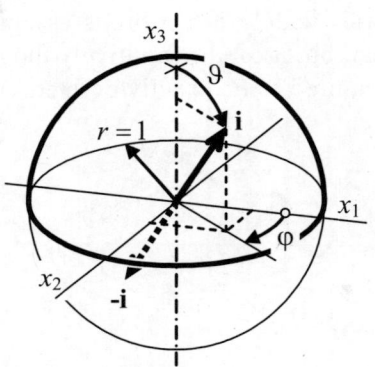

3.2 Spherical coordinates of orientation.

Note: More precisely, if $\vartheta = \pi/2$ then $\varphi \in \langle 0, \pi \rangle$, but if $\vartheta = 0$ then φ is not defined. Nevertheless, these details do not play any role when we think about continuous directional distribution of fiber segments. It is therefore sufficient to define the range of possible directions more easily by using a couple of open intervals $\vartheta \in (0, \pi/2)$ and $\varphi \in (0, 2\pi)$. Furthermore, the range of directions of fiber segments can be represented by the symbol ω as shown below

$$\omega : \vartheta \in (0, \pi/2) \wedge \varphi \in (0, 2\pi). \qquad \qquad ... (3.1)$$

Probability density functions. Let us take that the joint probability density function $w(\vartheta, \varphi)$ describes the distribution of directions of the defined fiber segments in the fibrous assembly. Of course, it is valid to write that

$$\int_\omega w(\vartheta,\varphi)\,d\vartheta\,d\varphi = \iint_{\substack{\vartheta \in (0,\pi/2), \\ \varphi \in (0,2\pi)}} w(\vartheta,\varphi)\,d\vartheta\,d\varphi = 1. \qquad \qquad \dots (3.2)$$

Let us remember the logical sense of the expression $w(\vartheta, \varphi)\,d\vartheta\,d\varphi$. This expresses the relative frequency and/or probability[1] that an orientation vector falls in an elementary "class" of vectors, where the first angle lies in an interval ranging from ϑ to $\vartheta + d\vartheta$, and the second angle lies in another interval ranging from φ to $\varphi + d\varphi$ – see the shaded area EFGH shown in Fig. 3.3.

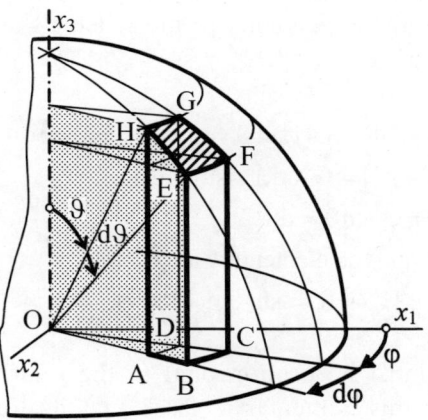

3.3 The graphical scheme of elemental "class".

Often, we need to know the distribution (marginal distribution) of the angle ϑ only, i.e., the distribution of angle of fiber segments with respect to a given direction (here, x_3-axis). The corresponding probability density function $u(\vartheta)$ of the angle ϑ is defined as follows

$$u(\vartheta) = \int_0^{2\pi} w(\vartheta,\varphi)\,d\varphi. \qquad \qquad \dots (3.3)$$

Of course, the expression $\int_0^{\pi/2} u(\vartheta)\,d\vartheta = 1$ must be valid.

---

1. The relative frequency is usually determined after experimentation or similar activity and we obtain it "ex post" – after our activity. The value of the relative frequency in a class can be utilized to determine (estimate) the probability of occurrence of that value in the mentioned class and we obtain it "ex ante" – before our activity.

Isotropic orientation – easiest case. If the relative frequencies and/or probabilities of the orientation vectors have an identical value in each possible direction then such orientation is known to be isotropic orientation. We can imagine that the set of all orientation vectors, going out from the origin of coordinates, as a "hedgehog" of arrows, whose end-points are lying on the surface of the unitary hemisphere. The "areal density" of such end-points of the orientation vectors is just constant in the case of isotropic structure. This idea allows us to derive the joint probability density function w (ϑ, φ) in this case.

The elementary area EFGH shown in Fig. 3.3 represents an elementary "class" that is determined by the angles ranging from ϑ to $\vartheta + d\vartheta$ and from φ to $\varphi + d\varphi$. From the geometry of the scheme shown in Fig. 3.3, it is valid to write that

$$\left. \begin{aligned} OA &= OD = OH \sin \vartheta = \sin \vartheta, \\ HG &= AD = OA\, d\varphi = \sin \vartheta\, d\varphi, \\ HE &= OH\, d\vartheta = d\vartheta, \\ &\text{and the elementary area} \\ EFGH &= HG \cdot HE = \sin \vartheta\, d\varphi\, d\vartheta \end{aligned} \right\} . \qquad \ldots (3.4)$$

The area EFGH must be proportional to the relative frequency of orientation vectors in this elementary "class", i.e., the area is proportional to the expression $w(\vartheta, \varphi)\, d\vartheta d\varphi$. Thus we obtain

$$w(\vartheta, \varphi)\, d\vartheta\, d\varphi = k \sin \vartheta\, d\varphi\, d\vartheta, \quad w(\vartheta, \varphi) = k \sin \vartheta. \qquad \ldots (3.5)$$

We can determine the proportionality constant k, common for all directions, by substituting the last expression from Eq. (3.5) to Eq. (3.2) as shown below

$$1 = \iint\limits_{\substack{\vartheta \in (0, \pi/2), \\ \varphi \in (0, 2\pi)}} k \sin \vartheta\, d\vartheta\, d\varphi = k \int_0^{\pi/2} \sin \vartheta \left(\int_0^{2\pi} d\varphi \right) d\vartheta = 2\pi k, \quad k = \frac{1}{2\pi}. \qquad \ldots (3.6)$$

We can then find the joint probability density function of orientation vectors in the case of isotropic orientation in space by substituting the value of k from Eq. (3.6) to Eq. (3.5). This is shown below

$$w(\vartheta, \varphi) = \frac{\sin \vartheta}{2\pi}. \qquad \ldots (3.7)$$

The corresponding distribution (marginal distribution) of the angle ϑ can be obtained by using Eqs. (3.3) and (3.7) as follows

$$u(\vartheta) = \int_{0}^{2\pi} \frac{\sin \vartheta}{2\pi} \, d\varphi = \sin \vartheta. \qquad \qquad \dots (3.8)$$

3.2   Fiber orientation in a sectional plane

We often theoretically work with the idea of imaginary sections of a fibrous assembly for studying different physical phenomena, especially in mechanics. In some other cases, it is possible to work with the real sections of a fibrous assembly (e.g., preparation for microscopic analysis), or with real clamping line (jaws of dynamometer). In these cases, a question may arise, what is the directional distribution of the very short fiber segments that are just intersected by the real or imaginary sectional plane?

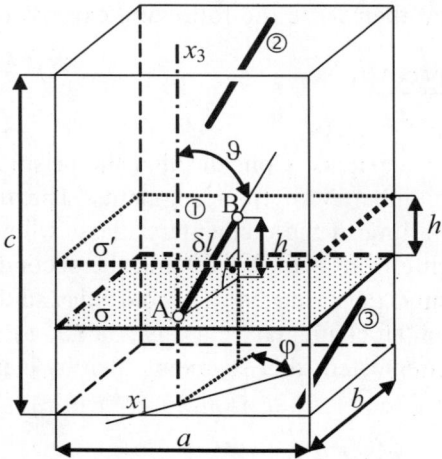

3.4 Scheme of intersection of a fibrous assembly by a sectional planes.

Modeling concept. Let us think about the distribution of very short fiber segments, so that they have a straight shape as short abscissas. A prism of dimensions a, b, c shown in Fig. 3.4 represents either a fibrous assembly or a part of the fibrous assembly. The dotted sectional plane σ, perpendicular to x_3-axis[2], can cut a large number of fiber segments of very short constant length. One such fiber segment of length δl is shown in Fig. 3.4. The directions of the fiber segments are described by the angles ϑ and φ.

---

2.   If the sectional plane σ is not perpendicular to the original x_3-axis, it is necessary to do the corresponding orthogonal transformation of the coordinate system.

The fiber segment ① has its lower end A just touching the sectional plane σ and upper end B lying over the sectional plane. The distance between the lower and upper ends of this fiber segment is given by

$$h = \delta l \cos \vartheta. \qquad \qquad \text{... (3.9)}$$

Another parallel plane σ' lying over the sectional plane σ at a distance h is also shown in Fig. 3.4. Evidently, it contains the upper end B of the fiber segment ①.

Probability of intersection. Let us now think about all fiber segments whose directions are determined by the values of angles ϑ and φ. The sectional plane σ cuts some of these segments, while it cannot cut others such as segments ② and ③ as shown in Fig. 3.4. Evidently, each intersected segment must have its upper end B lying between the sectional plane σ and the parallel plane σ'. If the distribution of directions of fiber segments in the prism is homogenous then the probability P_ϑ of section is given by the ratio of the volume between the planes σ and σ' to the volume of the prism[3]. Using Eq. (3.9) we can then write the following expression

$$P_\vartheta = \frac{abh}{abc} = \frac{h}{c} = \frac{\delta l \cos \vartheta}{c}. \qquad \qquad \text{... (3.10)}$$

Number of intersected fiber segments. Consider that the prism shown in Fig. 3.4 contains a large number N of fiber segments. The relative frequency of fiber segments falling in the elementary class, whose first angle lies in the interval ranging from ϑ to $\vartheta + d\vartheta$ and the second angle lies in the interval ranging from φ to $\varphi + d\varphi$, is $w(\vartheta, \varphi) \, d\vartheta \, d\varphi$, so that the number of fibers falling in such an elementary class is $N \, w(\vartheta, \varphi) \, d\vartheta \, d\varphi$. If dn denotes the number of intersected fiber segments then by using Eq. (3.10), we can write

$$dn = P_\vartheta \left[N \, w(\vartheta, \varphi) \, d\vartheta \, d\varphi \right] = \frac{N \delta l \cos \vartheta}{c} w(\vartheta, \varphi) \, d\vartheta \, d\varphi. \qquad \text{... (3.11)}$$

The number of all intersected fiber segments in the prism can be found out by means of integration of the previous expression over all possible directions. This is shown by using Eq. (3.3) as follows

$$n = \int_\omega dn = \frac{N \delta l}{c} \int_\omega \cos \vartheta \, w(\vartheta, \varphi) \, d\vartheta \, d\varphi, \qquad \qquad \text{... (3.12a)}$$

---

3.   This is in accordance with the geometrical definition of probability.

$$n = \frac{N\delta l}{c} \int\limits_0^{\pi/2} \cos\vartheta \left[\int\limits_0^{2\pi} w(\vartheta,\varphi)\, d\varphi \right] d\vartheta = \frac{N\delta l}{c} \int\limits_0^{\pi/2} \cos\vartheta\, u(\vartheta)\, d\vartheta. \quad \cdots (3.12b)$$

Probability density function of fiber orientation in a section. The joint probability density function of the directional distribution of the intersected fiber segments is denoted by $w^*(\vartheta, \varphi)$. The relative frequency of the intersected fiber segments falling in the elementary class ranging from ϑ to $\vartheta + d\vartheta$ and from φ to $\varphi + d\varphi$ is $w^*(\vartheta, \varphi)\, d\vartheta\, d\varphi$, but this – based on the general meaning of relative frequency – is also given by the ratio dn/n. So, it is valid to write that $w^*(\vartheta,\varphi)\, d\vartheta\, d\varphi = dn/n$. This expression can be written by applying Eqs. (3.11), (3.12) and (3.3) as follows in order to obtain the following expression for $w^*(\vartheta, \varphi)$

$$w^*(\vartheta,\varphi)\, d\vartheta\, d\varphi = \frac{dn}{n} = \frac{\cos\vartheta\, w(\vartheta,\varphi)\, d\vartheta\, d\varphi}{\int\limits_\omega \cos\vartheta\, w(\vartheta,\varphi)\, d\vartheta\, d\varphi},$$

$$\cdots (3.13a)$$

$$w^*(\vartheta,\varphi) = \frac{\cos\vartheta\, w(\vartheta,\varphi)}{\int\limits_\omega \cos\vartheta\, w(\vartheta,\varphi)\, d\vartheta\, d\varphi},$$

$$w^*(\vartheta,\varphi)\, d\vartheta\, d\varphi = \frac{dn}{n} = \frac{\cos\vartheta\, w(\vartheta,\varphi)\, d\vartheta\, d\varphi}{\int\limits_0^{\pi/2} \cos\vartheta\, u(\vartheta)\, d\vartheta},$$

$$\cdots (3.13b)$$

$$w^*(\vartheta,\varphi) = \frac{\cos\vartheta\, w(\vartheta,\varphi)}{\int\limits_0^{\pi/2} \cos\vartheta\, u(\vartheta)\, d\vartheta}.$$

Often we need to know the distribution (marginal distribution) of the angle ϑ of the intersected fiber segments only. The corresponding probability density function $u^*(\vartheta)$ can be found out by using Eqs. (3.13) and (3.3) as follows

$$u^*(\vartheta) = \int\limits_0^{2\pi} w^*(\vartheta,\varphi)\, d\varphi = \frac{\cos\vartheta \int\limits_0^{2\pi} w(\vartheta,\varphi)\, d\varphi}{\int\limits_0^{\pi/2} \cos\vartheta\, u(\vartheta)\, d\vartheta} = \frac{\cos\vartheta\, u(\vartheta)}{\int\limits_0^{\pi/2} \cos\vartheta\, u(\vartheta)\, d\vartheta}. \quad \cdots (3.14)$$

3.3   Mean sectional area of fiber, coefficient k_n and number of fibers in a section

Areas of fiber sections. Figure 3.5 illustrates a very short fiber segment of length δl. It makes an angle ϑ to the normal x_3 of the sectional plane. The sectional area of the fiber is s^* and the cross-sectional area, perpendicular to the fiber axis is s. It is evident that $s \leq s^*$. The height of the fiber segment perpendicular to the sectional plane is denoted by $\delta y \leq \delta l$. The expression $\cos \vartheta = \delta y / \delta l$ can be found out from Fig. 3.5. The volume of the observed (shaded) fiber section can be expressed in two ways: either by the product $s\,\delta l$, or by the product $s^* \delta y$. It is valid that $s\,\delta l = s^* \delta y$. Accordingly, the following expression can be obtained for the fiber sectional area

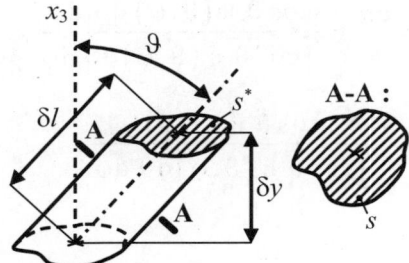

3.5 Scheme of inclined fiber section.

$$s^* = \frac{s}{\delta y / \delta l} = \frac{s}{\cos \vartheta}. \qquad \dots (3.15)$$

In the sectional plane of the fibrous assembly, we find many fiber segments that have different values of the angle ϑ. Consequently, we obtain different values for the sectional area s^*. We assume that all the fibers in the fibrous assembly have the same cross-sectional area[4] s. The mean value of the fiber sectional area $\overline{s^*}$ can then be expressed by $\overline{s^*} = \int_0^{\pi/2} s^* u^*(\vartheta)\,d\vartheta$.

(The distribution of angle ϑ is described by the probability density function $u^*(\vartheta)$). Using Eqs. (3.14) and (3.15) the following expression can be obtained for $\overline{s^*}$

---

4.   In general, it is assumed that the fiber cross-sectional area is a random variable, but it is statistically independent to the angle ϑ. Then, the magnitude of s can be considered as the mean area of fiber cross-sections.

$$\overline{s^*} = \int_0^{\pi/2} \left[\frac{s}{\cos \vartheta} \right] \left[\frac{\cos \vartheta\, u(\vartheta)}{\int_0^{\pi/2} \cos \vartheta\, u(\vartheta)\, d\vartheta} \right] d\vartheta$$

$$= \frac{s}{\int_0^{\pi/2} \cos \vartheta\, u(\vartheta)\, d\vartheta} \int_0^{\pi/2} u(\vartheta)\, d\vartheta = \qquad \text{... (3.16)}$$

$$= \frac{s}{\int_0^{\pi/2} \cos \vartheta\, u(\vartheta)\, d\vartheta}.$$

Coefficient k_n. Let us define a coefficient k_n as follows

$$k_n = s/\overline{s^*}, \quad k_n \le 1 \qquad \text{... (3.17)}$$

It expresses the ratio of the area of fiber cross-section s to the mean value of fiber sectional area $\overline{s^*}$. The expression $\overline{s^*} = s$ corresponds to a cross-section of perfectly parallel fiber bundle; $k_n = 1$ in such case. Otherwise, the expression $k_n < 1$ is valid. Comparing Eqs. (3.16) and (3.17) we find the following expression for k_n

$$k_n = \int_0^{\pi/2} \cos \vartheta\, u(\vartheta)\, d\vartheta. \qquad \text{... (3.18)}$$

Note: The quantity k_n is also equal to the arithmetic mean of $\cos\vartheta$, calculated using all fiber segments in the fibrous assembly. (The angle ϑ is measured from the x_3-axis which is chosen to be perpendicular to the sectional plane).

Applying Eq. (3.18) into Eqs. (3.13) and (3.14), we can write

$$w^*(\vartheta, \varphi) = \frac{\cos \vartheta\, w(\vartheta, \varphi)}{k_n}, \qquad \text{... (3.19)}$$

$$u^*(\vartheta) = \frac{\cos \vartheta\, u(\vartheta)}{k_n}. \qquad \text{... (3.20)}$$

Isotropic orientation. Generally, the value of the coefficient k_n depends on the direction of intersection of the fibrous assembly in space. Nevertheless, the coefficient k_n takes on a constant value for each direction of intersection in an isotropically orientated assembly, for which the probability density function as expressed in Eq. (3.8) is valid. Then, the following value can be obtained for k_n using Eq. (3.18)

$$k_n = \int_0^{\pi/2} \cos\vartheta\, u(\vartheta)\, d\vartheta = \int_0^{\pi/2} \cos\vartheta \sin\vartheta\, d\vartheta = \left(\frac{\sin^2\vartheta}{2}\right)_0^{\pi/2} = \frac{1}{2}. \qquad \ldots (3.21)$$

Substituting Eqs. (3.7), (3.8), and (3.21) into Eqs. (3.19) and (3.20), we obtain the following expressions

$$w^*(\vartheta,\varphi) = \frac{\cos\vartheta\, \dfrac{\sin\vartheta}{2\pi}}{1/2} = \frac{\sin 2\vartheta}{2\pi}, \qquad \ldots (3.22)$$

$$u^*(\vartheta) = \frac{\cos\vartheta \sin\vartheta}{1/2} = \sin 2\vartheta. \qquad \ldots (3.23)$$

The behaviors of these two functions are shown in Fig. 3.6.

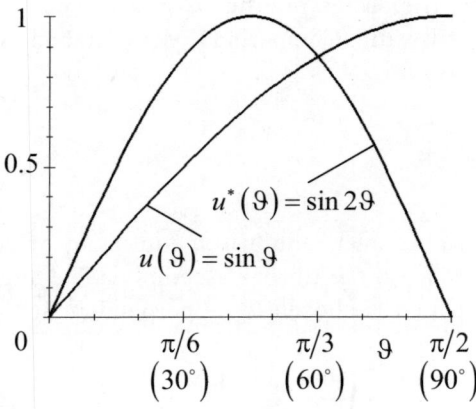

3.6 Behavior of probability density functions for isotropic orientation in space.

Note: Let us intuitively think the spatial isotropic orientation as a homogenous "hedgehog" of arrows. A number (frequency) of such arrows in the surrounding of $\vartheta \to \pi/2$ is much more higher than that in the surrounding of $\vartheta \to 0$; the function $u(\vartheta)$ is increasing. On the other hand, the number (frequency) of intersected arrows is small not only in the surrounding of $\vartheta \to 0$ (small number of arrows), but also in the surrounding of $\vartheta \to \pi/2$ (a large number of arrows, but with small probability of intersection – see P_ϑ as stated in Eq. (3.10)).

Number of sectioned fibers per unit sectional area. Let us consider a general fibrous assembly as shown in Fig. 3.7. This is intersected by a plane

σ, perpendicular to x_3-axis. The intersected section is characterized by the total sectional area S_c, packing density μ, and coefficient k_n. The (shaded) area occupied by the fiber sections is equal to $S_c\mu$, the mean sectional area per one fiber is equal to $\overline{s^*}$, and the number of fibers (inside the sectional area S_c) is equal to $n = S_c\mu/\overline{s^*}$. Finally, the number of sectioned fibers per unit sectional area is equal to $\upsilon_S = n/S_c$. Applying Eqs. (1.5), (1.25), (1.27) and (3.17), we can write the following expression for υ_S

$$\upsilon_S = \frac{n}{S_c} = \frac{\mu}{\overline{s^*}} = \mu\frac{k_n}{s} = \frac{\mu\rho}{t}k_n = \frac{\rho^*}{t}k_n. \qquad \qquad \dots (3.24)$$

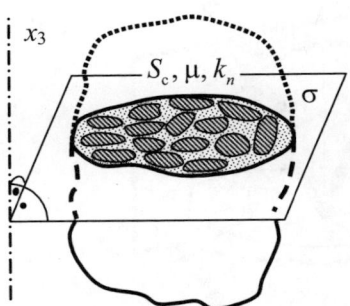

3.7 Cross-section of a general fibrous assembly.

Example 3.1: A bale of cotton fibers of fineness $t = 1.6$ dtex has dimensions 1.6m × 0.7m × 0.6m, and its mass is $m = 230$ kg. The fibers in the bale are distributed randomly, i.e., isotropic distribution in a three-dimensional space. Accordingly, the bale volume is calculated as $V_c = 0.672$ m^3. According to Eq. (1.26), the bale density is determined as $\rho^* = 342.3$ kg m^{-3}. According to Eq. (3.21), the value of coefficient k_n is obtained as 0.5. The number of sectioned fibers by the sectional plane per unit area according to Eq. (3.24) is obtained as $\upsilon_S = 1069.7$ mm^{-2}.

3.4   Model of fiber orientation in plane

It is possible, in principle, to find an application of the earlier expressions for fiber orientation in space, but this is practically very difficult. The joint probability density function $w(\vartheta, \varphi)$ is necessary to be found out and/or verified experimentally and this is usually very complicated[5].

---

5. It is sometimes possible to obtain a special set of sections of fibrous assembly experimentally and evaluate this section by using some regulations from stereology.

Nevertheless, a variety of fibrous assemblies (e.g., thin fibrous layers like card web, etc.) have their structures similar to an ideal model of two-dimensional fibrous structure. In such case we assume that each fiber curvature follows a planar curve and all such curves are lying on one plane only.

Coordinates and orientation vectors in plane. Let us consider that all the orientation vectors are lying only in one plane α containing x_3-axis as shown in Fig. 3.8. The spherical co-ordinate φ may take only two values, $\varphi_\alpha < \pi$ and $\varphi_\alpha + \pi$. This is, for example, in case of vectors $\mathbf{i}_1$ and $\mathbf{i}_2$ that have the same value of angle ϑ.

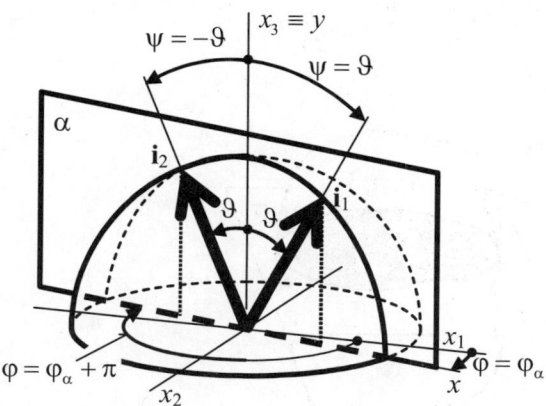

3.8 Orientation in plane.

It is easier to transfer the spherical coordinates in the plane α shown in Fig. 3.8 to the polar coordinates of radius r and coordinate angle ψ as stated below:

1. Rename x_3 axis by y-axis,
2. Rename the intersecting line of plane α and the plane of axes x_1, x_2 by "x-axis",
3. Define the radius coordinate $r = 1$ (orientation vectors are unitary), similar to the spherical coordinate,
4. Describe the orientation angle by the following expressions

$$\left.\begin{array}{l} \psi = \vartheta, \quad \text{when } \varphi < \pi \\ \psi = -\vartheta, \text{when } \varphi \geq \pi \end{array}\right\} \Rightarrow \ \psi \in (-\pi/2, \pi/2). \qquad \ldots (3.25)$$

Example 3.2: The spherical coordinates of vector $\mathbf{i}_1$ shown in Fig. 3.8 are $r = 1$, $\vartheta = \pi/6\,(30°)$, $\varphi = \pi/12\,(15°)$. For vector $\mathbf{i}_2$, the spherical coordinates are $r = 1$, $\vartheta = \pi/6\,(30°)$, $\varphi = \pi/12 + \pi/2 = \pi\,7/12\,(195°)$. According to Eq. (3.25), the polar coordinates of $\mathbf{i}_1$ and $\mathbf{i}_2$ are given by $r = 1$, $\psi = \pi/6\,(30°)$ and $r = 1$, $\psi = -\pi/6\,(-30°)$, respectively.

Pure random (isotropic) fiber orientation in plane. Let us consider a fiber from a fibrous assembly in plane and divide this fiber into very (infinitely) short segments. The direction of the fiber segments can be described by their orientation angles $\psi_0 \in (-\pi/2, \pi/2)$ to the *y*-axis. In case of isotropic orientation, the fiber segments are equally distributed in all directions; therefore, we can describe their orientation by a constant probability density function $f_0(\psi_0) =$ constant. It is then possible to write the following expression

$$1 = \int_{-\pi/2}^{\pi/2} f_0(\psi_0)\, d\psi_0 = f_0(\psi_0) \int_{-\pi/2}^{\pi/2} d\psi_0 = f_0(\psi_0)\, \pi, \quad f_0(\psi_0) = \frac{1}{\pi}. \quad \dots (3.26)$$

Preferential fiber orientation in one direction. In a real fibrous assembly, the orientation of fiber segments is never purely random. A lot of technological methods dealing with the processing of fibers produce a wide variety of fiber arrangements. Most of the technological methods used for manufacturing of textile products produce fibrous assemblies where the fibers are preferentially oriented in one particular direction. The fibers are often longitudinally arranged in the direction of the material output (e.g., card sliver or drawn sliver). The cross-lapping technology in nonwovens arranges the fibers in the perpendicular direction to the direction of the material output. In other cases, the fibers are somehow oriented in the perpendicular direction to the direction of the material output (e.g., pneumatic fleece). We will initially consider that the preferential direction of orientation is given by the angle $\psi = 0$, i.e., in the direction of *y*-axis (Figure 3.8).

During the processing of fibrous assemblies, the fiber segments tend to take a direction near to the preferential direction, because they are mechanically affected by

1. Other fiber segments
    (a)   adjacent segments of the same fiber,
    (b)   segments of other fibers, and
2. Textile machine elements (e.g., pins, cylinders, etc.).

In fact, the influential actions of the surrounding fiber segments are different; therefore, it is necessary to represent a suitable simplified concept, which is able to express these different actions. Figure 3.9a illustrates a very short (infinitely small) fiber segment[6], shown by thick

---

6.   If we consider that the fiber curvature is a smooth one, then the short fibers can be satisfactorily considered as fiber segment. (If a very short segment is cut from a very crumpled wire, it will be "straight").

black line, and it is laying on an imaginary flexible belt equipped with perpendicular spikes. The spikes are designated by "•" symbol in Fig. 3.9. The concept of flexible belt and spikes[7] represent the action of the surrounding fiber segments. Let us take a fiber segment which is laying

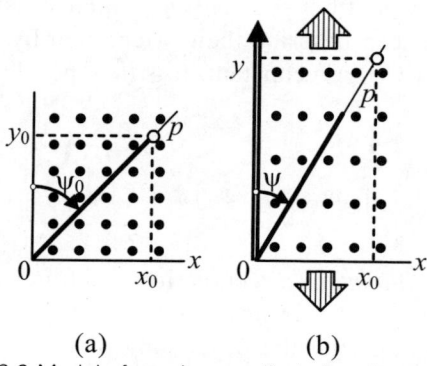

(a)   (b)

3.9 Model of one (perpendicular) preferential direction.

on the line p. Its initial point is located at the origin of the Cartesian coordinates, the end point is located at (x_0, y_0) and a point "below" the end point of fiber segment lying on the flexible belt is designated by "o" symbol. The direction of the fiber segment is defined by the orientation angle $\psi_0 \in (-\pi/2, \pi/2)$, and then we can write

$$\tan\psi_0 = x_0/y_0.$$ ... (3.27)

Let us now stretch the flexible belt in the direction of the shaded arrows (direction ↑ of y-axis) as shown in Fig. 3.9b. The fiber segment slips between the spikes of the belt, but it is still laying on the line p, which passes through the origin and the point o. The coordinate x_0 of point o remains the same (The lateral contraction of the imaginary belt is not considered), y_0 is changed to a higher value y. The ratio C corresponds to the "drafting value" of the imaginary flexible belt and it is expressed as follows

$$C = \frac{y}{y_0}, \quad C \geq 1.$$ ... (3.28)

---

7. This imagination has no direct relation with the spiked lattice found in textile machines. It is only an "assisted" imaginary representation, which simply simulates the surrounding actions on the fiber segments (in other words, such representations facilitate easy modeling). For example, in mechanical engineering, the elastic deformation is represented by the compression of a spring, which, in reality, is a completely different phenomenon.

Due to the stretching of the imaginary flexible belt, the spikes will try to swing the fiber segment in such a manner that the segment will make an angle ψ (smaller) to y-axis. According to Fig. 3.9b and by using Eqs. (3.27) and (3.28), we can write

$$\tan \psi = \frac{x_0}{y} = \frac{x_0}{C\, y_0} = \frac{\tan \psi_0}{C}. \qquad \ldots (3.29)$$

Differentiating the last expression we obtain the following expression

$$\frac{d\psi}{\cos^2 \psi} = \frac{d\psi_0}{C\cos^2 \psi_0} = \frac{d\psi_0 \left(1+\tan^2 \psi_0\right)}{C} = \frac{d\psi_0 \left(1+C^2 \tan^2 \psi\right)}{C} \qquad \ldots (3.30)$$

$$\frac{d\psi_0}{d\psi} = \frac{C}{\left(1+C^2 \tan^2 \psi\right)\cos^2 \psi}$$

$$\frac{d\psi_0}{d\psi} = \frac{C}{\cos^2 \psi + C^2 \sin^2 \psi} = \frac{C}{\cos^2 \psi + C^2 - C^2 \cos^2 \psi} \qquad \ldots (3.31)$$

$$= \frac{C}{C^2 - \left(C^2 - 1\right)\cos^2 \psi}.$$

*Probability density function of fiber orientation in plane.*Due to the mechanical actions of various machine elements, the very short (infinitely short) fiber segments in a fibrous assembly often change their orientation from their original purely random orientation to one defined preferential direction. The original constant probability density f_0 (ψ_0), according to Eq. (3.26), is changed to a final probability density function $f(\psi)$. In case of purely random fiber orientation, we deal with an elementary angular class; which ranges from ψ_0 to $\psi_0 + d\psi_0$, and this is described by the dotted wedge in Fig. 3.10. The relative frequency of fiber segments (black lines) in this class is given by f_0 (ψ_0) $d\psi_0$. The preferential orientation mechanism is now applied to the fiber segments that are lying in this elementary class. As a result of drafting, the whole elementary class is shifted to a new position and the angle ψ_0 is changed to angle ψ, the class width in this elementary class is also changed from the original value $d\psi_0$ to $d\psi$ (see the second dotted wedge in Fig. 3.10). The relative frequency of fiber segments in the elementary class after drafting is given by the expression $f(\psi)\, d\psi$. The relative frequency of fiber segments after drafting must be the same as those before drafting, because all of the fiber segments in the elementary class (thick abscissas on the Fig. 3.10) are displaced to their new position. In other words, $f_0\left(\psi_0\right)d\psi_0 = f\left(\psi\right)d\psi$. By applying Eqs. (3.26) and (3.30),

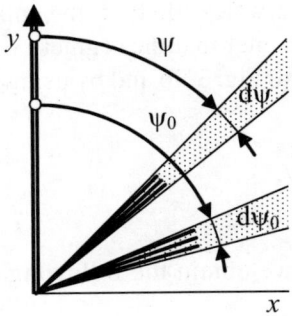

3.10 Frequency of fiber segments in elementary class.

or (3.31); we get the following expression for the probability density function $f(\psi)$

$$f(\psi) = f_0(\psi_0)\frac{d\psi_0}{d\psi} = \frac{1}{\pi}\frac{C}{\left(1+C^2\tan^2\psi\right)\cos^2\psi},\qquad \text{... (3.32)}$$

$$f(\psi) = f_0(\psi_0)\frac{d\psi_0}{d\psi} = \frac{1}{\pi}\frac{C}{C^2-\left(C^2-1\right)\cos^2\psi}.\qquad \text{... (3.33)}$$

The behavior of the probability density function according to Eq. (3.32) or (3.33) is illustrated in Fig. 3.11 for different values of the parameter C. It is evident that the maximum value of the probability density function f_{max} is obtained at angle $\psi = 0$, and then according to Eq. (3.33), we obtain

$$f_{max} = f(0) = \frac{C}{\pi}\qquad \text{... (3.34)}$$

Similarly, the minimum value of the probability density function f_{min} is obtained at angle $\psi = \pm\pi/2$, and then according to Eq. (3.33), we obtain

$$f_{min} = f\left(\frac{\pi}{2}\right) = \frac{1}{C\pi}\qquad \text{... (3.35)}$$

Thus, we can write

$$\frac{f_{max}}{f_{min}} = C^2\qquad \text{... (3.36)}$$

The parameter C corresponds to the drafting value of the imaginary belt considered in our present model. In actual process, the preferential orientation of fiber segments is governed by some other mechanisms. The

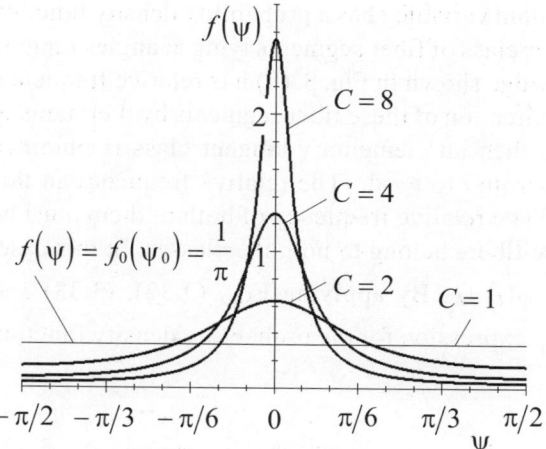

3.11 Probability density function of orientation of fiber segments at preferential direction $\psi = 0$.

parameter C has comparatively general meaning - preferential intensity (measure) of orientation at a given direction.

Distribution function. The distribution function $F(\psi)$ of fiber orientation in plane is obtained from the integration of the probability density function expressed in Eq. (3.32) as follows

$$F(\psi) = \frac{1}{\pi} \int_{-\pi/2}^{\psi} \frac{C}{\left(1 + C^2 \tan^2 \psi^*\right) \cos^2 \psi^*} \, d\psi^*$$

$$= \frac{1}{\pi} \int_{-\infty}^{C \tan \psi} \frac{C}{\left(1 + x^2\right) \cos^2 \psi^*} \frac{\cos^2 \psi^*}{C} \, dx \qquad \qquad \text{... (3.37)}$$

$$x = C \tan \psi^*; \, dx = \left(C/\cos^2 \psi^*\right) d\psi^*; \, d\psi^* = \left(\cos^2 \psi^*/C\right) dx$$

$$= \frac{1}{\pi} \left[\arctan x \right]_{-\infty}^{C \tan \psi} = \frac{1}{\pi} \arctan \left(C \tan \psi\right) + \frac{1}{2}.$$

(Here, ψ^* is an integration variable).

Cauchy's distribution of tangents. Let us define a random variable t as follows

$$t = \tan \psi, \quad t \in \left(-\infty, \infty\right). \qquad \qquad \text{... (3.38)}$$

By differentiating the above expression, we obtain

$$\frac{dt}{d\psi} = \frac{1}{\cos^2 \psi}. \qquad \qquad \text{... (3.39)}$$

We consider that the random variable t has a probability density function $\varphi(t)$. The elementary angular class of fiber segments lying at angles ranging from ψ to $\psi + d\psi$ (doted wedge shown in Fig. 3.10) has relative frequency $f(\psi)\,d\psi$. If we express the direction of these fiber segments by their tangent t instead of their angle ψ, then an elementary tangent class is obtained including the values lying from t to $t + dt$. The relative frequency in this elementary class is $\varphi(t)\,dt$. The relative frequency of both of them must be the same, because the same fibers belong to both the classes. In this case, it is valid that $f(\psi)\,d\psi = \varphi(t)\,dt$. By applying Eqs. (3.32), (3.38) and (3.39), we get the following expression for the probability density function $\varphi(t)$

$$\varphi(t) = f(\psi)\frac{d\psi}{dt} = \frac{1}{\pi}\frac{C}{\left(1 + C^2 \tan^2 \psi\right)\cos^2 \psi}\cos^2 \psi = \frac{1}{\pi}\frac{C}{1 + C^2 t^2}. \quad \dots (3.40)$$

Let us now consider two independent random variables x and y, where

1. both the random variables follow Gaussian (normal) distribution,
2. the mean values of both the random variables are equal to zero, and
3. their standard deviations σ_x and σ_y are generally different.

The random variable t is defined by $t = x/y$. Let us now find its probability density function.

Note: This reminds us about "the shooting practice" as illustrated in Fig. 3.12. The two coordinates x_A and y_A describe the striking position of the "bullet" A, the ratio x_A/y_A corresponds to the value of the tangent of angle ψ_A. The distribution of values t can be considered as the distribution of tangents of angles ψ, which is represented by the lines connecting the origin to each individual bullet.

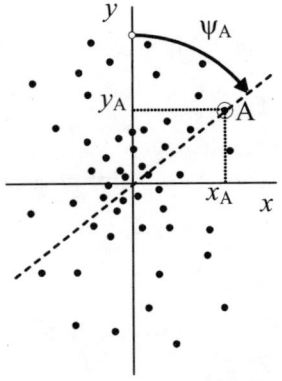

3.12 Cauchy's distribution of variable x/y.

The solution of this problem by using probability theory leads us to the so-called "generalized" Cauchy's distribution as shown below

$$\varphi(t) = \frac{1}{\pi} \frac{\left(\sigma_y/\sigma_x\right)}{1+\left(\sigma_y/\sigma_x\right)^2 t^2}. \qquad \ldots (3.41)$$

By comparing Eqs. (3.40) and (3.41), we recognize that we are dealing with the same probability density function, and the "measure" of intensity of preferential orientation parameter C is equal to the ratio of their standard deviations, shown below

$$C = \sigma_y/\sigma_x. \qquad \ldots (3.42)$$

Generalized probability density function of fiber orientation in plane. In general, the preferential direction of fiber segments is described by the preferential angle $\alpha \in (-\pi/2, \pi/2)$ to the y-axis (see Fig. 3.13). Accordingly, the orientation angle ψ (to the y-axis) is expressed as the summation of the preferential angle α and another angle ξ, which is described by the angle that the fiber segments makes to the preferential direction as shown in Fig. 3.13. Then it is valid to write

$$\psi = \alpha + \xi \quad \left(\xi = \psi - \alpha\right). \qquad \ldots (3.43)$$

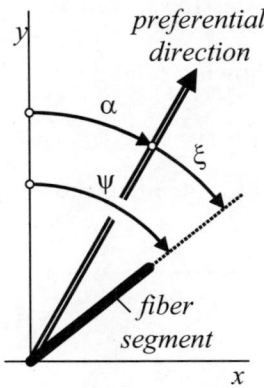

3.13 Angles ψ and ξ.

The probability density functions expressed by Eqs. (3.32) and (3.33) are derived for the case where the preferential direction coincides with the direction of the y-axis, i.e., where $\alpha = 0$. It is evident that the angle ψ was earlier used with the sense of the angle ξ; i.e., the angle between the fiber segment and the preferential direction. The probability density function of the angle ψ is $g(\psi)$ and this must be equal to the function $f(\xi)$ according to Eqs. (3.32) and/or (3.33). From Eq. (3.43), we obtain

$$g(\psi) = f(\xi) = \frac{1}{\pi} \frac{C}{\left[1 + C^2 \tan^2 \xi\right] \cos^2 \xi}$$

$$= \frac{1}{\pi} \frac{C}{\left[1 + C^2 \tan^2 (\psi - \alpha)\right] \cos^2 (\psi - \alpha)}, \qquad \ldots (3.44)$$

$$g(\psi) = f(\xi) = \frac{1}{\pi} \frac{C}{C^2 - (C^2 - 1) \cos^2 \xi}$$

$$= \frac{1}{\pi} \frac{C}{C^2 - (C^2 - 1) \cos^2 (\psi - \alpha)}. \qquad \ldots (3.45)$$

It is evident that if $\alpha = 0$ then $g(\psi) = f(\psi)$.

Distribution of non-oriented angles of fibers. The oriented angle ψ, describing fiber directions, is defined from $-\pi/2$ to $\pi/2$. This angle is related to the original angle ϑ shown in Fig. 3.8 as stated in Eq. (3.25). Then we can write that

$$\vartheta = |\psi|, \vartheta \in (0, \pi/2), \qquad \ldots (3.46)$$

and we call angle ϑ as non-oriented angle in this case of planar orientation; see Fig. 3.8. The probability density function of angle ϑ is denoted by $u(\vartheta)$ and it is of the same sense as the marginal probability density function $u(\vartheta)$, expressed in Eq. (3.3).

It is evident that the following relation is valid[8]

$$u(\vartheta) = g(-\vartheta) + g(\vartheta). \qquad \ldots (3.47)$$

Substituting Eq. (3.44) or (3.45) into the above expression, we obtain

$$u(\vartheta) = \frac{1}{\pi} \frac{C}{\left[1 + C^2 \tan^2 (\vartheta + \alpha)\right] \cos^2 (\vartheta + \alpha)} +$$

$$\frac{1}{\pi} \frac{C}{\left[1 + C^2 \tan^2 (\vartheta - \alpha)\right] \cos^2 (\vartheta - \alpha)}, \qquad \ldots (3.48)$$

---

8. Let us denote the distribution functions as follows: $U(\vartheta) = \int_0^\vartheta u(\vartheta^*) d\vartheta^*$, $G(\psi) = \int_{-\pi/2}^\psi g(\psi^*) d\psi^*$. Because Eq. (3.46) is valid, we can write $U(\vartheta) = \int_{-\vartheta}^\vartheta g(\psi) d\psi = G(\vartheta) - G(-\vartheta)$ and after differentiation of the last expression we obtain Eq. (3.47).

$$u(\vartheta) = \frac{1}{\pi} \frac{C}{C^2 - (C^2 - 1)\cos^2(\vartheta + \alpha)} + \frac{1}{\pi} \frac{C}{C^2 - (C^2 - 1)\cos^2(\vartheta - \alpha)}.$$

... (3.49)

Case study and experimental results. It is useful to study the orientation of fibers in a carded web, which is used for production of carded yarn or for production of non-wovens. There are several methods reported in literature to estimate the orientation of fibers in planar structures [6–11]. One such method, known as a direct method (e.g. tracer fiber technique according to Morton [11]), can be applied. A small quantity of black colored fibers is blended with white colored input fiber material, and a carded web is produced. The samples of the web are put in-between two transparent disks (glass, hard foil, etc.). By applying a suitable immersion liquid (for example, methyl-silicate is usually used for cellulose fibers), the non-colored fibers become glass transparent and the tracer fibers can be optically observed. The curvature of fibers can be observed by means of "image processing system", where the image of the fibers is digitized in a form of coordinates of many points. By means of a special software, the observed fibers are "divided" into many short fiber segments of length δl; the direction of each segment is determined and transferred to the respective class interval. The interval width is usually chosen as 5°.

The histograms presented in Fig. 3.14 describe the orientation of short fiber segments ($\delta l = 0.1$mm). Both carded webs are produced from viscose fibers, and are used for production of non-wovens. The values of the parameters C and α are obtained by applying a suitable statistical regression method, then those values are substituted into Eq. (3.44) or (3.45), and the calculated probability density curves are obtained as shown in Fig. 3.14.

It is evident that there exists a very good agreement between the calculated and the observed values. The close values of C around 1.9 indicate that the effect of fiber fineness is not significant. The small value of the angle α can be explained by the error occurred during the measurements of the web in the longitudinal direction.

The distribution of longer fiber segments ($\delta l = 12.8$ mm) obtained from the experimental data corresponding to the same web is evaluated in Ref. [9]; the resulting histogram is displayed in Fig. 3.15. It shows that the preferential longitudinal direction of relatively longer fiber segments is significantly noticeable. The values of the parameters C and α are also established and the probability density function is illustrated in Fig. 3.15. This result should be understood as an empirical only as the lengths of the fiber segment chosen are different. It can be seen that the increase in the

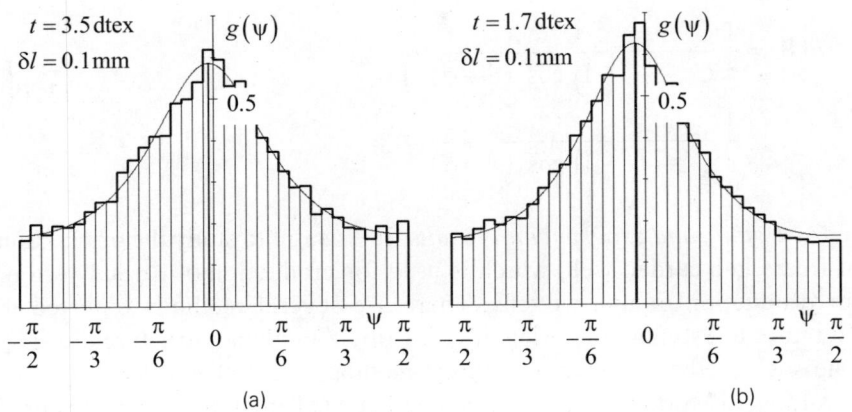

3.14 Probability density function of short fiber segments of length δl = 0.1mm, measured from a roller card web.

(a) Fibers of 3.5 dtex, 60 mm length; C = 1.84, α = –0.0401rad (–2.3°), see [9].

(b) Fibers of 1.7 dtex, 38mm length; C = 1.97, α = –0.0855rad (–4.9°), see [10].

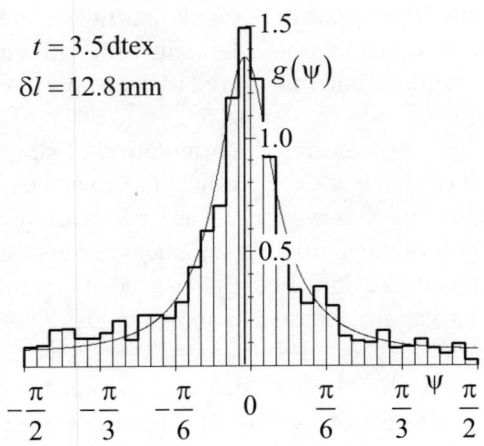

3.15 Orientation of viscose fiber segments of length δl = 12.8mm, taken from carding web, [9]. Fibers are of 3.5 dtex, 60mm *length*; C = 4.28 and α = –0.0401rad (–2.3°).

value of the parameter C from 1.84 to 4.28 is associated with the increase in length δl of the fiber segments chosen from 0.1 mm to 12.8 mm. A fiber shown in Fig. 3.16 is drawn by thin line. Its "macro-trend" follows the preferential direction but its "micro-shape" is full of loops, waves, etc. Therefore, the short fiber segments, whose orientation is illustrated by the set of short arrows, are dispersed to many directions whereas the directional orientation of longer fiber segments, marked by the longer arrows, strongly

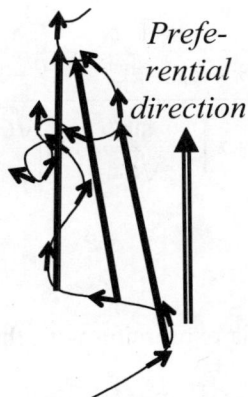

Prefe-rential direction

3.16 Orientation of short and long fiber segments.

follows the preferential direction. It means that the longer fiber segments correspond to a higher value of C and vice-versa.

3.5   Section of planar fiber assembly

Coefficient k_n. Substituting the expression for the probability density function $u(\vartheta)$ as stated in Eq. (3.49) to the general formula shown in Eq. (3.18), we obtain the following expression for k_n

$$k_n = \int_0^{\pi/2} \cos\vartheta \left[\frac{1}{\pi} \frac{C}{C^2 - (C^2 - 1)\cos^2(\vartheta + \alpha)} + \frac{1}{\pi} \frac{C}{C^2 - (C^2 - 1)\cos^2(\vartheta - \alpha)} \right] d\vartheta =$$

$$= \frac{2C\cos\alpha}{\pi\sqrt{C^2 - 1}} \arctan\left[\sqrt{C^2 - 1}\,\cos\alpha \right] +$$

$$\frac{\sin\alpha}{\pi\sqrt{C^2 - 1}} \ln\left| \frac{\sqrt{C^2 - 1}\,\sin\alpha + C}{\sqrt{C^2 - 1}\,\sin\alpha - C} \right|. \qquad \qquad \dots (3.50)^9$$

Distribution of the angle ϑ of intersected fiber segments. Substituting the expression for the probability density function $u(\vartheta)$ from Eq. (3.49) and the expression for the coefficient k_n from Eq. (3.50) to the general formula shown in Eq. (3.20), we obtain the expression for the probability density function of fiber segments in section $u^*(\vartheta)$ as stated in Eq. (3.51).

Isotropic orientation. If the orientation of fiber segments is purely random, i.e. isotropic orientation, then the value of "drafting ratio" is $C = 1$. Then, by using Eqs. (3.33) and (3.45), we obtain the expression for the probability density functions as stated in Eq. (3.52).

---

9.   The analytical integration is little complicated. The step-by-step integration is reported in Appendix A1.

$$u^*(9) = \frac{\cos 9 \left[\dfrac{1}{\pi} \dfrac{C}{C^2 - (C^2-1)\cos^2(9+\alpha)} + \dfrac{1}{\pi} \dfrac{C}{C^2 - (C^2-1)\cos^2(9-\alpha)} \right]}{\dfrac{2C\cos\alpha}{\pi\sqrt{C^2-1}} \arctan\left[\sqrt{C^2-1}\cos\alpha\right] + \dfrac{\sin\alpha}{\pi\sqrt{C^2-1}} \ln\left|\dfrac{\sqrt{C^2-1}\sin\alpha + C}{\sqrt{C^2-1}\sin\alpha - C}\right|}.$$

$$\qquad\qquad\qquad\qquad\qquad\qquad\qquad\qquad\qquad\qquad\qquad ... \ (3.51)$$

$$f(\psi) = g(\psi) = 1/\pi. \qquad\qquad\qquad\qquad\qquad ... \ (3.52)$$

Note: Compare the behavior of this expression with that expressed in Eq. (3.26).

Substituting $C = 1$ in Eq. (3.49), we obtain the following expression

$$u(9) = 2/\pi. \qquad\qquad\qquad\qquad\qquad ... \ (3.53)$$

Further, substituting the expression for the probability density function $u(9)$ from Eq. (3.53) to the general formula shown in Eq. (3.18), we obtain k_n as follows

$$k_n = \int_0^{\pi/2} \cos 9 \, (2/\pi) \, d9 = 2/\pi. \qquad\qquad ... \ (3.54)$$

Furthermore, substituting the expression for the probability density function $u(9)$ from Eq. (3.53) and the expression for the coefficient k_n from Eq. (3.54) to the general formula shown in Eq. (3.20), we obtain the probability density function of fiber segments in section $u^*(9)$ as follows

$$u^*(9) = \frac{\cos 9 \, (2/\pi)}{2/\pi} = \cos 9. \qquad\qquad (3.55)$$

Graphical illustration. Let us consider a carded web with preferential orientation intensity $C = 1.9$. Let us cut the web in such a manner that the preferential direction makes angles $\alpha = 0(0°), \pi/6(30°), \pi/3(60°), \pi/2(90°)$ with the normal to the intersecting line (with y-axis). The probability density function $u(9)$ of non-oriented angles 9 can be calculated from Eq. (3.49). The probability density function $u^*(9)$ of very short fiber segments in this section can be calculated from Eq. (3.51). The behavior of the calculated probability densities is shown in Figs. 3.17a–d.

It is obvious from the previous example that the orientation of fiber segments in the whole fibrous assembly differs significantly from the orientation of fiber segments in a section of the fibrous assembly.

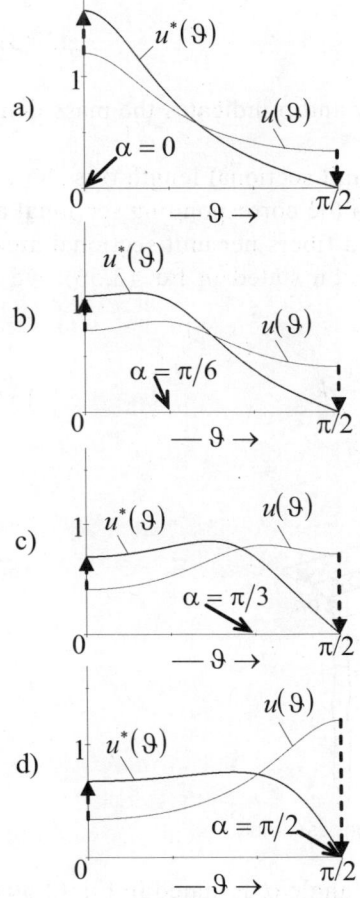

3.17 Probability density function $u(\vartheta)$ and $u^*(\vartheta)$ at preference level of $C = 1.9$. (a) $\alpha = 0$, (b) $\alpha = \pi/6(30°)$, (c) $\alpha = \pi/3(60°)$, (d) $\alpha = \pi/2(90°)$.

The section "chooses" mainly the fiber segments that are inclined at smaller values of angle ϑ and at these values it is always valid that $u^*(\vartheta) > u(\vartheta)$. On the other hand, the section "misses" the fiber segments that are inclined at higher values of angle ϑ and at these values it is always valid that $u^*(\vartheta) < u(\vartheta)$.

Note: The similar behavior can also be obtained for the negative values of angle α.

Number of sectioned fibers per unit sectional length. A section of very thin (planar) fibrous assembly with thickness δh, which is cut by a sectional plane σ perpendicular to the y-axis is shown in Fig. 3.18. (Compare this with Fig. 3.7). The thick lines determine an areal unit whose volume is $1 \times 1 \times \delta h$. The mass per unit area ("areal weight") G is expressed as follows

$$G = (1 \cdot 1 \cdot \delta h) \, \mu\rho = \delta h \, \mu\rho, \quad \frac{G}{\delta h} = \mu\rho, \qquad \qquad \dots (3.56)$$

where μ denotes the packing density and ρ indicates the mass density of the fibers used.

The number of sectioned fibers per unit sectional length υ is shown in Fig. 3.18 as a set of shaded "islands" in the corresponding sectional area $1 \cdot \delta h$. Using the number of the sectioned fibers per unit sectional area υ_s as stated in Eq. (3.24) and the expression stated in Eq. (3.56), we can write the following expression

$$\upsilon = (1 \cdot \delta h) \upsilon_S = \delta h \frac{\mu\rho}{t} k_n = \delta h \frac{G}{t \, \delta h} k_n = \frac{G}{t} k_n. \qquad \qquad \dots (3.57)$$

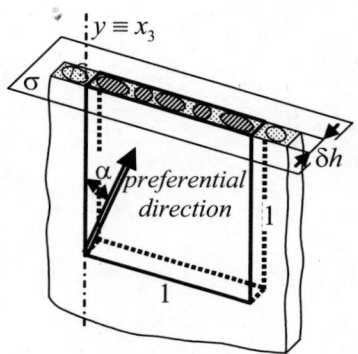

3.18 Section of a planar fiber assembly.

Note: The quantity k_n depends on the angle α as stated in Eq. (3.50) so that the quantity υ depends on this angle. If the values υ for a set of different angles α are known experimentally then the equations allow us to find a suitable value for the parameter C and then to obtain the distribution of orientation of fiber segments in a planar fiber assembly. Method – "intersecting method" – is derived and described in Ref. [1].

Nonwoven fleece. The nonwoven fleeces are usually produced by layering of webs of fibers as illustrated in Fig. 3.19. The fleece is composed of two fibrous webs, one with preferential direction 1 which makes angle $\alpha_1 > 0$ to the y-axis and the other with preferential direction 2 which makes angle $\alpha_2 < 0$ to the same y-axis. Let us assume that the preferential direction of the fibers in the webs follows the technological direction of the production machine. The probability density function of orientation (angle ψ related to y-axis) of fibers in the web with preferential direction 1 can be expressed as follows

$$g_1(\psi) = \frac{1}{\pi} \frac{C}{C^2 - (C^2 - 1) \cos^2(\psi - \alpha_1)}, \quad \alpha_1 > 0. \qquad \dots (3.58)$$

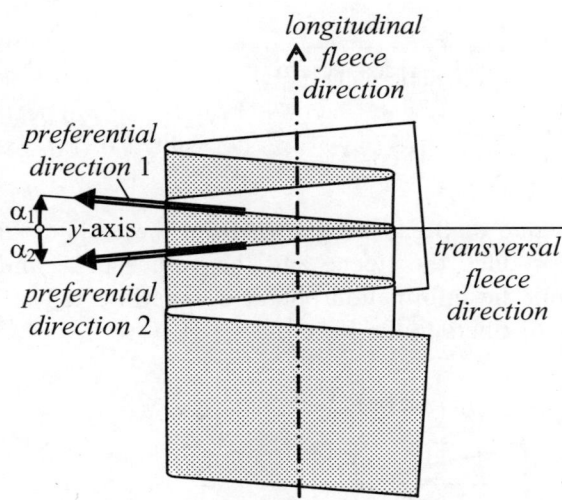

3.19 Formation of a fleece from two webs.

Similarly, the probability density function of orientation (angle ψ related to the y-axis) of fibers in the web with preferential direction 2 can be expressed as follows

$$g_2(\psi) = \frac{1}{\pi} \frac{C}{C^2 - (C^2 - 1) \cos^2(\psi - \alpha_2)}, \quad \alpha_2 < 0. \qquad \dots (3.59)$$

Usually, it is true that $|\alpha_1| = |\alpha_2|, \alpha_1 = -\alpha_2$. Nevertheless, it must be valid for a more general case that $\alpha_1 - \alpha_2 = \beta$ and the value of β ("double α-value") must be a constant which is decided by the technological process employed to produce the fleece. It is then valid to write that $\alpha_2 = \alpha_1 - \beta$. Then, the following expression if valid to write for the probability density function of orientation (angle ψ related to the y-axis) of fibers in the web with preferential direction 2

$$g_2(\psi) = \frac{1}{\pi} \frac{C}{C^2 - (C^2 - 1) \cos^2(\psi - \alpha_1 + \beta)}, \quad \beta > \alpha_1. \qquad \dots (3.60)$$

Evidently, the one half of the webs in the fleece follows the preferential direction 1 and the other half of the webs in the fleece follows the preferential direction 2. Then, the probability density function $g_f(\psi)$ of fiber orientation in the fleece (related to the same y-axis) can be written as follows

$$g_f(\psi) = \frac{0.5}{\pi} \frac{C}{C^2 - \left(C^2 - 1\right)\cos^2\left(\psi - \alpha_1\right)} +$$

$$\frac{0.5}{\pi} \frac{C}{C^2 - \left(C^2 - 1\right)\cos^2\left(\psi - \alpha_1 + \beta\right)}, \quad \beta > \alpha_1, \qquad \ldots (3.61)$$

where the value of β can be known from the technological process employed to produce the fleece and the values of C and α_1 can be determined from the information obtained experimentally in relation to the orientation of fibers in the fleece.

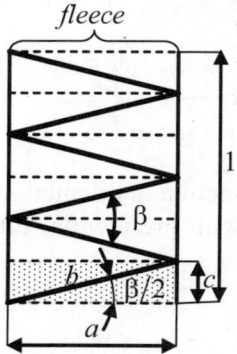

fleece

3.20 Scheme of angles in the web and fleece.

The value of β can also be determined by the following way. Let us consider that the areal densities (mass per unit area) of the web and the fleece are denoted by m_w and m_f respectively, and the widths of the web and the fleece are indicated by h_w and a, respectively. The area occupied by the rectangular fleece, shown in Fig. 3.20, is $1 \cdot a$; then, the mass of the fleece can be expressed as $M_f = m_f \cdot 1 \cdot a = m_f a$. The thick "zig-zag" line, shown in Fig. 3.20, represents the upper edge of the web used to make the fleece. The two adjacent dotted lines, comprising a web of length b, represent a repeat unit of the fleece and the number of such units present in the rectangular fleece is taken as n. Then, the total length of the web in the Fleece is $L_w = nb$ and its mass is $M_w = m_w L_w h_w = m_w nbh_w$.

Nevertheless, it must be valid that $M_w = M_f$, $m_w nbh_w = m_f a$. It is evident from Fig. 3.20 that $n = 1/c$, then the following expression is valid to write

$$m_w \frac{1}{c} bh_w = m_f a, \quad \frac{b}{c} = \frac{m_f a}{m_w h_w}, \quad \frac{c}{b} = \frac{m_w h_w}{m_f a}. \qquad \ldots (3.62)$$

Also, it is evident from Fig. 3.20 that $c/b = \sin(\beta/2)$, then the following expression can be written

$$\sin \frac{\beta}{2} = \frac{m_w h_w}{m_f a}. \qquad \ldots (3.63)$$

This expression can be used to find out the value of angle β.

Example 3.3: Consider that a fibrous fleece is prepared for production of a nonwoven fabric by using polyester fibers of 51 mm staple length and 6 denier fineness and employing carding and cross-lapping technologies. The areal density of the carded web is 18 g/m² and the width of the carded web is 440 mm. The areal density of the fleece is 90 g/m² and the width of the fleece is 500 mm. By using Eq. (3.63), the value of the angle β is found as $\beta = 0.3538$ radian.

Case study. A real nonwoven fleece, made up of polyester fibers of 0.11 tex fineness, was produced by layering of carded webs, illustrated in Fig. 3.21. A sample of this fleece was placed on a mirror, and the light was allowed to pass through the fleece and reflect off the mirror surface vertically back to the camera. The fibers, regardless of their position within the fleece, could merely block the light, appeared dark, and were in focus. The result was an image with excellent contrast and uniformity. The image was "thresholded" to separate the fibers from the black and white background to obtain a binary image. This binary image was then analyzed to determine the orientation of 1500 fixed 24-pixel fiber segments. Thirty such images were taken randomly from different parts of the fleece, thus the orientation of 45000 fiber segments was determined. This large set of orientation data was summarized by frequency distribution in 10 classes each of 18 degree width. The resulting histogram is displayed in Fig. 3.21. The continuous line corresponds to the probability density function of fiber orientation in fleece as expressed by Eq. (3.61). This was obtained by employing the standard non-linear statistical regression technique using the value of $\beta = 5.74$ degree $= 0.1$ rad, calculated from Eq. (3.63). The resulting value of C was obtained as $C = 1.53$ and the value of α_1 was obtained as $\alpha_1 = 2.87$ degree $= 0.05$ rad. Evidenlty, the theoretical result corresponded well to the experimental one.

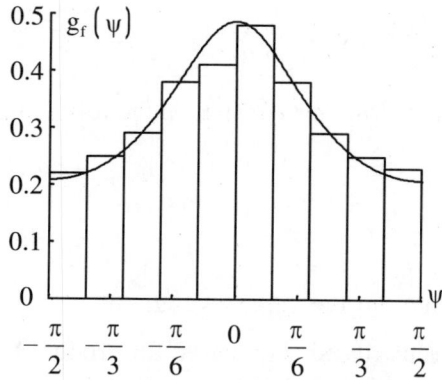

3.21 Comparison between theoretical and experimental results of fiber orientation in the fleece.

3.6   Model of fiber orientation in a linear fibrous assembly - sliver

Sliver is considered to be a linear fibrous assembly which is required to prepare staple fiber yarns. The orientation of fibers in the slivers is known to be a very useful parameter for evaluating the effectiveness of the fibre preparation processes namely, carding process and drawing process. Also, the fiber orientation is known to determine the fiber length utilization in the slivers. But, the measurement of fiber orientation in the slivers is a very complex task as the cross-section of a sliver typically contains several thousands of fibers. One of the methods of ascertaining fiber orientation in the slivers is a direct method of measurement of inclination of the fibers to the axis of the slivers, using a fluorescent tracer fiber technique used by Morton and Summers [12]. The other is an indirect method, developed by Lindsley [13], based on the weighing of suitable combed-out and cut-out fringes using a special apparatus and evaluating fiber orientation in terms of some empirical ratios of fringe weights namely cutting ratio, combing ratio, fiber orientation index, and projected mean fiber length. This method has been found to be widely followed in practice for evaluation of fiber orientation in the carded and the drawn slivers. Later on, Simpson and Patureau [14] modified Lindslay's apparatus to measure and evaluate the orientation of fibers in the slivers more accurately and comprehensively. Using Lindsley's apparatus and methodology a larger number of research studies were conducted to characterize the orientation of fibers in the carded and drawn slivers and also to establish the effect of carding and drawing process parameters on the fiber orientation in the slivers [15–23]. However, Lindsley's methodology for evaluation of fiber orientation in the slivers has been understood as empirical only. In order to understand Lindsley's methodology in a better way, a mathematical model of fiber orientation in slivers is derived and demonstrated in support of a practical example of polyester drawn sliver [24].

Lindsley's methodology. Lindsley developed an apparatus which is schematically shown in Fig. 3.22. The orientation of fibers in the slivers can be evaluated by using this appratus. The step-by-step procedure of evaluation of fiber orientation in slivers based on Lindsley's methodology is described hereunder.

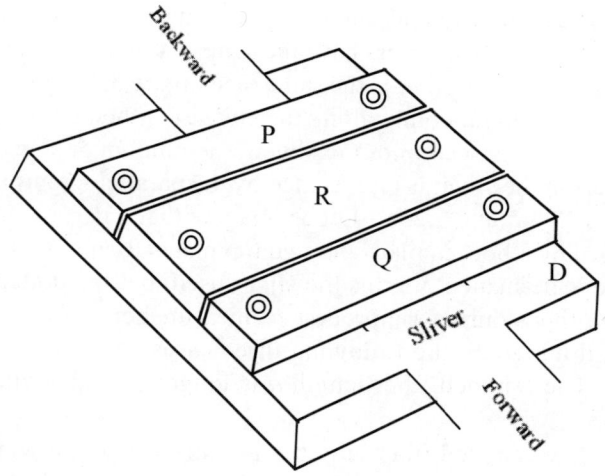

3.22 Lindsley apparatus.

Step 1: Take a sufficiently long sliver. Twist one end of the sliver slightly so as to mark the direction by which it was delivered by the machine, i.e. forward or backward. Take out the top three plates P, Q, R (Figure 3.22) and place the sliver onto the bottom plate D and clamp it by repositioning the three top plates.

Step 2: Comb gently the sliver in the forward direction in order to remove all the loose fibers that are not clamped by the plates Q and D. Discard the combed-out fibers. Then cut the fibers using a sharp razor blade at the right edge of the plate Q and weigh the cut fiber portion. Let this weight be W_f. (The subscript f refers to the forward direction of the sliver).

Step 3: Remove the top plate Q. Then, comb the fibers held below it. Retain the combed-out fiber portion and weigh it. Let this weight be C_f.

Step 4: Put the top plate Q back to its original position. Then, cut all the fiber ends that are extending beyond the edge of the plate Q. Collect the cut fiber portion and weigh it. Let this weight be E_f.

Step 5: Remove the plate Q again. Then, cut the fibers at the right edge of the plate R. Collect the cut fiber portion and weight it. Let this weight be N_f.

Step 6: Repeat the steps from 1 to 5 for the backward direction. Let the corresponding weights of fibers portions be W_b, C_b, E_b, and N_b, respectively. (The subscript b refers to the backward direction of the sliver).

Step 7: Repeat the steps from 1 to 6 for many samples of the sliver. Then, calculate the average of the weights. Use these weights to determine the index of fiber orientation by using the following formulas: index of fiber orientation in forward direction $\xi_f = 1 - E_f/N_f$ and index of fiber orientation in backward direction $\xi_b = 1 - E_b/N_b$.

Modeling scheme. Let us now consider the following assumptions: (1) all fibers in the sliver have the same (straight) length l [10] and the same linear density (fineness) t, (2) all fibers have the same waviness so that the shorter crimped length a of each fiber is the same (see Figure 3.5 preliminarily), (3) fibers are distributed randomly along the sliver, (4) the number of fibers is very high in the cross-section of the sliver. The random organization of the crimped fibers in the sliver is represented by the parallelograms as shown in Figs. 3.23 a', 3.24a' and 3.25a'. Let us imagine that a part of such sliver is firmly gripped by a bottom plate and two top plates R and Q. The vertically shaded plate R permanently grips the sliver used, but the dotted plate Q is removed two times during the process of measurement.

We must think about the following three cases.

Case (1): The crimped fiber length a is longer than the width d of the top plate Q,

Case (2): The crimped fiber length a is shorter than the width d of the top plate Q, but the straight fiber length l is longer than d,

Case (3): The crimped fiber length a as well as the straight fiber length l is shorter than the width d of the top plate Q.

Figure 3.23 illustrates the first case $(a > d)$ – see sliver in Fig. 3.23a'. Consider that the fibers protruding from the right-hand edge of the top (dotted) plate Q are combed as shown in Fig. 3.23a. As a result, the fibers which were not gripped by the top and bottom plates are removed and the fibers which were gripped by the plates are straightened. The straightened fibers protruding from the right-hand edge of the top plate Q are then cut and the first fringe of fibers of weight W is thus obtained. In the next step, the top plate Q is removed and the rectangle of crimped fibers is seen to be lying under it – see Fig. 3.23b'. Let us imagine that we straighten all these fibers so that we obtain a wider rectangle of straight fibers as shown in Fig. 3.23b. Of course, in reality, only the fibers protruding from the right-hand edge of the top plate R are straightened by combing, whereas the other fibers are combed out and contribute to the fringe weight C. Now the plate Q is replaced back on the straight fibers gripped by the

---

10. This assumption is generalized later on.

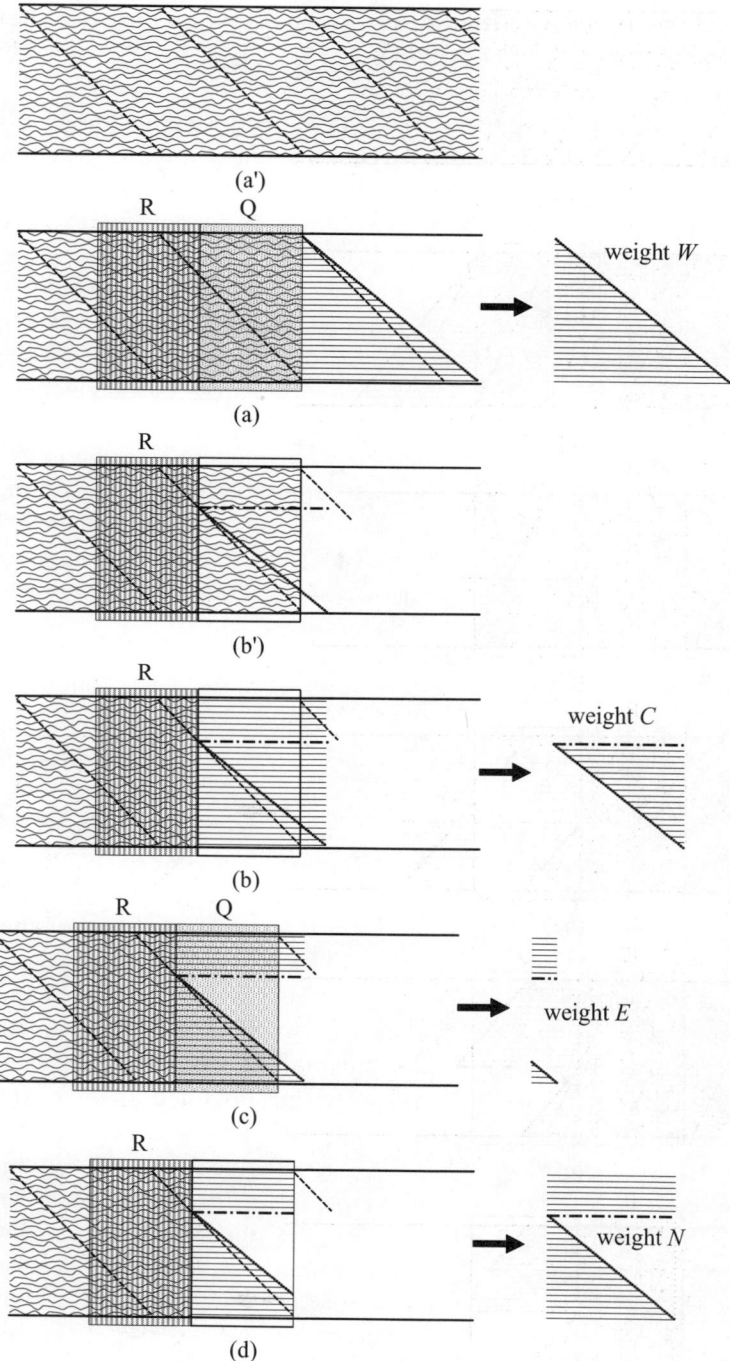

3.23 Scheme of modeling in accordance with Case (1) when *a* > *d*.

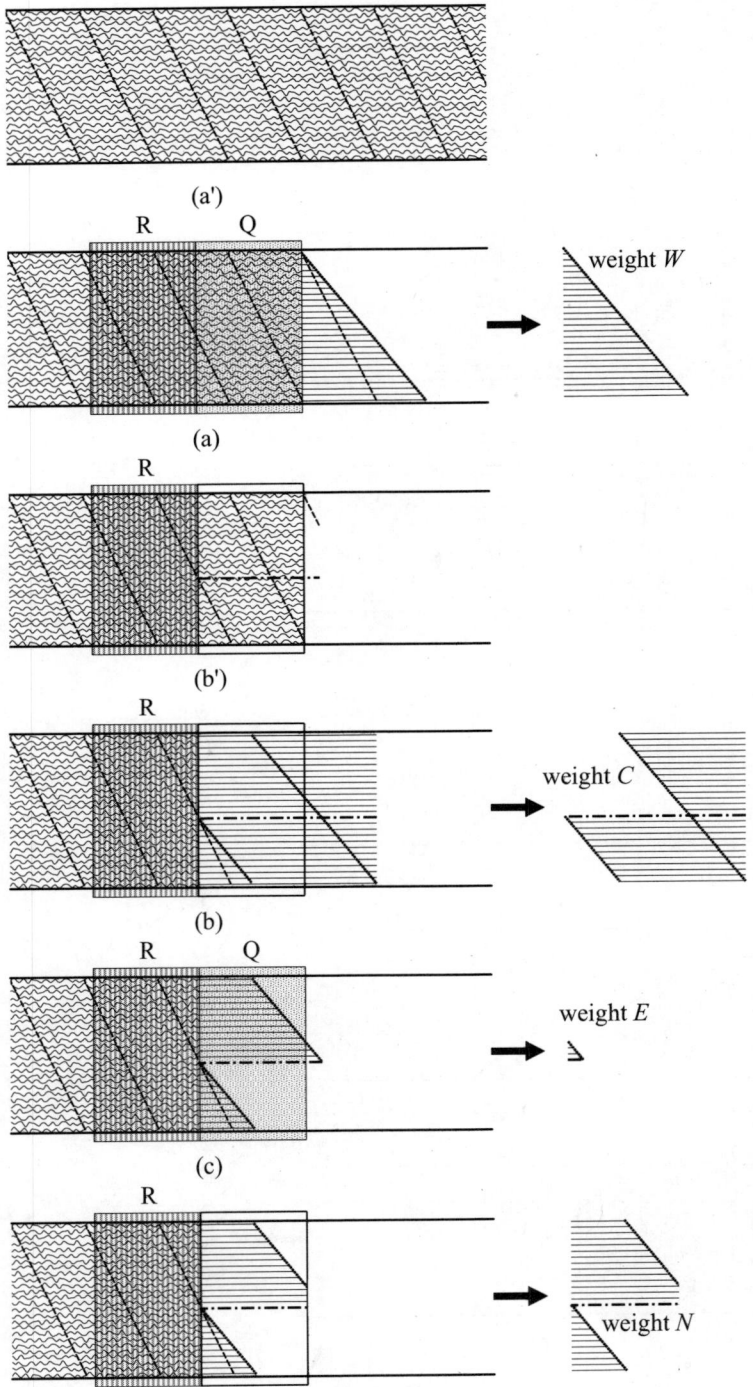

3.24 Scheme of modelling in accordance with Case (2) when $a < d$ and $l > d$.

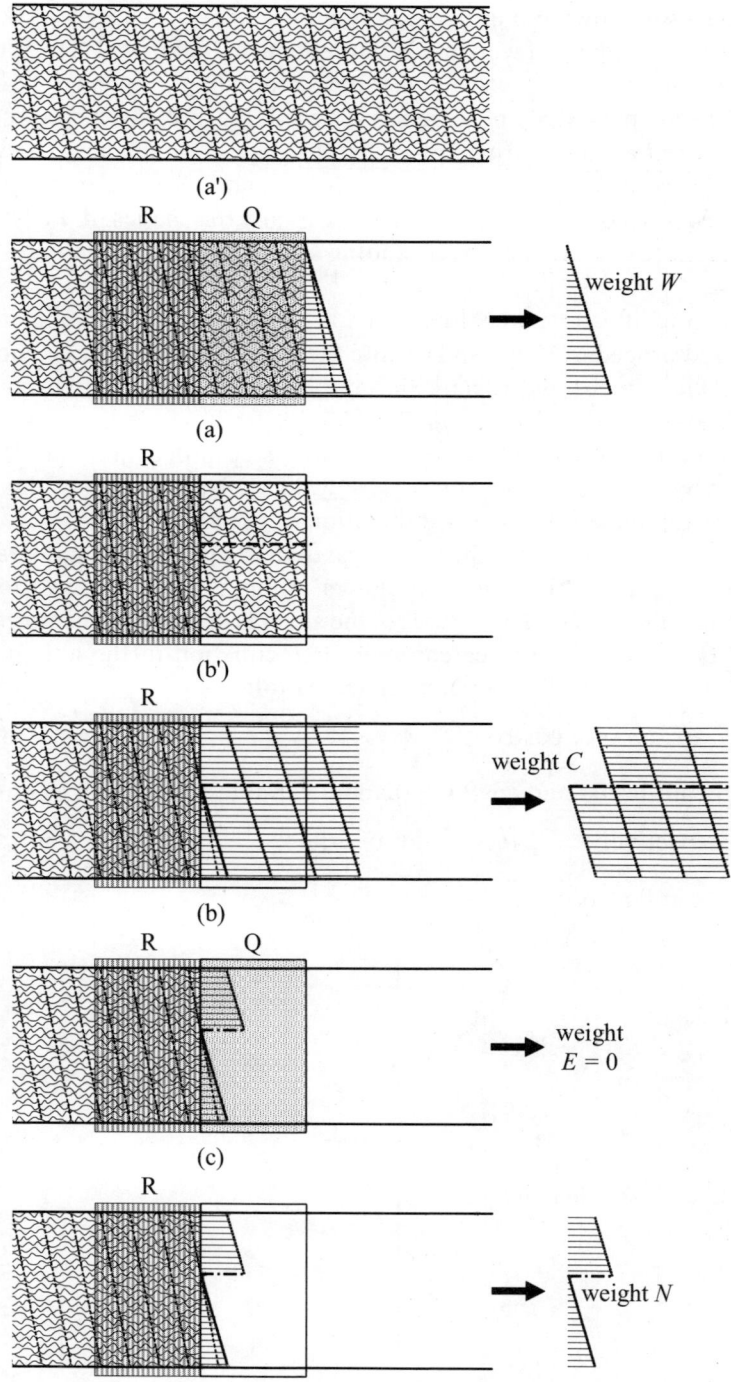

3.25 Scheme of modeling in accordance with Case (3) when $a < d$ and $l < d$.

plate R. This is shown in Fig. 3.23c. The protruding fibers are then cut and a small fringe of fibers of weight E is thus obtained. In the final step, the top plate Q is once again removed and the fibers protruding from the right-hand edge of the top plate R are observed as shown in Fig. 3.23d. The protruding fibers are then cut and a fringe of fibers of weight N is obtained.

Figure 3.24 illustrates the second case ($a < d$ and $l > d$). The commentary of the used procedure can be quite the same, only the shapes of the fringes are different (Compare the corresponding schemes displayed in Figs. 3.23 and 3.24).

Figure 3.25 illustrates the third case ($a < d$ and $l < d$). The commentary of the used procedure can also be quite the same. We only notice another shape of the fringes and remark that the "cut off fringe" shown in Fig. 3.25c does not exist – its weight E is equal to zero.

It can be noted that the aforesaid step-by-step procedure can also be followed by putting another top plate P at the left-hand edge of the left-hand side top plate for backward direction of the sliver.

Fiber orientation. Each fiber is interpreted as a chain of small straight segments of constant lengths δl as shown in Fig. 3.26. The projection of a segment in the direction of the axis of the sliver is denoted by the "crimped length" δa, and its non-oriented angle of inclination to the axis of the sliver is indicated by ϑ. They are related as follows

$$\delta a = \delta l \cos\vartheta. \qquad \qquad \dots (3.64)$$

The quantities δa and $\cos\vartheta$ are random variables with mean at $\overline{\delta a}$ and $\overline{\cos\vartheta}$, respectively. It is then valid to write

$$\overline{\delta a} = \delta l \ \overline{\cos\vartheta}, \qquad \qquad \dots (3.65)$$

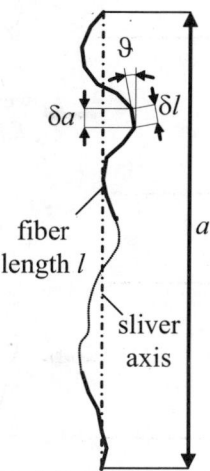

3.26 Scheme of a fibre and its segments.

It is valid to express $\overline{\cos \vartheta}$ as follows

$$\overline{\cos \vartheta} = \int_{0}^{\pi/2} \cos \vartheta \, u(\vartheta) \, d\vartheta = k_n, \qquad \qquad \dots (3.66)$$

where $u(\vartheta)$ denotes the probability density function of non-oriented angle ϑ to sliver axis. The last integral is also called as k_n as described earlier in Eq. (3.18). Using this, we can rewrite Eq. (3.66) as follows

$$k_n = \overline{\delta a}/\delta l . \qquad \qquad \dots (3.67)$$

It is possible to derive the following expression for k_n by substituting $u(\vartheta)$ from Eq. (3.49) to Eq. (3.66) and then integrating it.

$$k_n = \frac{2C \arctan\left(\sqrt{C^2 - 1}\right)}{\pi\left(\sqrt{C^2 - 1}\right)}. \qquad \qquad \dots (3.68)$$

The step-by-step derivation of the above equation is shown in Eq. (A1.10) in Appendix A1, when $\alpha = 0$ (i.e., preferential direction creates the sliver axis). Let us remark that when $C = 1$ (isotopic orientation) then $k_n = 2/\pi$ according to Eq. (3.54).

Because of the assumptions made earlier the following expression is valid to write

$$a/l = k_n.^{11} \qquad \qquad \dots (3.69)$$

Let us denote the linear density (fineness) of a fiber by the symbol t which is defined by $t = m/l$, where m indicates the mass of the fiber. Let us divide the mass m of the fiber by the crimped length a of the fiber and a quantity t_a is obtained such that $t_a = m/a$, where t_a is called as the linear density of the crimped fiber. It is then valid to write that $m = tl = t_a a$. Using Eq. (3.69) the following expression can be written

$$\frac{t_a}{t} = \frac{l}{a} = \frac{1}{k_n}. \qquad \qquad \dots (3.70)$$

If it is assumed that there are n number of fibers present in the cross-section of the sliver then the expression (Eq. 3.71) is valid to write

---

11. We use this equation also more generally; each crimped fiber length divided by the straightened fiber length is equal to k_n in this model.

$$T = nt_a = n\frac{t}{k_n}, \quad n = \frac{T}{t}k_n, \qquad \qquad \dots (3.71)$$

where T denotes the linear density of the sliver.

Geometry and weights of fringes when $a > d$. The following description is valid for the fringes when $a > d$. The detailed geometry of these fringes, introduced generally in Fig. 3.23, is characterized in the following four schemes displayed in Fig. 3.27.

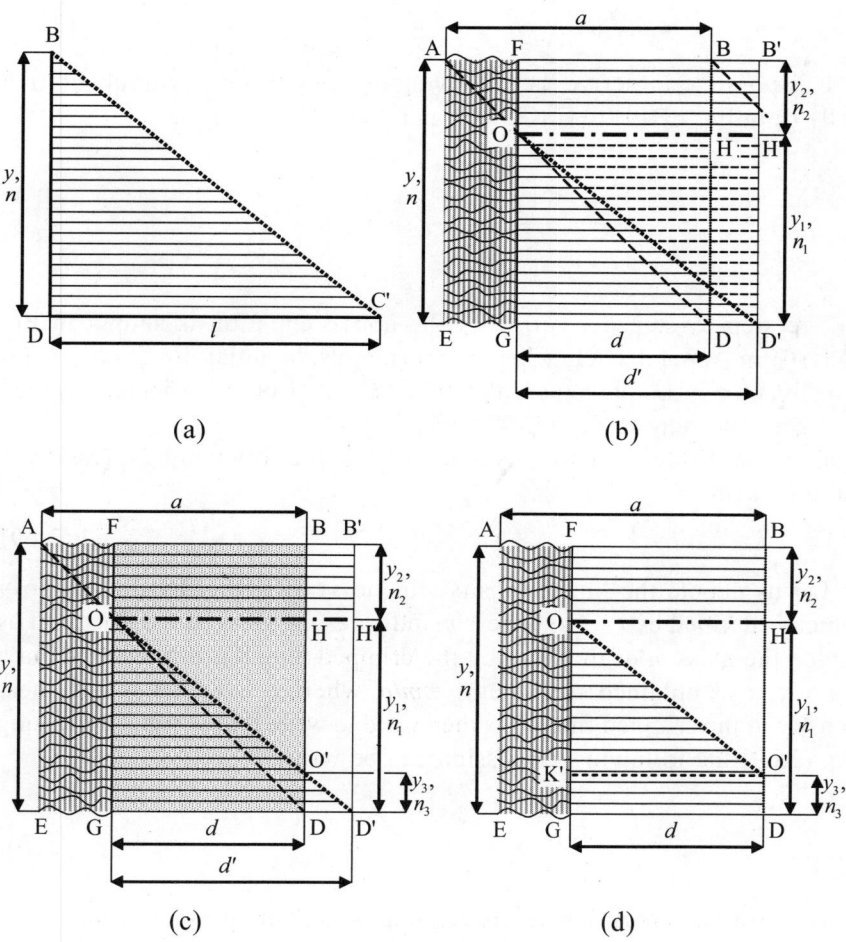

(a)   (b)

(c)   (d)

3.27 Schematic representation of fiber geometry in Case (1) when $a > d$.

The first fringe, earlier shown in Fig. 3.23a, is now shown in detail in Fig. 3.27a. Here, the number of fibers gripped along the clamping line BD of length y is equal to the total number n of fibers present in the cross-section of the sliver. This fringe of straight fibers has the triangular shape BC'D with the longest fiber of length l. The total length of fibers in such a fringe is $n\,l/2$. By applying Eq. (3.71) we obtain the expression for the weight (mass) W of the fringe using fiber fineness t as follows

$$W = n\frac{l}{2}t = \frac{T}{t}k_n\frac{l}{2}t = T\frac{l}{2}k_n. \qquad \ldots (3.72)$$

The second fringe, introduced in Fig. 3.23b, is now displayed in Fig. 3.27b. The fibers after straightening are shown by a set of horizontal lines; the continuous lines show the fibers gripped by the clamping line FG and the dashed lines show the fibers to be combed out. The earlier position of edge of plate Q is marked by the thin dotted line BD. The oblique dash line AOD represents the ends of the fibers in the parallelogram of fibers before straightening of fibers, the dotted line OD' represents it after straightening of fibers. The distance AB is equal to the crimped length a of fibers (Compare it with Fig. 3.23b').

The crimped length d (plate width) is elongated to the straight length d' and we obtain the following equation valid similarly to Eq. (3.69)

$$d' = d/k_n. \qquad \ldots (3.73)$$

Let the number of combed-out fibers be n_1 and these fibers are lying at a distance y_1, the remaining n_2 fibers are lying at a distance y_2. Let us take that the distance $y = y_1 + y_2$ is proportional to the number of fibers $n = n_1 + n_2$, y_1 is proportional to n_1 and y_2 is proportional to n_2, all with a common constant of proportionality.

It is shown that the triangle ABD is similar to the triangle OHD. Therefore,

$$\frac{a}{y_1 + y_2} = \frac{d}{y_1},$$

$$\frac{a}{d} = \frac{y_1 + y_2}{y_1} = 1 + \frac{y_2}{y_1},$$

$$\frac{y_2}{y_1} = a/d - 1. \qquad \ldots (3.74)$$

According to the proportionality the following equations are valid to write

$$y_2/y_1 = n_2/n_1, \qquad \ldots (3.75)$$

$$n_1 + n_2 = n. \qquad \ldots (3.76)$$

Combining Eqs. (3.74), (3.75), and (3.76) it is possible to write that

$$
\begin{aligned}
&n_2 = n_1(a/d - 1) = (n - n_2)(a/d - 1), \\
&n_2 + n_2(a/d - 1) = n(a/d - 1), \\
&n_2\left[1 + (a/d - 1)\right] = n_2\, a/d = n(a/d - 1), \\
&n_2 = n\frac{a/d - 1}{a/d} = n\left(1 - \frac{d}{a}\right),
\end{aligned}
$$

... (3.77)

and

$$
n_1 = n - n_2 = n\frac{d}{a}.
$$

... (3.78)

By using of Eqs. (3.71) and (3.73) it is possible to write the following expression for the total weight of the sliver (fibers in the rectangle FGD′B′)

$$
G_{\text{TOTAL}} = nd't = \frac{T}{t}k_n\frac{d}{k_n}t = Td\ .^{12}
$$

... (3.79)

Using Eqs. (3.78), (3.73), (3.69), and (3.71), the weight of the combed-out fibers (dashed lines in the triangle OH′D′) is expressed as follows

$$
C = n_1\frac{d'}{2}t = \left(n\frac{d}{a}\right)\frac{1}{2}\left(\frac{d}{k_n}\right)t = n\frac{d}{lk_n}\frac{d}{2k_n}t =
$$

$$
= \frac{T}{t}k_n\frac{d}{lk_n}\frac{d}{2k_n}t = T\frac{d^2}{2lk_n}\ .
$$

... (3.80)

Figure 3.27c displays the arrangement of fibers after combing-out the second fringe of fibers and returning the top plate Q back to its original position (Compare it with Fig. 3.23c). The straight fibers, touching the edge BD of the plate Q, are lying in the rectangle BB′D′D in two parts – in the rectangle BHH′B′ and in the triangle O′DD′. Let us consider that the number of fibers held in the distance y_3 is n_3. It is then valid to write that

$$
\frac{d'}{y_1} = \frac{d' - d}{y_3}.
$$

$$
y_3/y_1 = 1 - d/d'
$$

... (3.81)

---

12. This result is immediately visible with a view to the sliver shown in Fig. 3.25b'.

Nevertheless, according to the proportionality it must be also valid to write that

$$y_3/y_1 = n_3/n_1, \qquad \qquad \text{... (3.82)}$$

Substituting Eqs. (3.82) and (3.73) into Eq. (3.81) and then using Eq. (3.78), the following expression for n_3 is obtained

$$n_3 = n_1\left(1-k_n\right) = n\frac{d}{a}\left(1-k_n\right). \qquad \qquad \text{... (3.83)}$$

By using Eqs. (3.73), (3.77), (3.83), (3.71), and (3.69), the weight E of the third fringe of fibers (rectangle BB′H′H and triangle O′DD′) is expressed as follows

$$E = n_2\left(d'-d\right)t + n_3\frac{d'-d}{2}t = t\left(d'-d\right)\left(n_2 + \frac{n_3}{2}\right)$$

$$= t\left[\frac{d}{k_n} - d\right]\left[n\left(1-\frac{d}{a}\right) + \frac{1}{2}n\frac{d}{a}\left(1-k_n\right)\right]$$

$$= tdn\left(\frac{1}{k_n} - 1\right)\left[1 - \frac{d}{a} + \frac{1}{2}\frac{d}{a} - \frac{1}{2}\frac{d}{a}k_n\right]$$

$$= tdn\left(\frac{1}{k_n} - 1\right)\left[1 - \frac{d}{2a} - \frac{1}{2}\frac{d}{a}k_n\right] = td\frac{T}{t}k_n\left(\frac{1}{k_n} - 1\right)\left[1 - \frac{d}{2lk_n} - \frac{1}{2}\frac{d}{lk_n}k_n\right]$$

$$= Td\left(1-k_n\right)\left[1 - \frac{d}{2l} - \frac{d}{2lk_n}\right]. \qquad \qquad \text{... (3.84)}$$

Figure 3.23d displays the arrangement of fibers after cutting the third fringe of fibers. The weight N of the last fringe of fibers, lying in the rectangle FBO′K′, can be expressed by using of Eqs. (3.79), (3.80), and (3.84) as follows

$$N = G_{\text{TOTAL}} - C - E = Td - T\frac{d^2}{2lk_n} - Td\left(1-k_n\right)\left[1 - \frac{d}{2l} - \frac{d}{2lk_n}\right]$$

$$= Td\left(1 - \frac{d}{2lk_n} - 1 + \frac{d}{2l} + \frac{d}{2lk_n} + k_n - \frac{dk_n}{2l} - \frac{d}{2l}\right) \qquad \qquad \text{... (3.85)}$$

$$= Tdk_n\left(1 - \frac{d}{2l}\right).$$

Naturally, an identical result can also be obtained by using the geometrical dimensions directly from Fig. 3.23d, i.e., after rearrangement of the following equation: $N = \left[\left(n_1 - n_3\right)d/2 + \left(n_2 + n_3\right)d\right]t$.

Geometry and weights of fringes when a < d and l > d. The detailed geometry of these fringes, introduced generally in Fig. 3.24, is characterized in the following four schemes shown in Fig. 3.28.

The first fringe, introduced in Fig. 3.24a, is now shown in Fig. 3.28a. This scheme is fully analogical to the scheme shown in Fig. 3.27a so that Eq. (3.72) is valid for the weight W in this case too. Also, Eq. (3.79) is valid for the total weight G_{TOTAL} of the sliver, i.e., for all fibers in the rectangle FGD'B' in Fig. 3.28b – gripped fibers (continuous line) and to-be-combed-out fibers (dashed lines).

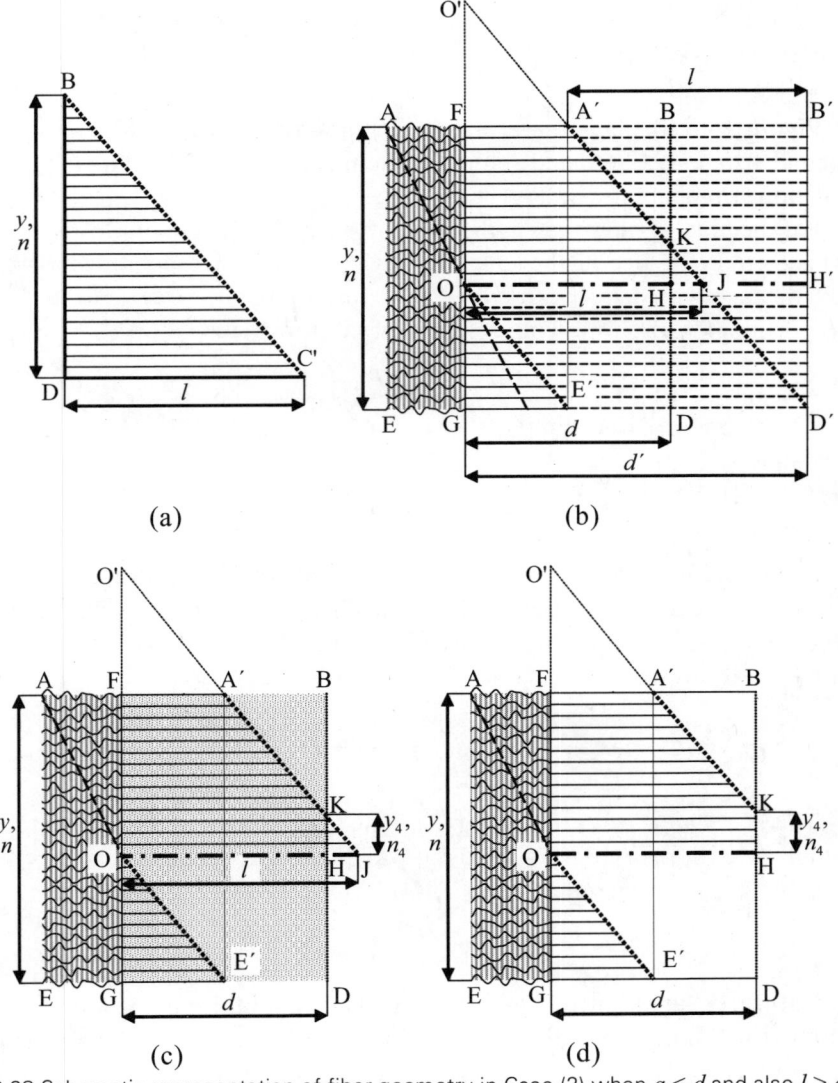

3.28 Schematic representation of fiber geometry in Case (2) when $a < d$ and also $l > d$.

The fibers gripped by clamping line FG are lying in the trapezoid OJA'F and in the triangle GE'O. Nevertheless, the triangle GE'O can be "replaced" onto the position FA'O'. If the length $y = GF = OO'$ then the weight of gripped fibers can be expressed as follows

$$\Phi = n\frac{l}{2}t = \frac{T}{t}k_n\frac{l}{2}t = Tk_n\frac{l}{2}. \qquad \ldots (3.86)$$

The weight C of the combed-out fibers (dashed lines) is given by the following equation

$$C = G_{TOTAL} - \Phi = Td - Tk_n\frac{l}{2} = T\left(d - \frac{lk_n}{2}\right). \qquad \ldots (3.87)$$

Figure 3.7c displays the arrangement of fibers after combing-out the second fringe of fibers and returning the top plate Q back to its original position (Compare it with Fig. 3.3c). The straight fibers, touching the edge BD of the plate Q, are lying in the triangle KHJ. The length of the abscissa HJ is $l - d$. Let us denote the length KH by y_4 and the corresponding number of fibers be protruding beyond this length be n_4. Because of the proportionality the following relation is valid to write

$$y_4/y = n_4/n. \qquad \ldots (3.88)$$

The triangle KHJ is similar to the triangle O'OJ and the line O'O has the same length as that of FG. Then,

$$\frac{y_4}{y} = \frac{n_4}{n} = \frac{l-d}{l}, \quad n_4 = n\frac{l-d}{l}. \qquad \ldots (3.89)$$

The weight E of the triangular fringe KHJ can be expressed using Eqs. (3.71) and (3.89) as follows

$$E = n_4\frac{l-d}{2}t = n\frac{l-d}{l}\frac{l-d}{2}t = \frac{T}{t}k_n\frac{(l-d)^2}{2l}t = Tk_n\frac{(l-d)^2}{2l}. \qquad \ldots (3.90)$$

The last fringe, after removing the plate Q, is shown in Fig. 3.28d. The weight N of this fringe is equal to the weight Φ, derived earlier, minus the weight E of the triangular fringe KHJ. This is written below

$$N = \Phi - C = Tk_n\frac{l}{2} - Tk_n\frac{(l-d)^2}{2l} = \frac{Tk_n}{2}\left(l - l + 2d - \frac{d^2}{l}\right)$$

$$= Tdk_n\left(1 - \frac{d}{2l}\right) \qquad \ldots (3.91)$$

Geometry and weights of fringes when a < d and also l < d. The detailed geometry of these fringes, introduced generally in Fig. 3.25, is characterized in the following four schemes displayed in Fig. 3.29.

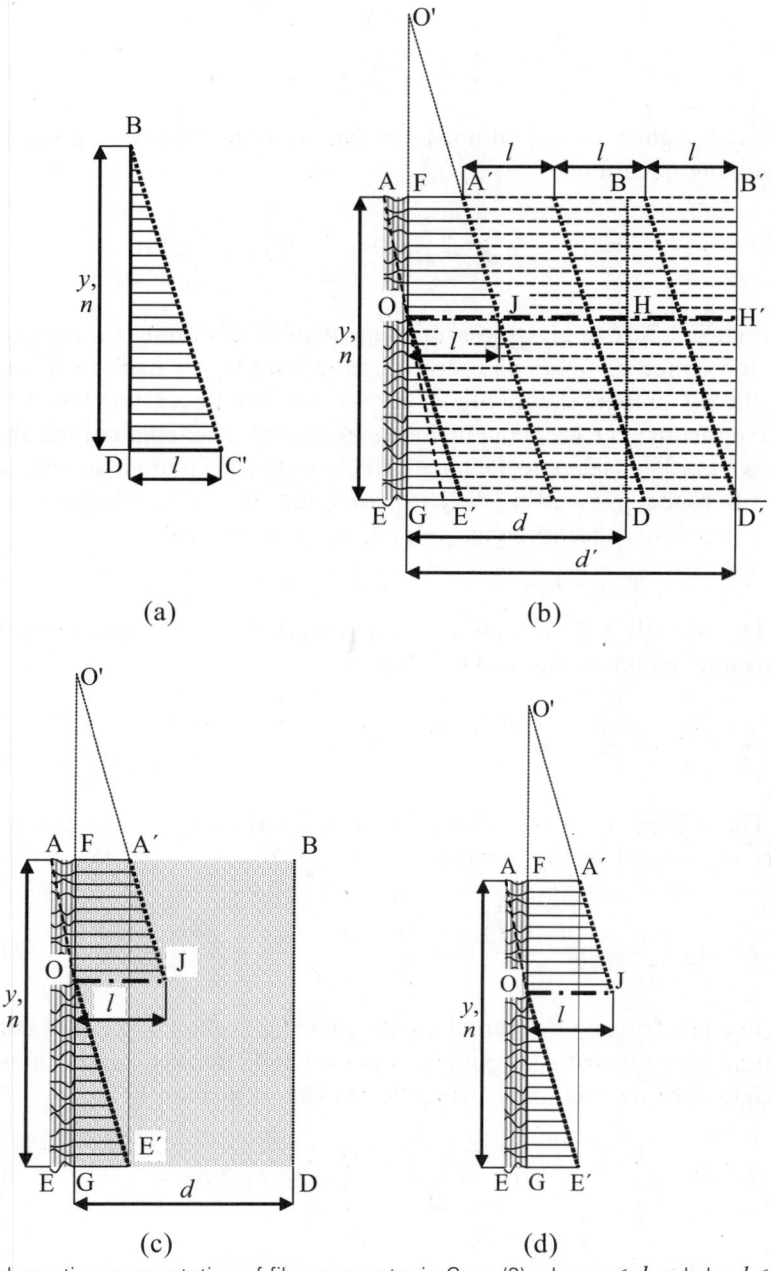

(a)   (b)

(c)   (d)

3.29 Schematic representation of fiber geometry in Case (3) when *a* < *d* and also *l* < *d*.

The first fringe, introduced in Fig. 3.25a, is now displayed in Fig. 3.29a. This scheme is fully analogical to the scheme shown in Fig. 3.27a so that Eq. (3.72) is valid for the weight W in this case too. Also, Eq. (3.79) is valid for the total weight G_{TOTAL} of the sliver, i.e., for all fibers in the rectangle FGD'B' in Fig. 3.29b – gripped fibers (continuous line) and to-be-combed-out fibers (dashed lines).

In analogy to the previous discussion for obtaining Eq. (3.86), the fibers gripped by the clamping line FG are lying in the trapezium OJA'F and in the triangle GE'O, and the triangle GE'O can be "replaced" onto the position FA'O'. So, Eqs. (3.86) and (3.86) are also valid in this case for the weight Φ of the gripped fibers and for the weight C of the combed-out fibers (dashed lines).

Nevertheless, in this case, no one fiber is touching the edge BD after returning the top plate Q back to its original position. This is shown in Fig. 3.29c. Therefore, the following equation is valid to write

$$E = 0. \qquad \qquad \dots (3.92)$$

The last fringe obtained after removing the plate Q is shown in Fig. 3.29d. The weight N of this fringe is equal to the weight Φ of the fibers gripped by the plates along the edge FG. Applying Eq. (3.86) we obtain

$$N = \Phi = Tk_n \frac{l}{2}. \qquad \qquad \dots (3.93)$$

Summary of results. The results of weight of the fiber fringes derived earlier are summarized in Table 3.1.

Table 3.1 Summary of results of weight of fiber fringes

Fiber length[13]:	Case (1)	Case (2)	Case (3)
	$l > d/k_n$	$l \in (d, d/k_n)$	$l < d$
Weight W	Equation (3.72)		
Weight C	Equation (3.80)	Equation (3.87)	
Weight E	Equation (3.84)	Equation (3.90)	Equation (3.92)
Weight N	Equation (3.85) or Equation (3.91)		Equation (3.93)

Generalization for fiber length distribution. The model, derived for geometry and weights of fringes, assumes a constant length l of fibers and a constant value of the parameter k_n. However, both of them are usually random quantities, hence they are generally described by a conjugate probability density function. Usually, we cannot find the variability of the parameter k_n, but it is very easy to determine the distribution of fiber lengths. Therefore, let us keep the constant value of k_n for all fibers, but think about the distribution of fiber lengths.

---

13.   Equation (3.69) is used for the crimped fiber length a.

Let the probability density function of mass distribution of fibers in relation to their length be $\gamma(l)$. Then the relative frequency of mass of fibers in each elementary class defined by the lower limit of length l and the upper limit of length $l + dl$ is $\gamma(l)dl$. Then the "elementary sliver" has the fineness (linear density) $dT = T\gamma(l)dl$, where T denotes the fineness (linear density) of the sliver. Then it is valid to write the following expressions

$$W = \int_0^{l_{max}} W_{(3.72)}\gamma(l)\,dl, \qquad\qquad\qquad \ldots (3.94)$$

$$C = \int_0^{l_{max}} C\gamma(l)\,dl = \int_0^{d/k_n} C_{(3.87)}\gamma(l)\,dl + \int_{d/k_n}^{l_{max}} C_{(3.80)}\gamma(l)\,dl, \qquad \ldots (3.95)$$

$$E = \int_0^{l_{max}} E\gamma(l)\,dl = \int_0^{d} E_{(3.92)}\gamma(l)\,dl + \int_d^{d/k_n} E_{(3.90)}\gamma(l)\,dl + \int_{d/k_n}^{l_{max}} E_{(3.84)}\gamma(l)\,dl, \ \ldots (3.96)$$

$$N = \int_0^{l_{max}} N\gamma(l)\,dl = \int_0^{d} N_{(3.93)}\gamma(l)\,dl + \int_d^{l_{max}} N_{(3.85)}\gamma(l)\,dl. \qquad\qquad \ldots (3.97)$$

The numeral subscripts in the brackets indicate the number of relevant equations, which correspond to Table 3.1.

However, in practice, the integrands mentioned in Eqs. (3.94) to (3.97) are often difficult to solve analytically. But, they can be solved numerically. The easiest of the approaches to solve them is stated below. If M denotes the weight of the original sliver and L denotes the length of the original sliver then the linear density (fineness) T of the original sliver can be expressed by $T = M/L$.

Let us assume that this sliver consists of m number of partial slivers (i = 1, 2, ..., m) according to Fig. 3.30. Each partial sliver has the common length L and is created from fibers of constant length l_i. (We assume in the original sliver are only the fibers of lengths $l_1, l_2, ..., l_m$). The linear density (fineness) T_i of the i-th partial sliver is $T_i = M_i/L$, where M_i denotes the weight of such partial sliver. It is then possible to write that $M_i = M\gamma_i$, where γ_i denotes the relative frequency of weight of i-th partial sliver in the weight of the original sliver. Then each partial sliver will have values for W_i, C_i, E_i, and N_i according to the fiber length l_i – see Table 3.1. The summation of each of these values for all partial slivers will give the

Original sliver	$T = M/L$
1-st partial sliver, fiber length l_1,	$T_1 = M_1/L = \gamma_1 T$
2-nd partial sliver, fiber length l_2,	$T_2 = M_2/L = \gamma_2 T$
$\vdots$	
i-th partial sliver, fiber length l_i,	$T_i = M_i/L = \gamma_i T$
$\vdots$	
m-th partial sliver, fiber length l_m,	$T_m = M_m/L = \gamma_m T$
L	

3.30 Scheme of original and partial slivers.

corresponding values for the original sliver, that is $W = \sum_{i=1}^{m} W_i$, $C = \sum_{i=1}^{m} C_i$,

$E = \sum_{i=1}^{m} E_i$, and $N = \sum_{i=1}^{m} N_i$.

Practical example. A polyester drawn sliver of 5.37 ktex linear density was taken for this study. The weight-based fiber length distribution of this sliver is shown in Table 3.2. The fineness of the polyester fiber was found to be 1.67 dtex.

The methodology as reported in mathematical model was followed to obtain the values of W, C, E, and N in the forward and the backward directions of the sliver. The average of one hundred such readings carried out on the aforementioned sliver is reported in the column named experimental in Table 3.3. The width of the plate d was kept at 12.7 mm. A computer program was developed to find out the corresponding values by using the equations derived earlier. They are reported in the column named theoretical in Table 3.3. It was observed that the summation of the squares of the deviations between the experimental and theoretical readings for the four variables corresponding to the forward and backward directions was found to be minimum at $k_n = 0.73$ and $k_n = 0.71$, respectively.

Table 3.2 Weight-based length distribution of polyester fibres

Length (mm)	Relative frequency (–)
36	0.65625
35	0.19792
30	0.07812
14	0.06771
Total	1.00000

Table 3.3 Comparison between experimental and theoretical results

	Forward direction	
Variable	Weight (mg)	
	Experimental	Theoretical at $k_n = 0.73$
W_f	0.0590	0.0663
C_f	0.0157	0.0185
E_f	0.0067	0.0098
N_f	0.0461	0.0399
	Backward direction	
Variable	Weight (mg)	
	Experimental	Theoretical at $k_n = 0.71$
W_b	0.0568	0.0645
C_b	0.0163	0.0190
E_b	0.0048	0.0104
N_b	0.0466	0.0388

The coefficient of determination (R^2) was found to be 0.9405 and 0.9123, respectively at the forward and backward directions. The theoretical results are found in good agreement with the experimental results. By using Eq. (3.60), the values of the fiber orientation parameter C in the forward and backward directions were obtained as $C = 1.6$ and $C = 1.43$, respectively.

Let us mention that a set of experimental results of orientation of fibers in the carded viscose webs obtained by using the well-known tracer fiber technique was presented earlier in Section 3.4 The values of C were reported around 1.9 which is not too far from the values obtained here. It shows that the idea of transformation of fiber orientation from the web to the sliver without too significant change can be principally right.

By putting the values of C in Eq. (3.33) the probability density function of orientation angle ψ, where $\psi \in (-\pi/2, \pi/2)$, in the forward and backward directions of the sliver was obtained as $f(\psi) = 0.5096 / (2.56 - 1.56 \cos^2 \psi)$ and $f(\psi) = 0.4554 / (2.0449 - 1.0449 \cos^2 \psi)$, respectively. The behavior of these functions is displayed in Fig. 3.31. As expected, the fibers are more anisotropically oriented in the forward direction as compared to the backward direction in the case of this drawn sliver.

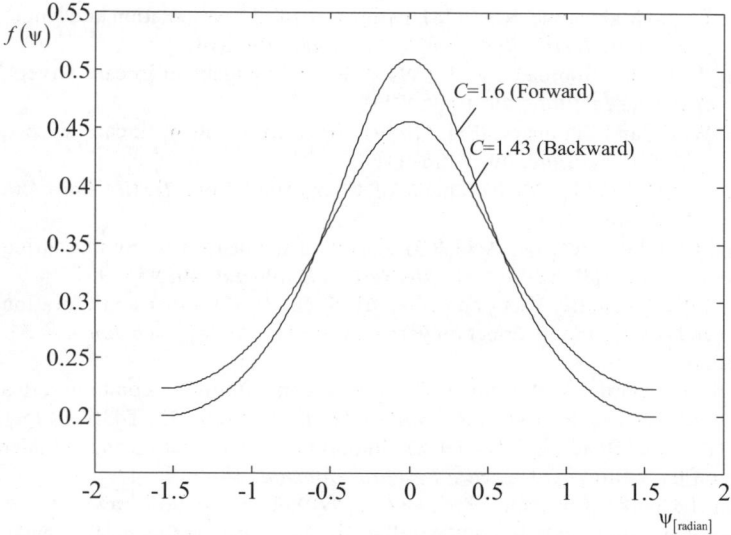

3.31 Behavior of probability density function of orientation of fiber in the polyester drawn sliver.

3.8   References

1. Nečkář, B. (1998). *Morphology and Structural Mechanics of General Fibrous Assemblies*, Technical University of Liberec, Czech Republic, pp. 21–39.
2. Folgar, F., and Tucker III, C. L. (1984). Orientation behaviour of fibres in concentrated suspensions, *Journal of Reinforced Plastics and Composites*, **3**, 98–119.
3. Jackson, G. W., and James, D. F. (1986). The permeability of fibrous porous media, *The Canadian Journal of Chemical Engineering*, **64**, 364–374.
4. Mao, N., and Russell, S. J. (2003). Anisotropic liquid absorption in homogeneous two-dimensional nonwoven structures, *Journal of Applied Physics*, **94**, 4135–4138.
5. Murugan, R., and Ramakrishna, S. (2007). Design strategies of tissue engineering scaffolds with controlled fibre orientation, *Tissue Engineering*, **13**, 1845–1868.
6. Pourdeyhimi, B., Ramanathan, R., and Dent, R. (1996). Measuring fibre orientation in nonwovens, Part II: Direct tracking, *Textile Research Journal*, **66**, 747–753.
7. Pourdeyhimi, B., Dent, R., and Davies, H. (1997). Measuring fibre orientation in nonwovens, Part III: Fourier transformation, *Textile Research Journal*, **67**, 143–151.

8. Pourdeyhimi, B., and Dent, R. (1997). Measuring fibre orientation in nonwovens, Part IV: Flow field analysis, *Textile Research Journal*, **67**, 181–190.

9. Blanc, R., Germain, C., Da costa, J. P., Baylou, P., and Cataldi, M. (2006). Fibre orientation measurements in composite materials, *Composites: Part A*, **37**, 197–206.

10. Komori, T., and Makishima, K. (1978). Estimation of fibre orientation and length in fibre assemblies, *Textile Research Journal*, **48**, 309–314..

11. Morton, W. E., and Summers, R. J. (1949). Fiber arrangement in card slivers, *Journal of Textile Institute*, **40**, P106–P116.

12. Morton, W. E., and Summers, R. J. (1949). Fiber arrangement in card slivers, *Journal of Textile Institute*, **40**, P106–116.

13. Lindsley, C. H. (1951). Measurement of fiber orientation, *Textile Research Journal*, **21**, 39–46.

14. Simpson, J., and Patureau, M. A. (1969). A method and instrument for measuring fiber hooks and parallelization, *Textile Research Journal*, **40**, 956–957.

15. Garde, A. R., Wakandar, V. A., and Bhaduri, S. N. (1961). Fiber configuration in sliver and roving and its effect on yarn quality, *Textile Research Journal*, **31**, 1026–1036.

16. Rao, J. S., and Garde, A. R. (1962). Theoretical computation of combing ratios of ideal and quasi-ideal slivers, *Journal of Textile Institute*, **53**, T430–T445.

17. Ghosh, G. C., and Bhaduri, S. N. (1968). Studies on hook formation and cylinder loading on the cotton card, *Textile Research Journal*, **38**, 535–543.

18. Simpson, J., Sands, J. E., and Flori, L. A. (1970). The effect of drawingframe variables on cotton fiber hooks and parallelization and processing performance, *Textile Research Journal*, **40**, 42–47.

19. Perel, J. (1982). Characterization of fiber length in slivers, *Textile Research Journal*, **52**, 376–379.

20. Ishtiaque, S. M., Mukhopadhyay, A., and Kumar, A. (2007). Impact of high-speed drawframe and its preparatory on fiber orientation parameters at sliver, *Journal of Textile Institute*, **98**, 501–512.

21. Kumar, A., Ishtiaque, S. M., and Salhotra, K. R. (2008). Measurements of fiber orientation parameters and effect of preparatory process on fiber orientation and properties, *Indian Journal of Fiber and Textile Research*, **33**, 451–467.

22. Salhotra, K. R., Ishtiaque, S. M., and Kumar, A. (2006). Analysis of spinning process using the Taguchi method. Part I: Effect of spinning process variables on fiber orientation and tenacities of sliver and roving, *Journal of Textile Institute*, **97**, 271–283.

23. Das, D., Ishtiaque, S. M., and Dixit, P. (2011). Influence of carding and drawing processes on the orientation of fibers in slivers, *Journal of Textile Institute*, DOI: 10.1080/00405000.2011.598667.

24. Nečkář, B., Das, D., and Ishtiaque, S. M. (2011). A mathematical model of fiber orientation in slivers, *Journal of Textile Institute*, DOI: 10.1080/00405000.2011.586153.

Fiber-to-fiber contacts

4.1 Contacts according to van Wyk [1]

The fibers contact with each other in a fibrous assembly. The region of contact, schematically shown by the dotted line in Fig. 4.1, is defined as contact between two fibers. The place on fiber surface, which is in contact with other fiber, is called contact place. Hence, it is clear that one contact is created from two contact places. The number and position of mutual contacts among the fibers is known to influence the mechanical behavior of a fibrous assembly, for example, the mutual forces causing the deformation of a fibrous assembly are transmitting due to fiber-to-fiber contacts, etc.

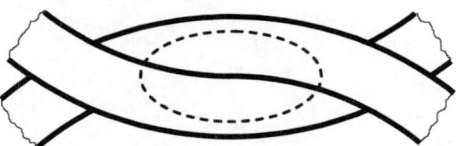

4.1 Contact between two fibers.

Basic idea of van Wyk model. The simple textile fibrous assemblies are usually consisted of randomly oriented fibers. Therefore, the contacts between fibers also originate randomly. In contact places, some fibers "try" to be shifted to the place of other fibers while the other fibers "resist" this shifting. As the fibers cannot penetrate into each other, this process is ended with creation of fiber contacts.

In an abstract sense, we can consider the fibers as geometrical bodies (negligible mass or weightless), which can mutually penetrate into each other. In such cases, the shifting of fibers will not end only with fiber contact, but they will penetrate into each other. In other words, the contact between fibers occurs in those places where the imaginatively geometrical fiber bodies together create a common penetration. With this great idea, van Wyk [1] converted the problem of contact to a "classical" concept of intersections of bodies.

Idealized fibers and their position in space. It is a fact that the geometry of fibers is very much complicated in a real fibrous assembly. The model of van Wyk introduces the following simplified assumptions for a fibrous assembly:

1. The fibrous assembly consists of straight fibers,
2. All fibers are of same length l,
3. All fibers follow cylindrical shape with diameter d, where $d \ll l$,
4. All fibers are distributed randomly in the fibrous assembly.

The location of each fiber in a (three-dimensional) space is given by its direction and position. According to Section 3.1, the direction of a fiber in a space can be expressed by a unit orientation vector $\mathbf{i}$, which is defined by its spherical coordinates ϑ and φ (Figure 3.2). The domain of fiber direction, i.e. $\vartheta \in (0, \pi/2)$ and $\varphi \in (0, 2\pi)$, is denoted by ω according to Eq. (3.1). Further, the coordinates of some definite point on a fiber express its position in a space. Such points can be, for example, one end-point of the fiber axis.

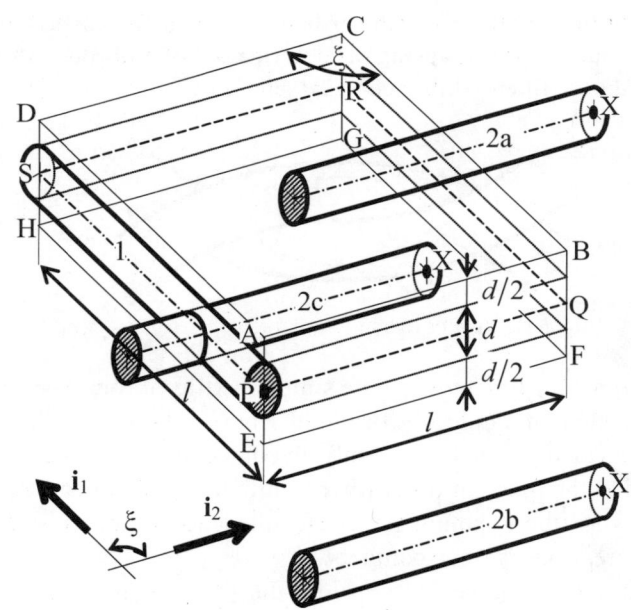

4.2 Intersection of two cylinders of length l.

Two fibers in a space. Let us now consider two fibers (fiber No. 1 and fiber No. 2) in a space. Let us also consider that fiber No. 1 has a given direction and position. Its direction is expressed by the unit orientation vector $\mathbf{i}_1$, which is defined by the two spherical coordinates ϑ_1, φ_1. The coordinates of end point P shown in Fig. 4.2 describe its position. Fiber No. 2 has only a given direction, expressed by the unit orientation vector $\mathbf{i}_2$, which is defined by the couple of spherical coordinates ϑ_2 and φ_2. This fiber is randomly positioned in space. (For example, its position can be 2a or 2b, as shown in Fig. 4.2). If we consider the fibers as geometrical (weightless) cylinders, then fiber No. 2 may take also the position 2c. In this case, both cylinders have a common intersection, as shown in Fig. 4.2.

An oblique prism ABCDEFGH is created around fiber No. 1 (Komori and Makishima [2] already reported such idea). Let us extend the end points P and S in the direction of vector $\mathbf{i}_2$ so that the abscissas PQ and SR of length l (fiber length) are formed. Further, we draw a perpendicular line in all apexes of the trapezoid PQRS and on both sides of them ("above" and "below" the plane PQRS in Fig. 4.2) we determine points A, B, C, D, and E, F, G, H at a distance d (fiber diameter); then we obtain AE = BF = CG = DH = $2d$. This drawing results in an oblique prism ABCDEFGH.

The angle ξ in the oblique prism corresponds to the angle between the orientation vectors $\mathbf{i}_1$ and $\mathbf{i}_2$. The unitary vector $\mathbf{i}_1$ with spherical coordinates ϑ_1, φ_1 has the (rectangular) Cartesian coordinates $\mathbf{i}_1 \equiv (\sin\vartheta_1\cos\varphi_1, \sin\vartheta_1\sin\varphi_1, \cos\vartheta_1)$ which follows from Fig. 3.2. Similarly, the other unitary vector $\mathbf{i}_2$ has the Cartesian coordinates $\mathbf{i}_2 \equiv (\sin\vartheta_2\cos\varphi_2, \sin\vartheta_2\sin\varphi_2, \cos\vartheta_2)$. The scalar product of these vectors is $\mathbf{i}_1\mathbf{i}_2 = |\mathbf{i}_1||\mathbf{i}_2|\cos\xi = 1\cdot1\cdot\cos\xi = \cos\xi$. If we express the scalar product of the vectors by the Cartesian coordinate system, we obtain the following expression for ξ.

$$\cos\xi = \sin\vartheta_1\cos\varphi_1\sin\vartheta_2\cos\varphi_2 + \sin\vartheta_1\sin\varphi_1\sin\vartheta_2\sin\varphi_2 + \cos\vartheta_1\cos\vartheta_2. \qquad \ldots (4.1)$$

Note: So, the angle ξ is always a function of four variables ϑ_1, φ_1, ϑ_2, φ_2 only.

The area of the trapezoid ABCD in Fig. 4.2 is $l\cdot l \sin\xi$ and the volume of the oblique prism is

$$V_{1,2} = AE\cdot ABCD = 2d\, l^2 \sin\xi. \qquad \ldots (4.2)$$

Probability of fiber intersection. We think about the two weightless cylinders No. 1 and No. 2, having known directions as shown in Fig. 4.2. Nevertheless, the position of cylinder No. 2, i.e., the position of its point X, is random. The two cylinders have no common intersection, if the following conditions are satisfied:

(a)   The point X lies above the plane ABCD (see e.g. the position 2a) or under the plane EGGH (see e.g. the position 2b),

(b) The point X lies at the right hand side of the plane BCGF or at the left hand side of the plane ADHE,[1]

(c) The point X lies in front of the plane ABFE or behind the plane DCGH.[2]

To the contrary, cylinders 1 and 2 have a common intersection if the point X lies inside the oblique prism ABCDEFGH (see e.g. the position 2c). The position of the point X is random and it may lie at any place in the fibrous assembly of total volume V_c. The probability that point X just lies inside the oblique prism is $P = V_{1,2}/V_c$ (geometrical definition of probability). By applying Eq. (4.2) we find

$$P = V_{1,2}/V_c = 2dl^2 \sin \xi/V_c . \qquad \qquad ... (4.3)$$

If point X lies inside the oblique prism, the intersection of both cylinders is realized. Under that condition, according to van Wyk's model, a contact between these (material) fibers occurs. Then, Eq. (4.3) expresses the probability P of occurrence of contact between two fibers.

Mean number of contact places on the fiber No. 1. Komori and Makishima [2] reported the number of contacts, density of contacts, and other quantitative characteristics regarding fiber-to-fiber contact in a fibrous assembly, based on C. M. van Wyk's model [1].

We assume that a fibrous assembly is created from a large number of (idealized) randomly organized fibers whose total number N is very large. The distribution of fiber orientation is described by the joint probability density function $w(\vartheta, \varphi)$ and the domain of directions is expressed by symbol $\omega : \vartheta \in (0, \pi/2) \wedge \varphi \in (0, 2\pi)$ according to Eq. (3.1).

Let us now choose (arbitrarily) fiber No. 1, having an orientation vector i_1 defined by spherical coordinates ϑ_1, φ_1. Hence, the number of other fibers in that assembly is

$$N_2 = N - 1. \qquad \qquad ... (4.4)$$

---

1. The concept is considered as a rough idea, because of neglecting fiber ends and fiber thickness. For example, if point X lies in the plane PQRS between the two lines PQ and RS and only a "small part" (less than $d/2$) in the right hand side of the plane BCGF, or in the left hand side of the plane ADHE, then intersection occurs. However, this is insignificant, because $d \ll l$.

2. This consideration is also an approximate one. For example, if point X just lies in the plane PQRS between the lines PS and QR and only a "small part" of it (less than $d/2$) lies in front of the plane ABFE or behind the plane DCGH, then intersection occurs. However, this is also insignificant, because $d \ll l$.

Each of these N_2 fibers acts as fiber No. 2 in relation to earlier selected fiber No. 1. These N_2 fibers have orientation vectors $\mathbf{i}_2$ defined by spherical coordinates ϑ_2, φ_2. Because N is very large and only one fiber (fiber No. 1) was taken away, the directional distribution of fibers does not change significantly. Hence, the directional distribution of fiber No. 2 is described by the same joint probability density function, i.e. $w(\vartheta_2, \varphi_2)$ and the domain of directions is expressed by symbol $\omega_2 : \vartheta_2 \in (0, \pi/2) \wedge \varphi_2 \in (0, 2\pi)$.

In accordance with the work [1] and [2], we assume that the probability that a selected fiber is in contact with fiber No. 1 is independent to other fibers. Then the probability P of each fiber No. 2 in contact with fiber No. 1 is the same and given by Eq. (4.3).

Note: In fact, the fibers, which are already in contact with fiber No. 1, "hinder" other fibers to contact with fiber No. 1. Therefore, the probability of occurrence of a new contact is reduced. We assume that the fibers in a fibrous assembly with small number of contacts (low densities) will face significantly less "hindering" effect.

Let us now imagine a directional elementary "class" of mentioned N_2 fibers determined by the elemental intervals $(\vartheta_2, \vartheta_2 + d\vartheta_2)$ and $(\varphi_2, \varphi_2 + d\varphi_2)$. (The same idea was used in the text before Eq. (3.4), relating to Fig. 3.3). The relative frequency of fibers in this elementary class is $w(\vartheta_2, \varphi_2)\, d\vartheta_2\, d\varphi_2$ and the absolute frequency ("number") of fibers in this elementary class is

$$dN_2 = N_2\, w(\vartheta_2, \varphi_2)\, d\vartheta_2\, d\varphi_2. \qquad \ldots (4.5)$$

From the fibers lying in the mentioned elementary "class", the mean value of number of contact places on fiber No. 1 can be expressed by $dm_1 = P\, dN_2$. By applying Eqs. (4.3) and (4.5), we get

$$dm_1 = P\, dN_2 = \frac{2dl^2 \sin\xi}{V_c} N_2\, w(\vartheta_2, \varphi_2)\, d\vartheta_2\, d\varphi_2$$

$$= \frac{2dl^2 N_2}{V_c} \sin\xi\, w(\vartheta_2, \varphi_2)\, d\vartheta_2\, d\varphi_2. \qquad \ldots (4.6)$$

The mean number m_1 of all contact places on fiber No. 1 (from all N_2 fibers) is

$$m_1 = \int_{\omega_2} dm_1 = \frac{2dl^2 N_2}{V_c} \iint_{\omega_2} \sin\xi\, w(\vartheta_2, \varphi_2)\, d\vartheta_2\, d\varphi_2, \qquad \ldots (4.7)$$

where angle ξ can be expressed as the function of spherical coordinates ϑ_1, φ_1 and ϑ_2, φ_2 according to Eq. (4.1).

Number of contact places and contacts in a fibrous assembly. Let us consider that each fiber from a fibrous assembly can be elected as fiber No. 1. So, the number of such fibers is

$$N_1 = N. \qquad \qquad \text{... (4.8)}$$

The directions of these fibers are expressed by the vector $\mathbf{i}_1$, which is defined by the couples of spherical coordinates ϑ_1, φ_1. The distribution of the directions of the considered N_1 fibers is given by the joint probability density function $w(\vartheta_1, \varphi_1)$ with defined domain $\omega_1 : \vartheta_1 \in (0, \pi/2) \wedge \varphi_1 \in (0, 2\pi)$.

A directional elementary "class" of mentioned N_1 fibers is determined by the intervals $(\vartheta_1, \vartheta_1 + d\vartheta_1)$ and $(\varphi_1, \varphi_1 + d\varphi_1)$. The relative frequency of fibers in such elementary class is $w(\vartheta_1, \varphi_1) d\vartheta_1 d\varphi_1$ and the absolute frequency ("number") of fibers in this elementary class is then

$$dN_1 = N_1 w(\vartheta_1, \varphi_1) d\vartheta_1 d\varphi_1. \qquad \qquad \text{... (4.9)}$$

The mean number of contact places m_1 on one fiber having this direction is given by Eq. (4.7). Also the other fibers belonging to the considered class have the same mean number of contacts. The number of contact places dM on all fibers in the elementary class is then $dM = m_1 \, dN_1$ and by applying Eqs. (4.7) and (4.9) we find

$$dM = m_1 dN_1 = \left[\frac{2d\,l^2 N_2}{V_c} \iint_{\omega_2} \sin\xi \, w(\vartheta_2, \varphi_2) d\vartheta_2 d\varphi_2 \right] \left[N_1 w(\vartheta_1, \varphi_1) d\vartheta_1 d\varphi_1 \right]$$

$$= \frac{2d\,l^2 N_2 N_1}{V_c} \left[\iint_{\omega_2} \sin\xi \, w(\vartheta_2, \varphi_2) d\vartheta_2 d\varphi_2 \right] w(\vartheta_1, \varphi_1) d\vartheta_1 d\varphi_1. \qquad \text{... (4.10)}$$

The number M of contact places on all fibers (not only on the considered fibers in one elementary class, but also on the fibers having other directions) is

$$M = \int_{\omega_1} dM = \iint_{\omega_1} \left\{ \frac{2d\,l^2 N_2 N_1}{V_c} \left[\iint_{\omega_2} \sin\xi \, w(\vartheta_2, \varphi_2) d\vartheta_2 d\varphi_2 \right] w(\vartheta_1, \varphi_1) d\vartheta_1 d\varphi_1 \right\}$$

$$= \frac{2d\,l^2 N_2 N_1}{V_c} \iint_{\omega_1, \, \omega_2} \iint \sin\xi \, w(\vartheta_1, \varphi_1) \, w(\vartheta_2, \varphi_2) d\vartheta_1 d\varphi_1 d\vartheta_2 d\varphi_2. \qquad \text{... (4.11)}$$

Let us introduce a dimensionless quantity I as follows

$$I = \iint_{\omega_1, \, \omega_2} \iint \sin\xi \, w(\vartheta_1, \varphi_1) \, w(\vartheta_2, \varphi_2) d\vartheta_1 d\varphi_1 d\vartheta_2 d\varphi_2. \qquad \qquad \text{... (4.12)}$$

Note: According to Eq. (4.1) the angle ξ is the given function of ϑ_1, φ_1, ϑ_2, φ_2. So, the definite integral I according to Eq. (4.12) depends only on the joint probability density function w of fiber orientation; I is a parameter of fiber orientation (evidently, $I \le 1$).

By substituting Eq. (4.12) into Eq. (4.11), we can write $M = 2d\,l^2 N_2 N_1 I / V_c$. If N is very large then according to Eqs. (4.4) and (4.8) it is valid to write that $N_2 N_1 = (N-1)N \cong N^2$. Hence the number M of contact places in the fibrous assembly is

$$M = \frac{2dl^2 N^2 I}{V_c}. \qquad \qquad \dots (4.13)$$

We know that one contact creates two contact places. Therefore, the number n of contacts in the fibrous assembly is

$$n = \frac{M}{2} = \frac{dl^2 N^2 I}{V_c}. \qquad \qquad \dots (4.14)$$

4.2   Density and distances of contacts

Density of contacts. The total volume V_c of the fibrous assembly can be expressed by Eq. (1.22) as a function of packing density μ and fiber volume V; $V_c = V/\mu$. The fibrous assembly is formed from N idealized fibers of diameter d and length l. Hence the fiber volume is $V = N\left(\pi d^2/4\right)l$. The total volume V_c is then expressed by the following equation

$$V_c = \frac{V}{\mu} = \frac{N\left(\pi d^2/4\right)l}{\mu} = \frac{N\pi d^2 l}{4\mu}. \qquad \dots (4.15)$$

The number of contacts per unit volume of fibrous assembly defines the density of contact υ. By applying Eqs. (4.14) and (4.15) we find the following expression

$$\upsilon = \frac{n}{V_c} = \frac{dl^2 N^2 I}{V_c^2} = dl^2 N^2 I \frac{16\mu^2}{N^2 \pi^2 d^4 l^2} = \frac{16I}{\pi^2 d^3}\mu^2. \qquad \dots (4.16)$$

This expression matches with the expression derived by Komori and Makishima [2] and Cheng and Duckett [3].

Now we introduce a parameter k_υ as follows

$$k_\upsilon = \frac{16I}{\pi^2 d^3}. \qquad \qquad \dots (4.17)$$

The parameter k_υ depends on the directional arrangement of fibers (via the quantity I) and on the considered fibrous assembly (via fiber diameter d). Finally, it can be stated that the parameter k_υ depends on the material characteristics and the structure of the fibrous assembly.

By substituting Eq. (4.17) into Eq. (4.16), the density of fiber contacts can be expressed by the following simple expression

$$\upsilon = k_\upsilon \mu^2. \qquad \qquad \dots (4.18)$$

Note: The quantity I is changed with the change in directional orientation which is generally changed with the increase in the value of packing density due to compression of fibrous assembly. So, the quantity I can be generally said to be a function of packing density μ. Nevertheless it is often possible assume that such changes are not too significant so that we can take the quantity k_υ as a constant parameter in Eqs. (4.17) and (4.18).

In order to verify whether van Wyk's model [1] corresponds to the reality, Taylor [4] made an attempt to determine the number of contacts per unit length of a wool sliver by radio-active tracer fiber technique. He experimentally found that there were 79 contacts on 1 cm length of a fiber when the fiber packing density in the sliver was determined as 0.077. At the same packing density, van Wyk deduced that there were 70 contacts on 1 cm length of fiber. Though it appears that the model is in agreement with the experimental result, but Taylor, however, had an apprehension that this agreement would appear as fortuitous.

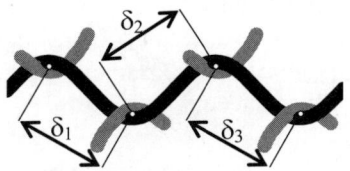

4.3 Distance between contact places.

Mean distance between neighboring contact places. If we move gradually along the black colored fiber shown in Fig. 4.3, we find many contact places marked by symbol "O". These contact places divide the black fiber to many sections of lengths δ_1, δ_2, δ_3,...; they express the distances between neighboring contact places (measured along the fiber curvature). As fiber contacts occur randomly, the quantity δ is considered to be a random variable.

The fibrous assembly contains N idealized fibers of length l; the total length of all fibers is Nl. In the same fibrous assembly, there are M contact places. The mean distance between neighboring contact places is then $\overline{\delta} = Nl/M$. By applying Eqs. (4.13) and (4.15), we find

$$\overline{\delta} = \frac{N\,l}{M} = \frac{N\,l}{2d\,l^2N^2I/V_c} = \frac{N\,l}{2d\,l^2N^2I} \frac{N\pi d^2 l}{4\mu} = \frac{\pi d}{8I}\frac{1}{\mu}. \qquad \text{... (4.19)}$$

Now we introduce the parameter k_δ in the form of

$$k_\delta = \frac{\pi d}{8I}. \qquad \text{... (4.20)}$$

(The note to the parameter k_υ – stated after Eq. (4.18) – is valid for the parameter k_δ similarly). Now the mean distance between the contact places can be expressed as follows

$$\overline{\delta} = \frac{k_\delta}{\mu}. \qquad \text{... (4.21)}$$

Note: The relationship between k_υ and k_δ can be found from Eqs. (4.17), (4.20), and (1.7) as follows

$$k_\upsilon k_\delta = \frac{16I}{\pi^2 d^3}\frac{\pi d}{8I} = \frac{2}{\pi d^2} = \frac{1}{2(\pi d^2/4)} = \frac{1}{2s}. \qquad \text{... (4.22)}$$

The value of the product $k_\upsilon k_\delta$ depends only the cross-sectional area of fibers s. The product $k_\upsilon k_\delta$ is independent of the arrangement of fibers.

The following examples illustrate the numerical values resulting from the previous equations.

Example 4.1: We consider a special regular arrangement of cylindrical fibers of diameter d as shown in Fig. 4.4a. The structure is created from cubes each of side d, as shown in Fig. 4.4b. The volume of the cube is $V_c = d^3$. The material volume creates two halves of fiber of length d, i.e., $V = \left(\pi d^2/4\right)d = \pi d^3/4$. The packing density is $\mu = V/V_c = \left(\pi d^3/4\right)/d^3 = \pi/4 \cong 0.7854$. In the cube, there is only one contact (the black arrow in Fig. 4.4b); $n = 1$. The density of contacts is $\upsilon = n/V_c = 1/d^3$. By applying μ and υ into Eq. (4.16), we find

$$1/d^3 = \left[16I/\left(\pi^2 d^3\right)\right]\left[\pi/4\right]^2 = I/d^3. \text{ Accordingly, we find } I = 1^3. \text{ For example,}$$

we consider a polyester fiber of fineness $t = 0.17$ tex and density $\rho = 1360$ kg m^{-1}. According to Eq. (1.6), fiber diameter is $d = 0.012616$ mm. We find $k_\upsilon = 807338$ mm^{-3} and $k_\delta = 0.00495430$ mm from Eqs. (4.17) and (4.20). The numerical results mentioned in Table 4.1 are obtained by applying

---

3.   We may get the same result if we realize that the contact fibers make always a right angle $\xi = \pi/2$; therefore, constantly, $\sin\xi = 1$ in Eq. (4.12). Nevertheless, a little problem can bring here the joint probability density function w, which is equal to zero for all angles except 0 and $\pi/2$ and is equal to infinity for these two angles. Therefore a suitable limitation procedure must be used in this case.

k_υ and k_δ into Eq. (4.18) and Eq. (4.21), respectively for similar type of structures (fibers contact at right angle) having different packing densities.

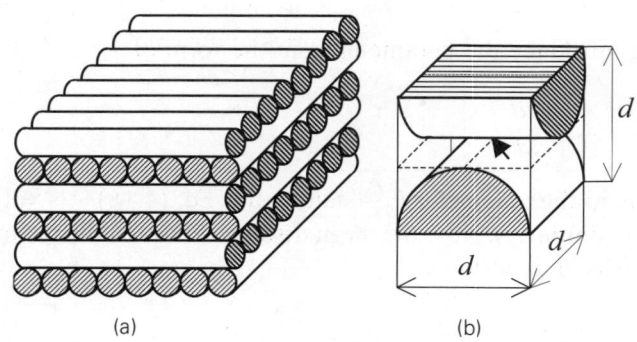

(a)　　　　　　　　　　　(b)

4.4 Example of a regularly arranged structure.

Table 4.1 Values of υ and $\bar{\delta}$ for $l = 1$.

Material. Polyester fibers, fineness $t = 0.17$ tex , density $\rho = 1360\,\mathrm{kg\,m^{-1}}$		
Packing density	Density of contacts $\upsilon\left[\mathrm{mm^{-3}}\right]$	Mean distance $\bar{\delta}$ [mm]
$\mu = 0.7854$ (according to Fig. 4.4)	498007	0.006308
$\mu = 0.5$ (orientation value for yarn)	201835	0.009909
$\mu = 0.3$	72660	0.016514
$\mu = 0.1$ (orientation value for roving)	8073	0.049543
$\mu = 0.01$ (orientation value for sliver)	80.73	0.495429

Example 4.2: We consider a fibrous assembly with spatial isotropic fiber orientation. The joint probability density function $w(\vartheta, \varphi)$ is given by Eq. (3.7) in this case. Eq. (4.1) expresses $\cos\xi$ and it is valid that $\sin\xi = \sqrt{1-\cos^2\xi}$. By applying Eqs. (3.7), (4.1), and expression of integrating borders according (3.1), into the Eq. (4.12), we get the following expression for calculating the quantity of I.

$$
I = \iint\limits_{\omega_1,\,\omega_2}\iint \sin\xi\; w(\vartheta_1,\varphi_1)\,w(\vartheta_2,\varphi_2)\,d\vartheta_1 d\varphi_1 d\vartheta_2 d\varphi_2
$$

$$
= \iint\limits_{\omega_1,\,\omega_2}\iint \sqrt{1-\cos^2\xi}\;\frac{\sin\vartheta_1}{2\pi}\frac{\sin\vartheta_2}{2\pi}\,d\vartheta_1 d\varphi_1 d\vartheta_2 d\varphi_2
$$

$$
= \iint\limits_{\substack{\vartheta_1\in(0,\pi/2)\\ \varphi_1\in(0,2\pi)\\ \vartheta_2\in(0,\pi/2)\\ \varphi_2\in(0,2\pi)}}\iint \left[1-\left(\sin\vartheta_1\cos\varphi_1\sin\vartheta_2\cos\varphi_2 + \sin\vartheta_1\sin\varphi_1\sin\vartheta_2\sin\varphi_2 + \cos\vartheta_1\cos\vartheta_2\right)^2\right]^{1/2}\frac{\sin\vartheta_1\sin\vartheta_2}{4\pi^2}\,d\vartheta_1 d\varphi_1 d\vartheta_2 d\varphi_2 .
$$

The value of I found by numerical integration is $I = 0.7854$ now[4]. The same value for this function was also reported by Komori and Makishima [2] and Stern [5]. Similarly to previous example, we also obtain the values $k_\upsilon = 634083$ mm^{-3}, $k_\delta = 0.00630799$ mm, and the values υ and $\bar\delta$ as shown in Table 4.2.

Table 4.2   Values of υ and $\bar\delta$ for $I = 0.7854$ (spatial isotropic fiber orientation)

Material: Polyester fibers, fineness $t = 0.17$ tex, density $\rho = 1360$ kg m^{-3}		
Packing density	Density of contacts $\upsilon \left[\text{mm}^{-3}\right]$	Mean distance $\bar\delta [\text{mm}]$
$\mu = 0.7854$	391136	0.008032
$\mu = 0.5$ (approx. yarn packing density)	158521	0.012616
$\mu = 0.3$	57067	0.021027
$\mu = 0.1$ (approx. roving packing density)	6341	0.063080
$\mu = 0.01$ (approx. sliver packing density)	63.41	0.630799

4.3   Distribution of contact places

Probability (p). In Section 4.1, Eq. (4.3) and Fig. 4.2 define the probability $P = 2d\,l^2 \sin\xi / V_c$ that fiber No. 2 contacts fiber No. 1. We may remind that the angle ξ can be expressed by Eq. (4.1) as a function of spherical coordinates ϑ_1, φ_1 and ϑ_2, φ_2. The probability of the randomly selected fiber No. 2 belonging to the elementary class, which is defined by the angle intervals $(\vartheta_2, \vartheta_2 + d\vartheta_2)$ and $(\varphi_2, \varphi_2 + d\varphi_2)$, is $w(\vartheta_2, \varphi_2)\,d\vartheta_2 d\varphi_2$ (see also the considerations mentioned before Eq. (4.5)). The probability d_p of the randomly selected fiber No. 2 belonging to the elementary class and at the same time is in contact with fiber No. 1 is given by the product of these independent probabilities

$$dp = P\,w\left(\vartheta_2,\varphi_2\right)d\vartheta_2 d\varphi_2 = \frac{2d\,l^2 \sin\xi}{V_c}\,w\left(\vartheta_2,\varphi_2\right)d\vartheta_2 d\varphi_2. \qquad \ldots (4.23)$$

The probability p of randomly selected fiber No. 2 (regardless of its direction) is in contact with given fiber No. 1 is

$$p = \iint_{\omega_2} dp = \frac{2d\,l^2}{V_c} \iint_{\omega_2} \sin\xi\; w\left(\vartheta_2,\varphi_2\right)d\vartheta_2 d\varphi_2. \qquad \ldots (4.24)$$

---

4.   This value will be later derived also analytically – see Eq. 4.44.

If we denote

$$J(\vartheta_1, \varphi_1) = \iint_{\omega_2} \sin \xi \, w(\vartheta_2, \varphi_2) \, d\vartheta_2 \, d\varphi_2 \qquad \qquad \dots (4.25)$$

then we can reformulate the above probability p in the following manner

$$p = \frac{2d \, l^2}{V_c} J(\vartheta_1, \varphi_1). \qquad \qquad \dots (4.26)$$

(As ξ is a function of ϑ_1, φ_1, ϑ_2, φ_2, the integral of J is a function of ϑ_1, φ_1).

It is possible to rearrange the last equation by the following manner. The length and equivalent diameter of an individual fiber are l and d, respectively. Hence, the volume of individual fiber is $(\pi d^2/4)l$ and the volume of N fibers in the fibrous assembly is $V = N(\pi d^2/4)l$. We also consider the total volume of the fibrous assembly is V_c. From the definition of packing density μ expressed in Eq. (1.22), we can write

$$\mu = \frac{V}{V_c} = \frac{N \dfrac{\pi d^2}{4} l}{V_c}, \quad N \frac{2d \, l^2}{V_c} = \frac{8 \mu l}{\pi d}, \quad \frac{2d \, l^2}{V_c} = \frac{8 \mu l}{N \pi d}. \qquad \dots (4.27)$$

Accordingly, it is valid that the probability p can be written as follows

$$p = \frac{8 \mu l}{N \pi d} J(\vartheta_1, \varphi_1). \qquad \qquad \dots (4.28)$$

Binomial distribution of contact places on fiber No. 1. Fibrous assembly contains $N_2 = N - 1$ fibers of type 2, which can be in contact with the given fiber No. 1. The theory of C. M. van Wyk assumes p as an independent parameter, then the distribution of number of contact places x on fibers of type 1 (fibers which have given direction ϑ_1, φ_1) must follow binomial distribution.

$$B(x) = \binom{N-1}{x} p^x (1-p)^{N-1-x}. \qquad \qquad \dots (4.29)$$

According to the properties of binomial distribution, the mean number of contact places m_1 on fiber of type 1 is $m_1 = (N-1)p$. By applying Eq. (4.28), we obtain

$$m_1 = (N-1)p = \frac{(N-1) 8 \mu l}{N \pi d} J(\vartheta_1, \varphi_1). \qquad \qquad \dots (4.30)$$

Poisson's distribution of contact places on fiber No. 1. If we assume that the number of fibers in a fibrous assembly tends to infinity, that is,

$N \rightarrow \infty$, then in all "successful" cases, according to Eq. (4.28), the probability will tend to zero, that is, $p \rightarrow 0$ and the mean value will be constant, that is, $m_1 \rightarrow$ constant. Then the following expression is obtained from Eq. (4.30)

$$m_1 = \lim_{N \to \infty} \left[\frac{(N-1)8\mu l}{N \pi d} J(\vartheta_1, \varphi_1) \right] = \frac{8\mu l}{\pi d} J(\vartheta_1, \varphi_1) . \qquad \ldots (4.31)$$

According to the above conditions, the binomial distribution $B(x)$ can be replaced by the Poison's distribution $P(x)$.

$$P(x) = e^{-m_1} m_1^x / x! . \qquad \ldots (4.32)$$

In other words,

$$P(0) = e^{-m_1}, \quad P(x) = \frac{m_1^x}{x!} P(0). \qquad \ldots (4.33)$$

The mean value of this distribution is $m_1 = \sum_{x=0}^{\infty} [x P(x)]$. In the given particular case, the mean value is found from Eq. (4.31).

Note: By substituting Eq. (4.27) into Eq. (4.31) and applying the integration from Eq. (4.25), we obtain

$$m_1 = \frac{8\mu l}{\pi d} J(\vartheta_1, \varphi_1) = N \frac{2d l^2}{V_c} J(\vartheta_1, \varphi_1)$$
$$= N \frac{2d l^2}{V_c} \iint_{\omega_2} \sin \xi \, w(\vartheta_2, \varphi_2) d\vartheta_2 \, d\varphi_2 . \qquad \ldots (4.34)$$

As expected, the last expression is identical with Eq. (4.7)[5].

Distribution of number of contact places on fiber. The probability of a randomly selected fiber No. 1, belonging to the directional elementary class, determined by the elementary intervals $(\vartheta_1, \vartheta_1 + d\vartheta_1)$ and $(\varphi_1, \varphi_1 + d\varphi_1)$, is $w(\vartheta_1, \varphi_1) d\vartheta_1 \, d\varphi_1$. The probability $dK(x)$ of the randomly selected fiber No. 1 belonging to the considered elementary class and simultaneously has x contact places is given by the product $P(x) [w(\vartheta_1, \varphi_1) d\vartheta_1 \, d\varphi_1]$. By applying Eq. (4.32), we obtain the following expression for $dK(x)$

$$dK(x) = P(x) \cdot w(\vartheta_1, \varphi_1) d\vartheta_1 \, d\varphi_1 = \frac{m_1^x}{x!} e^{-m_1} w(\vartheta_1, \varphi_1) d\vartheta_1 \, d\varphi_1 . \qquad \ldots (4.35)$$

---

5. According to Eq. (4.4), $N_2 = N - 1$ and for a large number of N, we can consider that $(N-1) \cong N$.

The probability $K(x)$ of the randomly selected fiber having just x contact places is obtained from the integration of the previous expression. By applying Eqs. (4.31) and (4.35), we obtain

$$K(x) = \iint_{\omega_1} dK(x) = \iint_{\omega_1} \frac{m_1^x}{x!} e^{-m_1} w(\vartheta_1, \varphi_1) d\vartheta_1 d\varphi_1$$

$$= \iint_{\omega_1} \frac{1}{x!} \left[\frac{8\mu l}{\pi d} J(\vartheta_1, \varphi_1) \right]^x \exp\left[-\frac{8\mu l}{\pi d} J(\vartheta_1, \varphi_1) \right] w(\vartheta_1, \varphi_1) d\vartheta_1 d\varphi_1,$$

$$\ldots (4.36)$$

where the integral of $J(\vartheta_1, \varphi_1)$ is defined by Eq. (4.25) and it implicates the function of $\sin\xi = \sqrt{1 - \cos^2\xi}$, which is deduced from Eq. (4.1).

In fact, $K(x)$ is a special type of distribution, which depends on fiber orientation (via joint probability density function w) and packing density of the fibrous assembly. In general, a suitable numerical integration method can be used for evaluation of the expression of $K(x)$ and of course, this is going to be difficult.

It is relatively easy to find out the mean value m of the number of contact places on the fiber, $m = \sum_{x=0}^{\infty} [x K(x)]$. By applying Eqs. (4.36), (4.32), (4.31), (4.25), and (4.12) step-by-step, we find

$$m = \sum_{x=0}^{\infty} \left[x \iint_{\omega_1} \overbrace{\frac{m_1^x}{x!} e^{-m_1}}^{=P(x)} w(\vartheta_1, \varphi_1) d\vartheta_1 d\varphi_1 \right]$$

$$= \iint_{\omega_1} \overbrace{\sum_{x=0}^{\infty} [x P(x)]}^{=m_1} w(\vartheta_1, \varphi_1) d\vartheta_1 d\varphi_1$$

$$= \frac{8\mu l}{\pi d} \iint_{\omega_1} J(\vartheta_1, \varphi_1) w(\vartheta_1, \varphi_1) d\vartheta_1 d\varphi_1$$

$$= \frac{8\mu l}{\pi d} \iint_{\omega_1} \left(\iint_{\omega_2} \sin\xi \, w(\vartheta_2, \varphi_2) d\vartheta_2 d\varphi_2 \right) w(\vartheta_1, \varphi_1) d\vartheta_1 d\varphi_1$$

$$= \frac{8\mu l}{\pi d} \overbrace{\iint_{\omega_1} \iint_{\omega_2} \sin\xi \, w(\vartheta_1, \varphi_1) w(\vartheta_2, \varphi_2) d\vartheta_2 d\varphi_2 d\vartheta_1 d\varphi_1}^{=I} = \frac{8\mu l I}{\pi d}. \ldots (4.37)$$

Note: The fibrous assembly contains $M = Nm$ contact places. By applying Eqs. (4.37) and (4.27), we obtain

$$M = N \frac{8 \mu l \, I}{\pi d} = N^2 \frac{2 d \, l^2 I}{V_c}. \qquad \qquad \dots (4.38)$$

Naturally, this result is identical with Eq. (4.13) as we expected.

Distribution of contact places in case of spatial isotropic orientation. The integral value of $J(\vartheta_1, \varphi_1)$ expressed by Eq. (4.25) depends on

(a) the angles ξ between fiber No. 1 (with given direction ϑ_1, φ_1) and the other fibers considered as fibers of type 2 (of angles ϑ_2, φ_2) – see Fig. 4.2, and

(b) on the joint probability density function $w(\vartheta_2, \varphi_2)$ of orientation of fibers of type 2. The angles ϑ_1, φ_1, ϑ_2, φ_2 are of spherical coordinates in space defined to the axis of the Cartesian coordinates x_1, x_2, x_3 – see Fig. 3.2.

Let us now shift and turn the Cartesian coordinates to some new position x'_1, x'_2, x'_3 (orthogonal transformation of coordinates). We determine the new spherical coordinates $\vartheta'_1, \varphi'_1, \vartheta'_2, \varphi'_2$ with respect to the new axes. Nevertheless, the angles ξ, which fiber No. 1 makes with the other fibers, are evidently not changed due to this transformation. With respect to the orthogonal transformation, they are invariants. Analogically to Eq. (4.1), it is also valid to write that

$$\cos \xi = \sin \vartheta'_1 \cos \varphi'_1 \sin \vartheta'_2 \cos \varphi'_2 +$$
$$+ \sin \vartheta'_1 \sin \varphi'_1 \sin \vartheta'_2 \sin \varphi'_2 + \cos \vartheta'_1 \cos \vartheta'_2. \qquad \dots (4.39)$$

In opposite to this, the joint probability density function $w(\vartheta_2, \varphi_2)$ is changed due to orthogonal transformation of coordinates. (For example, the angles ϑ_{2max} and φ_{2max} which describe the most frequent direction of fibers, take another values in the new coordinates system as $\vartheta'_{2\,max} \neq \vartheta_{2\,max}$ and $\varphi'_{2\,max} \neq \varphi_{2\,max}$).

A special case of fiber orientation is spatial isotropic orientation, which is distinguished by the property of same frequency of fibers in all directions. According to Eq. (3.7), the joint probability density function is $w(\vartheta_2, \varphi_2) = \sin \vartheta_2 / (2\pi)$. The frequency of fibers in all directions is same after the orthogonal transformation of coordinates too. In this case, the joint probability density function $w(\vartheta_2, \varphi_2)$ due to the orthogonal transformation of coordinates is invariant. For the new coordinates, it is valid to write

$$w(\vartheta'_2, \varphi'_2) = \sin \vartheta'_2 / (2\pi), \quad \omega'_2 : \vartheta' \in (0, \pi/2) \wedge \varphi' \in (0, 2\pi). \qquad \dots (4.40)$$

In this case, due to the orthogonal transformation of coordinates, the integral of $J(\vartheta_1, \varphi_1)$ is invariant, because according to Eq. (4.25), all its components are invariant. It is valid that

$$J(\vartheta_1, \varphi_1) = J(\vartheta'_1, \varphi'_1). \qquad \qquad \dots (4.41)$$

In case of spatial isotropic orientation, if we rotate the Cartesian axis in such a manner that fiber No. 1 will have the direction of x_3-axis as shown in Fig. 3.2 so that $\vartheta_1' = 0$, then it is valid from Eq. (4.39).

$$\cos\xi = \overbrace{\sin\vartheta_1' \cos\varphi_1'}^{=0} \sin\vartheta_2' \cos\varphi_2' + \overbrace{\sin\vartheta_1' \sin\varphi_1'}^{=0} \sin\vartheta_2' \sin\varphi_2' +$$
$$+ \overbrace{\cos\vartheta_1'}^{=1} \cos\vartheta_2' = \cos\vartheta_2', \quad \sin\xi = \sin\vartheta_2'. \qquad \ldots (4.42)$$

We can write the integration of Eq. (4.25), from Eqs. (4.40), (4.41), and (4.42).

$$J(\vartheta_1,\varphi_1) = J(\vartheta_1',\varphi_1') = \iint\limits_{\omega_2'} \sin\xi \, w(\vartheta_2',\varphi_2') \, d\vartheta_2' \, d\varphi_2'$$

$$= \iint\limits_{\omega_2'} \sin\vartheta_2' \frac{\sin\vartheta_2'}{2\pi} d\vartheta_2' \, d\varphi_2'$$

$$= \int\limits_0^{\pi/2} \sin^2\vartheta_2' \overbrace{\left(\frac{1}{2\pi} \int\limits_0^{2\pi} d\varphi_2'\right)}^{=1} d\vartheta_2' = \int\limits_0^{\pi/2} \sin^2\vartheta_2' \, d\vartheta_2' \qquad \ldots (4.43)$$

$$= \left[\frac{1}{2}\vartheta_2 - \frac{1}{4}\sin(2\vartheta_2')\right]_0^{\pi/2} = \frac{\pi}{4}.$$

By applying Eqs. (4.25) and (4.43) into Eq. (4.12), we obtain the value of the integral I for the fibrous assembly with spatial isotropic orientation as follows

$$I = \iint\limits_{\omega_1,\,\omega_2} \iint \sin\xi \, w(\vartheta_1,\varphi_1) \, w(\vartheta_2,\varphi_2) \, d\vartheta_1 d\varphi_1 d\vartheta_2 d\varphi_2$$

$$= \iint\limits_{\omega_1} w(\vartheta_1,\varphi_1) \overbrace{\left[\iint\limits_{\omega_2} \sin\xi \, w(\vartheta_2,\varphi_2) \, d\vartheta_2 d\varphi_2\right]}^{J(\vartheta_1,\varphi_1)=\pi/4} d\vartheta_1 d\varphi_1 \qquad \ldots (4.44)$$

$$= \frac{\pi}{4} \overbrace{\iint\limits_{\omega_1} w(\vartheta_1,\varphi_1) d\vartheta_1 \, d\varphi_1}^{=1} = \frac{\pi}{4} \quad (= 0,7854).$$

Komori and Makishima [2] and Stern [5] also found the constant $J(\vartheta_1,\varphi_1) = I = \pi/4$.

Note: The integral value of I for spatial isotropic orientation is calculated also by numerical integration and this is shown in Example 4.2 at the end of Section 4.2. The resultant values are naturally the same.

The mean value of the number of contact places is the same for each fiber regardless of its direction. By applying Eq. (4.43) into Eq. (4.31) and Eq. (4.44) into Eq. (4.37), we find

$$m_1 = \frac{8\mu l}{\pi d} J(\vartheta_1, \varphi_1) = \frac{8\mu l}{\pi d} \frac{\pi}{4} = \frac{2\mu l}{d}, \quad m = \frac{8\mu l \, I}{\pi d} = \frac{8\mu l}{\pi d} \frac{\pi}{4} = \frac{2\mu l}{d},$$

$$m = m_1 = \frac{2\mu l}{d}. \qquad \text{... (4.45)}$$

The distribution $K(x)$ of the contact places on fibers in a fibrous assembly with spatial isotropic orientation can be found by applying Eq. (4.45) into Eq. (4.36) as follows

$$K(x) = \iint_{\omega_1} \frac{m_1^x}{x!} e^{-m_1} w(\vartheta_1, \varphi_1) \, d\vartheta_1 \, d\varphi_1$$

$$= \iint_{\omega_1} \frac{1}{x!} \left(\frac{2\mu l}{d} \right)^x e^{-\frac{2\mu l}{d}} w(\vartheta_1, \varphi_1) \, d\vartheta_1 \, d\varphi_1 \qquad \text{... (4.46)}$$

$$= \frac{1}{x!} \left(\frac{2\mu l}{d} \right)^x e^{-\frac{2\mu l}{d}} \overbrace{\iint_{\omega_1} w(\vartheta_1, \varphi_1) \, d\vartheta_1 \, d\varphi_1}^{=1} = \frac{1}{x!} \left(\frac{2\mu l}{d} \right)^x e^{-\frac{2\mu l}{d}},$$

which is the Poisson distribution with a mean value $m = 2\mu l/d$.

Orientation of fibers in plane. In case of orientation of fibers in plane, the orientation vector for all fibers lie in a single plane α and its joint probability density function is described by $f(\psi)$, $\psi \in (-\pi/2, \pi/2)$ instead of $w(\vartheta, \varphi)$ (see Section 3.4 and Fig. 3.8). The relative frequency of fibers in orientation elementary class (or in other words the probability of a randomly chosen fiber belonging to this elementary class) is given by $f(\psi) \, d\psi$ instead of $w(\vartheta, \varphi) d\vartheta d\varphi$. The fiber orientation vector of fiber No. 1 and fiber No. 2 are described by only one set of angle i.e., ψ_1 and ψ_1. The non-oriented angle ξ is the angle between fiber No. 1 and fiber No. 2 (as shown in Fig. 4.2), then it is evident that $\xi = |\psi_2 - \psi_1|$. The integral of $J(\vartheta_1, \varphi_1)$ is defined by Eq. (4.25) in the following form

$$J(\vartheta_1, \varphi_1) = J(\psi_1) = \int_{-\pi/2}^{\pi/2} \sin\xi \, f(\psi_2) \, d\psi_2$$

$$= \int_{-\pi/2}^{\pi/2} \sin|\psi_2 - \psi_1| \, f(\psi_2) \, d\psi_2. \qquad \text{... (4.47)}$$

Integral of I is defined by Eq. (4.12) and using Eq. (4.25) it takes the following form

$$
\begin{aligned}
I &= \iint_{\omega_1,\,\omega_2} \iint \sin\xi\, w(\vartheta_1,\varphi_1)\, w(\vartheta_2,\varphi_2)\, d\vartheta_1\, d\varphi_1\, d\vartheta_2\, d\varphi_2 \\
&= \iint_{\omega_1} \left[\overbrace{\iint_{\omega_2} \sin\xi\, w(\vartheta_2,\varphi_2)\, d\vartheta_2\, d\varphi_2}^{J(\vartheta_1,\varphi_1)} \right] w(\vartheta_1,\varphi_1)\, d\vartheta_1\, d\varphi_1 \\
&= \int_{-\pi/2}^{\pi/2} J(\psi_1) f(\psi_1)\, d\psi_1 .
\end{aligned}
\qquad\ldots (4.48)
$$

From Eqs. (4.31) and (4.47), we can re-write the mean number of contacts on fiber No. 1 as follows

$$
m_1 = \frac{8\mu l}{\pi d} J(\psi_1).
\qquad\ldots (4.49)
$$

The distribution $K(x)$ of the number of contacts can be modified to the following form by applying Eq. (4.49) into Eq. (4.36)

$$
\begin{aligned}
K(x) &= \int_{-\pi/2}^{\pi/2} \frac{m_1^x}{x!} e^{-m_1} f(\psi_1)\, d\psi_1 \\
&= \int_{-\pi/2}^{\pi/2} \frac{1}{x!} \left[\frac{8\mu l}{\pi d} J(\psi_1) \right]^x \exp\left[-\frac{8\mu l}{\pi d} J(\psi_1) \right] f(\psi_1)\, d\psi_1 .
\end{aligned}
\qquad\ldots (4.50)
$$

Distribution of contact places in case of plane isotropic orientation. The special case is the plane of isotropic orientation, which is distinguished by the property of same frequency of fiber orientation vector in all directions. In this case, the constant value of the joint probability density function is obtained from Eq. (3.26) as $f(\psi) = 1/\pi$. The probability density in this case is also invariant with respect to the orthogonal transformation of coordinates, as this was in the case of spatial isotropic orientation.

Therefore, we can rotate the original coordinates to the new (dashed) coordinates without any restrictions in such a manner that the considered fiber No. 1 is parallel to the axis $x_3 \equiv y$ (see Fig. 3.8). In this case, $\psi_1' = 0$ and from Eq. (4.47) a new expression is obtained as mentioned below

$$J(\psi_1) = J(\psi_1') = J(0) = \int_{-\pi/2}^{\pi/2} \sin|\psi_2' - 0| \frac{1}{\pi} d\psi_2'$$

$$= \frac{1}{\pi} 2 \int_0^{\pi/2} \sin \psi_2' \, d\psi_2 \qquad \qquad \dots (4.51)$$

$$= \frac{2}{\pi} [-\cos \psi']_0^{\pi/2} = \frac{2}{\pi}.$$

From Eqs. (4.48) and (4.51), we obtain the value of the integral I as follows

$$I = \int_{-\pi/2}^{\pi/2} J(\psi_1') f(\psi_1') d\psi_1' = \frac{2}{\pi} \overbrace{\int_{-\pi/2}^{\pi/2} f(\psi_1') d\psi_1'}^{=1} = \frac{2}{\pi}. \qquad \dots (4.52)$$

Komori and Makishima [2] and Pan [6] also found the parameter $J(\psi_1) = I = 2/\pi$.

The mean value of contact places on each fiber is equal regardless to its direction. Accordingly, by applying Eq. (4.51) into Eq. (4.49) and Eq. (4.52) into Eq. (4.37), we find

$$m_1 = \frac{8\mu l}{\pi d} J(\psi_1) = \frac{8\mu l}{\pi d} \frac{2}{\pi} = \frac{16\mu l}{\pi^2 d}, \quad m = \frac{8\mu l \, I}{\pi d} = \frac{8\mu l}{\pi d} \frac{2}{\pi} = \frac{16\mu l}{\pi^2 d}, \qquad \dots (4.53)$$

$$m = m_1 = \frac{16\mu l}{\pi^2 d}.$$

The distribution $K(x)$ of the number of contact places on the fibers can be found by applying Eq. (4.53) into Eq. (4.50)

$$K(x) = \int_{-\pi/2}^{\pi/2} \frac{m_1^x}{x!} e^{-m_1} f(\psi_1) d\psi_1 = \int_{-\pi/2}^{\pi/2} \frac{1}{x!} \left(\frac{16\mu l}{\pi^2 d} \right)^x e^{-\frac{16\mu l}{\pi^2 d}} f(\psi_1) d\psi_1$$

$$= \frac{1}{x!} \left(\frac{16\mu l}{\pi^2 d} \right)^x e^{-\frac{16\mu l}{\pi^2 d}} \overbrace{\int_{-\pi/2}^{\pi/2} f(\psi_1) d\psi_1}^{=1} = \frac{1}{x!} \left(\frac{16\mu l}{\pi^2 d} \right)^x e^{-\frac{16\mu l}{\pi^2 d}}. \qquad \dots (4.54)$$

It is the Poison's distribution having the mean value $m = 16\mu l / (\pi^2 d)$.

The examples to estimate the distribution of $K(x)$ for fibrous assembly with isotropic orientation are illustrated in Fig. 4.5. For calculations, the fiber aspect ratio is assumed for cotton fibers as $\Lambda = l/d = 2000$ and the packing density is chosen as $\mu = 0.1, 0.3$ and 0.5. (The graphs are defined and therefore calculated only for integers of x values).

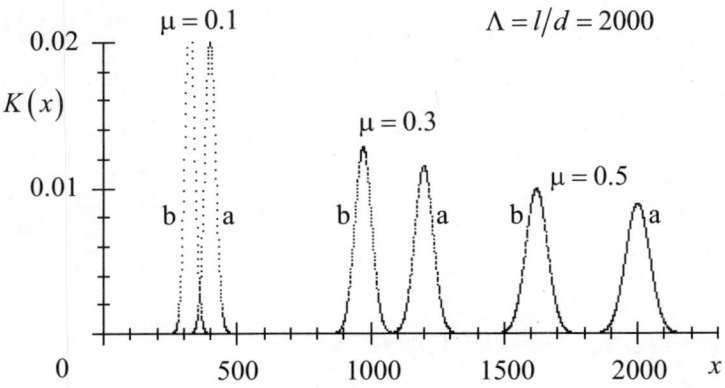

4.5 Probability density $K(x)$ of the number of contact places on fiber in case:
a... fibrous assembly with spatial isotropic orientation – Equation (4.46).
b...fibrous assembly with plane isotropic orientation – Equation (4.54).

4.4   Modified probability of fiber-to-fiber contacts

Introductory idea. In the previous chapters we assumed that each fiber No. 2 (Figure 4.2) is in contact with the selected fiber No. 1 independently to other fibers, i.e. with same probability P, given by Eq. (4.3). In fact, the fibers, which are already in contact with fiber No. 1, "obstruct" other fibers to make contacts with the fiber No. 1. Therefore, the probability of occurrence of another new contact is reduced. A similar idea was reported by Pan [6], but the mathematical derivations made by him to solve this problem were incorrect as reported by Komori and Itoh [7]. Though Komori and Itoh corrected the mistakes made by Pan, however, the solution given by them was too simplified.

Let us imagine that the fiber No. 2 is being already in contact with fiber No. 1 as shown in Fig. 4.6. Such fiber allocates a (horizontally shaded) section a_1 on fiber No. 1 and "blocks" this part for another future contact. Further, the next fiber – dotted fiber No. 3 on Fig. 4.6 – is coming close to fiber No. 1 and "wants" to be in contact, too. If this fiber should have the position e.g. according to 3a, then it will make a contact with fiber No. 1 without any difficulty and allocates a new, i.e. second "blocking" section a_2 on it. Nevertheless, if the dotted fiber No. 3 should have the position according to 3b on Fig. 4.6, i.e., if it "would like" to be in contact with fiber No. 1 in the blocked section a_1, then such fiber will not be "successful" because the earlier contacted fiber No. 2 obstructs to it. It can be then

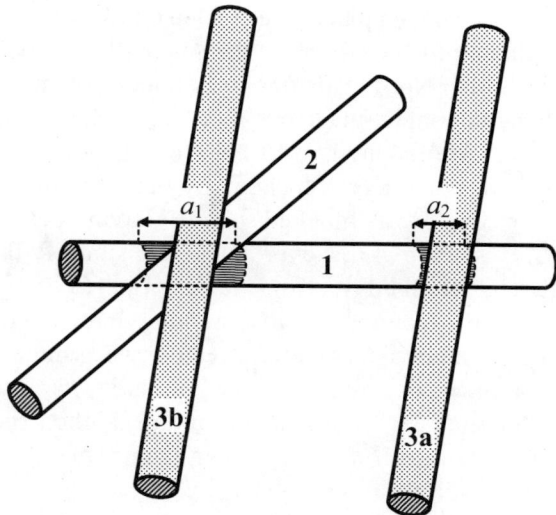

4.6 Scheme of modified idea of contacts.

generally said that every other fiber will realize its contact with fiber No. 1 only when its random position will be outside of the earlier created "blocking" sections $a_1, a_2, \ldots$. Evidently, the probability of every other contact with fiber No 1 is not the same but is a decreasing quantity.

Interaction. If a fiber "wants" to be in contact with another fiber then they must be mutually very close. The sufficient vicinity of fiber No. 2 to fiber No. 1 was earlier also the sufficient condition for creation of contact (Section 3.1, Fig. 4.2). This situation, where a fiber is very close to other fiber will be called by interaction, now. Fiber No. 1 may (but need not) contact fiber No. 2 only if fiber No. 2 is in interaction with fiber No. 1.

Earlier, van Wyk's probability p according to Eq. (4.26) meant the probability that a randomly selected fiber No. 2 (regardless of its direction) is in contact with the given fiber No. 1. The same equation says now that the so randomly selected fiber No. 2 is only in interaction with fiber No. 1. Similarly, the Poison distribution in Eq. (4.32) or (4.33) expresses only the probability $P(x)$ of the given fiber No. 1 having just x interactions with other fibers (never x contacts, as it is valid in the original theory according to van Wyk's concept).

Note: We assume number of fibers $N \to \infty$ in this model; then the mentioned Poison distribution of interactions is valid.

Occurrence of contact place. We imagine that a fibrous assembly is formed in such a manner that at first we place the given fiber No. 1 in the available space, and then in a random way, we place the other fibers. In this way, some of the fibers will interact with fiber No. 1 and some of the interacting fibers will create contact places with it.

After a while, $i - 1$ contact places are created on fiber No. 1. We continue the process of placing further fibers in the space till another fiber will be in interaction with fiber No. 1. This fiber may undergo some circumstances to create another i-th contact place on fiber No. 1. Naturally, for creating a contact place, the whole length l of fiber No. 1 is not available because a part of this length is already "blocked" by the previous $i - 1$ contacts. The contact places enclose a "blocked section" having generally different lengths a_1, a_2, ... – see Fig. 4.6. Nevertheless, we simplify this reality and assume that each "blocked section" have same (average) length a, independent to fiber directions. We also assume that on a fiber of length l, a maximum of z contact places can be created (we assume that $z \geq 1$), so that each contact place "occupy" the same length $a = l/z$. If there are $i - 1$ contact places on fiber No. 1 just at the moment, then the "occupied" length is $(i - 1)l/z$ and still a "free" fiber length of $l^* = l - (i-1)l/z$ is available for contacting on fiber No. 1.

Let us introduce the assumption that the probability r_i of a new interacting fiber creating i-th contact place just now on fiber No. 1 (similarly as fiber 3a on the Fig. 4.6) is $r_i = l^*/l$. Then it is valid to write that

$$r_i = \frac{l^*}{l} = \frac{l - (i-1)\dfrac{l}{z}}{l} = 1 - \frac{i-1}{z}, \quad i \leq z+1 \cdot \qquad \ldots (4.55)$$

The complementary probability s_i, that the new interacting fiber do not create i-th contact place (similarly as fiber 3b on Fig. 4.6) just now on fiber No. 1 is

$$s_i = 1 - r_i = \frac{i-1}{z}, \quad i \leq z+1. \qquad \ldots (4.56)$$

For $i = 1$, the probability of creating a contact place is $r_1 = 1$ and hence $s_1 = 0$; the first interacting fiber creates a contact place on fiber No. 1 for sure, because no other fiber prevents it to make a contact. In opposite to this, if already the whole fiber No. 1 was completely "occupied" then the probability of creating other contact place is equal to zero.

Like wise for the probability s_i, it is valid from Eq. (4.56)

$$s_2 = \frac{1}{z}, \quad s_i = (i-1)s_2, \quad s_{i+1} = s_i + s_2. \qquad \ldots (4.57)$$

Note: It must be $i \leq z$ in the last formula because the possible maximum of subscript by all s must be equal to $z + 1$ only; see Eq. (4.56).

Mathematical symbolism. It will be useful to introduce some mathematical conventions and symbols allowing us to formulate this modified model of fiber-to-fiber contacts:

(1) Let us imagine that e.g. eight fibers (sequence numbers I, II, ...,VIII) are interacting – step-by-step – with a given fiber No. 1. The interacting fibers I, IV, VI and VII will contact fiber No. 1, but the fibers II, III, V and VIII will not contact fiber No. 1. Fiber I surely create contact with probability $r_1 = 1$. Fiber II have a latent possibility to create the second contact, but it does not to realize it; the probability of non-creation of second contact is s_2. It therefore stays only one contact on fiber No. 1. Also, the fiber III can create the second contact, nevertheless it also does not realize it; the probability of non-creation of second contact is again s_2. The next interacting fiber IV successfully creates the second contact with the probability r_2. Now, there are two contacts on fiber No. 1. The following fiber V does not realize the possibility to create the third contact and the probability of this is s_3. The sixth and seventh fibers create step-by-step the third and fourth contacts with corresponding probabilities r_3 and r_4, respectively. Finally, the last, i.e. the eighth interacting fiber does not create the fifth contact with fiber No. 1 and the probability of this is s_5. Overall, the probability of the mentioned configuration of contacts from eight interacting fibers is the product of all individual probabilities and it can be write down by the expression $\underset{\text{I \; II \; III \; IV \; V \; VI \; VII \; VIII}}{r_1\, s_2\, s_2\, r_2\, s_3\, r_3\, r_4\, s_5}$. Nevertheless, this expression can be written in a simpler form, i.e. without the Roman numerals arising from the interacting fibers. Then, the expression will be $r_1 s_2 s_2 r_2 s_3 r_3 r_4 s_5$ in our example and analogical expressions will be used for each other configuration.

(2) If we create combinations with repetition of k-th class, from $j-1$ values $s_2, s_3, \cdots, s_j$ ($j \in \{2,3,...,z+1\}$), then we obtain number of combinations equals to $\binom{(j-1)+k-1}{k} = \binom{j+k-2}{k}$. Further, the values in each combination will be multiplied and then the resultant products will be added to obtain the final value which is denoted by the symbol σ_j^k .

Note: The following convention will be used in this part of text: a superscript written by a Greek letter will have the sense of upper index, not exponent; e.g. k in the symbol σ_j^k, but a subscript written by other quantities means an exponent, e.g. $s_2^k \equiv (s_2)^k$.

Example 4.3: Let us consider the values of s_2, s_3, s_4 (i.e., the highest index is $j = 4$), we create from them 2nd combinations ($k = 2$) with repetition.

The number of these combinations will be $\begin{pmatrix} 4+2-2 \\ 2 \end{pmatrix} = \begin{pmatrix} 4 \\ 2 \end{pmatrix} = 6$. These

combinations are (s_2, s_2), (s_2, s_3), (s_2, s_4), (s_3, s_3), (s_3, s_4), (s_4, s_4). Thus, we

obtain the value of $\sigma_4^2 = s_2 s_2 + s_2 s_3 + s_2 s_4 + s_3 s_3 + s_3 s_4 + s_4 s_4$.

If $j = 2$ then it is evidently valid that

$$\sigma_2^k = \overbrace{s_2 \cdot s_2 \cdots\cdots s_2}^{k\ \text{factors}} = s_2^k \, . \qquad \ldots (4.58)$$

For $k = 0$, we find the convention

$$\sigma_j^0 = 1, \quad j \in \{2, 3, \ldots, z+1\} \, . \qquad \ldots (4.59)$$

Finally, if $j > 2$ then, from the definition of σ_j^k and from Eqs. (4.57)
and (4.59), we can write the following expression

$$\sigma_j^k = \sigma_{j-1}^k + \overbrace{(j-1) s_2}^{s_j} \sigma_{j-1}^{k-1} + \overbrace{(j-1)^2 s_2^2}^{s_j^2} \sigma_{j-1}^{k-2} + \cdots + \qquad \ldots (4.60)$$

$$+ \overbrace{(j-1)^k s_2^k}^{s_j^k} \sigma_{j-1}^0 = \sum_{i=0}^{k} (j-1)^i s_2^i \sigma_{j-1}^{k-i}.$$

Example 4.4: According to the previous equation, it is valid that

$$\sigma_4^2 = \underbrace{\sigma_3^2}_{(s_2 s_2 + s_2 s_3 + s_3 s_3)} + \underbrace{3 s_2}_{s_4} \underbrace{\sigma_3^1}_{(s_2 + s_3)} + \underbrace{3^2 s_2^2 \sigma_3^0}_{s_4 s_4 \quad 1} = s_2^2 + s_2 s_3 + s_3^2 + s_2 s_4 + s_3 s_4 + s_4^2 \,; \text{ this is}$$

identical with the expression found from the previous example.

(3) Furthermore, we introduce ξ_j^k [6] which is defined by

$$\xi_j^k = \frac{\sigma_j^k}{s_2^k} \quad \left(\sigma_j^k = s_2^k \xi_j^k \right). \qquad \ldots (4.61)$$

By applying Eqs. (4.58) and (4.59) into Eq. (4.61), we get

$$\xi_j^0 = 1, \quad \xi_2^k = 1. \qquad \ldots (4.62)$$

---

6. According to our earlier convention, a superscript k written by the Greek letter
    denotes the upper index, not the exponent.

The following equation is obtained by applying Eq. (4.61) into Eq. (4.60)

$$\xi_j^k = \frac{\sigma_j^k}{s_2^k} = \sum_{i=0}^{k} \left[(j-1)^i \frac{s_2^i \sigma_{j-1}^{k-i}}{s_2^k} \right] = \sum_{i=0}^{k} \left[(j-1)^i \frac{\sigma_{j-1}^{k-i}}{s_2^{k-i}} \right] = \qquad \dots (4.63)$$

$$= \sum_{i=0}^{k} \left[(j-1)^i \xi_{j-1}^{k-i} \right].$$

Probability of occurrence of contact places on fiber No. 1. The Poison distribution according to Eq. (4.33) expresses the probability $P(x)$ of the given fiber No. 1 having just x interactions with other fibers. (We assumed that the number of fibers in a fibrous assembly is limiting to infinity). The probability of fiber No. 1 having y contact places ($y \le x$) is given by the symbol $Q(y)$. We will now express $Q(y)$ for different values of y.

0 contact ($y = 1$). No contact will occur, if there is no interaction. (It is showed that $s_1 = 0$). By using the symbols used in Eq. (4.33), it is valid to write that

$$Q(0) = P(0). \qquad \dots (4.64)$$

1 contact ($y = 1$). For realizing one contact place, the number x of all possible interactions with fiber No. 1 must be at least 1, i.e., $x = 1, 2, \dots$.

1 interaction ($x = 1$). The interacting fibers create further contact place ($r_1 = 1$). The probability of possible occurrence of such interaction is found by applying Eqs. (4.33) and (4.62) as follows

$$\kappa_1 = P(1) r_1 = P(0) \frac{m_1}{1!} \frac{r_1}{s_2} s_2 = P(0) \frac{r_1}{s_2} \underbrace{\xi_2^0}_{=1} \frac{s_2 m_1}{1!}. \qquad \dots (4.65)$$

2 interactions ($x = 2$). The first interacting fiber creates for sure a contact place ($r_1 = 1$), 2nd interacting fiber will not realize a contact place. The probability of this possibility is estimated by applying Eqs. (4.33) and (4.62) as follows

$$\kappa_2 = P(2) r_1 s_2 = P(0) \frac{m_1^2}{2!} \frac{r_1}{s_2} s_2^2 = P(0) \frac{r_1}{s_2} \underbrace{\xi_2^1}_{=1} \frac{s_2^2 m_1^2}{2!}. \qquad \dots (4.66)$$

3 interactions ($x = 3$). The first interacting fiber creates for sure a contact place ($r_1 = 1$). Neither the 2nd nor the 3rd fiber creates contact places. The probability of this possibility is found by applying Eqs. (4.33) and (4.62) as follows

$$\kappa_3 = P(3) r_1 s_2 s_2 = P(0) \frac{m_1^3}{3!} \frac{r_1}{s_2} s_2^3 = P(0) \frac{r_1}{s_2} \underbrace{\xi_2^2}_{=1} \frac{s_2^3 m_1^3}{3!}. \qquad \dots (4.67)$$

4 interaction (x = 4) and more. The analogous technique may be used for expressing $\kappa_4,\ldots$. Generally, the probability $Q(1)$ of creating one contacting place is expressed by the summation of the following probabilities

$$Q(1) = \kappa_1 + \kappa_2 + \kappa_3 + \cdots = P(0)\frac{r_1}{s_2}\left(\xi_2^0\frac{s_2 m_1}{1!} + \xi_2^1\frac{s_2^2 m_1^2}{2!} + \xi_2^2\frac{s_2^3 m_1^3}{3!} + \cdots\right)$$

$$= P(0)\frac{r_1}{s_2}\sum_{i=1}^{\infty}\left[\xi_2^{i-1}\frac{s_2^i m_1^i}{i!}\right]. \qquad \ldots (4.68)$$

<u>2 contacts</u> *(y = 2)*. For occurrence of 2 contact places, the number of all interactions (with fiber No. 1) must be at least 2, i.e., $x = 2, 3, \ldots$.

2 interactions (x = 2). Both the interacting fibers must create contact places. The probability of this possibility can be found by applying Eqs. (4.33) and (4.62) as follows

$$\lambda_2 = P(2)r_1 r_2 = P(0)\frac{m_1^2}{2!}\frac{r_1 r_2}{s_2^2}s_2^2 = P(0)\frac{r_1 r_2}{s_2^2}\underset{=1}{\xi_3^0}\frac{s_2^2 m_1^2}{2!}. \qquad \ldots (4.69)$$

3 interactions (x = 3). The 1st interacting fiber creates for sure a contact $(r_1 = 1)$. Then followed by a) the 2nd interaction fiber creates a contact place and the 3rd does not or b) the 2nd interacting fiber does not create a contact place and the 3rd fiber creates a contact place. The probability of this possibility is found by applying Eq. (4.33), definition of σ_j^k and Eq. (4.61)

$$\lambda_3 = P(3)\left(\overbrace{r_1 r_2 s_3}^{a)} + \overbrace{r_1 s_2 r_2}^{b)}\right) = P(3)r_1 r_2 \overbrace{(s_3 + s_2)}^{\sigma_3^1}$$

$$= P(0)\frac{m_1^3}{3!}\frac{r_1 r_2}{s_2^2}s_2^2\overbrace{\left(\frac{\sigma_3^1}{s_2}\right)}^{\xi_3^1}s_2 = P(0)\frac{r_1 r_2}{s_2^2}\xi_3^1\frac{s_2^3 m_1^3}{3!}. \qquad \ldots (4.70)$$

4 interactions (x = 4). The 1st interacting fiber creates for sure a contact place $(r_1 = 1)$. Then, follows a) the 2nd interacting fiber creates a contact place, and the 3rd and 4th do not create a contact place or, b) the 2nd interacting fiber does not create a contact place, but the 3rd fiber creates a contact place and the 4th does not create a contact place or c) the 2nd and 3rd interacting fibers do not create a contact place and the 4th fiber creates a contact place. The probability of these possibilities is calculated by applying Eq. (4.33), definition of σ_j^k and Eq. (4.61) as shown below

$$\lambda_4 = P(4)\left(\overbrace{r_1 r_2 s_3 s_3}^{a)} + \overbrace{r_1 s_2 r_2 s_3}^{b)} + \overbrace{r_1 s_2 s_2 r_2}^{c)}\right) = P(4) r_1 r_2 \overbrace{\left(s_3^2 + s_2 s_3 + s_2^2\right)}^{\sigma_3^2}$$

$$= P(0)\frac{m_1^4}{4!}\frac{r_1 r_2}{s_2^2} s_2^2 \overbrace{\left(\frac{\sigma_3^2}{s_2^2}\right)}^{\xi_3^2} s_2^2 = P(0)\frac{r_1 r_2}{s_2^2} \xi_3^2 \frac{s_2^4 m_1^4}{4!}. \qquad \ldots (4.71)$$

5 interactions ($x = 5$) *and more* can be found by the analogous process expressed by $\lambda_5, \cdots$. Generally, the probability $Q(2)$ of realizing two contacting places is expressed by the addition rule

$$Q(2) = \lambda_2 + \lambda_3 + \lambda_4 + \cdots = P(0)\frac{r_1 r_2}{s_2^2}\left(\xi_3^0 \frac{s_2^2 m_1^2}{2!} + \xi_3^1 \frac{s_2^3 m_1^3}{3!} + \xi_3^2 \frac{s_2^4 m_1^4}{4!} + \cdots\right)$$

$$= P(0)\frac{r_1 r_2}{s_2^2}\sum_{i=2}^{\infty}\left[\xi_3^{i-2}\frac{s_2^i m_1^i}{i!}\right]. \qquad \ldots (4.72)$$

<u>3 contacts</u> ($y = 3$). In order to occur 3 contacting places, the number of all possible interactions (with fiber No. 1) should be at least 3; i.e., $x = 3, 4, \ldots$.

3 interactions ($x = 3$). All the 3 interacting fibers must create contact places, the probability of this possibility is found by applying Eqs. (4.33) and (4.62) as shown below

$$\upsilon_3 = P(3) r_1 r_2 r_3 = P(0)\frac{m_1^3}{3!}\frac{r_1 r_2 r_3}{s_2^3} s_2^3 = P(0)\frac{r_1 r_2 r_3}{s_2^3}\underbrace{\xi_4^0}_{=1}\frac{s_2^3 m_1^3}{3!}. \qquad \ldots (4.73)$$

4 interactions ($x = 4$). The 1st interacting fibers create a contact place ($r_1 = 1$). Then a) the 2nd and 3rd interacting fibers create contact places and the 4th one never creates a contact place or b) the 2nd interacting fiber creates a contact place, the 3rd does not create a contact place and the 4th interacting fiber creates a contact place or c) the 2nd interacting fiber does not create a contact place, the 3rd and 4th create contact places. The probability of these possibilities can be calculated by applying Eq. (4.33), definition of σ_j^k and Eq. (4.61) as shown below

$$\upsilon_4 = P(4)\left(\overbrace{r_1 r_2 r_3 s_4}^{a)} + \overbrace{r_1 r_2 s_3 r_3}^{b)} + \overbrace{r_1 s_2 r_2 r_3}^{c)}\right) = P(0)\frac{m_1^4}{4!} r_1 r_2 r_3 \overbrace{\left(s_4 + s_3 + s_2\right)}^{\sigma_4^1}$$

$$= P(0)\frac{m_1^4}{4!}\frac{r_1 r_2 r_3}{s_2^3} s_2^3 \overbrace{\left(\frac{\sigma_4^1}{s_2}\right)}^{\xi_4^1} s_2 = P(0)\frac{r_1 r_2 r_3}{s_2^3}\xi_4^1 \frac{s_2^4 m_1^4}{4!}. \qquad \ldots (4.74)$$

5 interactions ($x = 5$). The 1st interacting fiber creates for sure a contact place ($r_1 = 1$). Then further a) the 2nd and 3rd interacting fibers create contact places, the 4th and 5th do not create or b) the 2nd interacting fiber creates a contact place, the 3rd do not create a contact place, the 4th creates a contact place and the 5th does not create a contact place or c) the 2nd interacting fiber creates a contact place, the 3rd and 4th do not create a contact place and the 5th creates a contact place or d) the 2nd interacting fiber does not create a contact place, the 3rd and 4th create a contact place and the 5th does not create any contact or e) the 2nd interacting fiber does not create a contact place, the 3rd creates a contact place, the 4th does not create a contact place, the 5th creates a contact place or f) the 2nd and 3rd interacting fibers do not create any contact, the 4th and 5th realize contact. The probability of these possibilities is estimated by applying Eq. (4.33), definition of σ_j^k and Eq. (4.61) as follows

$$
\begin{aligned}
\upsilon_5 &= P(5)\Big(\overbrace{r_1 r_2 r_3 s_4 s_4}^{a)} + \overbrace{r_1 r_2 s_3 r_3 s_4}^{b)} + \overbrace{r_1 r_2 s_3 s_3 r_3}^{c)} + \overbrace{r_1 s_2 r_2 r_3 s_4}^{d)} + \overbrace{r_1 s_2 r_2 s_3 r_3}^{e)} + \overbrace{r_1 s_2 s_2 r_2 r_3}^{f)} \Big) \\
&= P(0)\frac{m_1^5}{5!} r_1 r_2 r_3 \Big(\overbrace{s_4^2 + s_3 s_4 + s_3^2 + s_2 s_4 + s_2 s_3 + s_2^2}^{\sigma_4^2} \Big) \\
&= P(0)\frac{m_1^5}{5!}\frac{r_1 r_2 r_3}{s_2^3} s_2^3 \Big(\overbrace{\frac{\sigma_4^2}{s_2^2}}^{\xi_4^2} \Big) s_2^2 = P(0)\frac{r_1 r_2 r_3}{s_2^3}\xi_4^2 \frac{s_2^5 m_1^5}{5!}. \qquad \ldots(4.75)
\end{aligned}
$$

6 interactions ($x = 6$) *and more.* It can be analogously expressed by the symbol $\upsilon_6, \ldots$. The general probability $Q(3)$ of 3 contact places is expressed by the addition rule as follows

$$
Q(3) = \upsilon_3 + \upsilon_4 + \upsilon_5 + \cdots = P(0)\frac{r_1 r_2 r_3}{s_2^3}\Big(\xi_4^0 \frac{s_2^3 m_1^3}{3!} + \xi_4^1 \frac{s_2^4 m_1^4}{4!} + \xi_4^2 \frac{s_2^5 m_1^5}{5!} + \cdots \Big)
$$

$$
= P(0)\frac{r_1 r_2 r_3}{s_2^3}\sum_{i=3}^{\infty}\Big[\xi_4^{i-3}\frac{s_2^i m_1^i}{i!} \Big]. \qquad \ldots (4.76)
$$

In the same manner, one can establish the probability of occurrence of more contact places ($y = 4, 5, \ldots$).

4.5   Modified distribution of fiber contacts

It is possible to generalize Eqs. (4.64), (4.68), (4.72), and (4.76) to express the probability y of occurring contact places on fiber No. 1 as shown below

$$Q(0) = P(0), \quad Q(y) = P(0)\frac{\prod\limits_{t=1}^{y} r_t}{s_2^y}\sum_{i=y}^{\infty}\left[\xi_{y+1}^{i-y}\,\frac{s_2^i m_1^i}{i!}\right], \quad y = 1, 2\cdots \quad \ldots (4.77)$$

This equation expresses the distribution of contact places on fiber No. 1. Nevertheless, it requires further modification.

Correction of function Q (y). In Appendix A2, the value of ξ_{n+1}^{i-n} is given by Eq. (A2.29), in a similar way, ξ_j^k is also expressed by Eqs. (4.62) and (4.63). In Appendix A2, other symbols are used: $n + 1$ instead of j, $i - n$ instead of k, index t instead of index i. The final Eq. (A2.41) is also mentioned in Appendix A2. We find the following equation by designating n by y and x by $s_2 m_1$.

$$\left(e^{s_2 m_1} - 1\right)^y = \sum_{i=y}^{\infty}\left[\frac{s_2^i m_1^i}{i!}\,y!\,\xi_{y+1}^{i-y}\right] = y!\sum_{i=y}^{\infty}\left[\frac{s_2^i m_1^i}{i!}\,\xi_{y+1}^{i-y}\right], \quad y = 1, 2\cdots \quad \ldots (4.78)$$

The summation of the right hand of this equation is naturally identical with the summation of the right hand of Eq. (4.77). Therefore it is valid to write that

$$Q(0) = P(0), \quad Q(y) = P(0)\frac{\prod\limits_{t=1}^{y} r_t}{y!\,s_2^y}\left(e^{s_2 m_1} - 1\right)^y, \quad y = 1, 2\cdots \quad \ldots (4.79)$$

Further, rearranging and applying Eqs. (4.56) and (4.57) we find the following equation

$$\frac{\prod\limits_{t=1}^{y} r_t}{y!\,s_2^y} = \frac{\prod\limits_{t=1}^{y}(1-s_t)}{y!\,s_2^y} = \frac{\prod\limits_{t=1}^{y}\left(\frac{1}{s_2} - \frac{s_t}{s_2}\right)}{y!} = \frac{\prod\limits_{t=1}^{y}\left(z - z\frac{t-1}{z}\right)}{y!} = \frac{\prod\limits_{t=1}^{y}(z - t + 1)}{y!}$$

$$= \frac{\prod\limits_{j=z}^{z-y+1} j}{y!} = \frac{\prod\limits_{j=z-y+1}^{z} j}{y!} = \frac{\prod\limits_{j=1}^{z} j}{y!\prod\limits_{j=1}^{z-y} j} = \frac{z!}{y!(z-y)!} = \binom{z}{y} \quad \ldots (4.80)$$

In this way, a new multiplying index $j = z - t + 1$ is introduced instead of the initial multiplying index t.

Finally, by applying Eqs. (4.57) and (4.33) the following equation is obtained

$$P(0)\left(e^{s_2 m_1} - 1\right)^y = e^{-m_1}\left(e^{\frac{m_1}{z}} - 1\right)^y$$

$$= e^{-m_1}\left(\frac{1}{e^{\frac{m_1}{z}}} - \frac{e^{\frac{m_1}{z}}}{e^{\frac{m_1}{z}}}\right)^y = e^{-m_1}\frac{\left(1 - e^{-\frac{m_1}{z}}\right)^y}{e^{-\frac{m_1}{z}y}} \qquad \dots (4.81)$$

$$= \left(1 - e^{-\frac{m_1}{z}}\right)^y e^{-m_1 + \frac{m_1}{z}y} = \left(1 - e^{-\frac{m_1}{z}}\right)^y \left(e^{-\frac{m_1}{z}}\right)^{z-y}.$$

By applying Eqs. (4.33), (4.80) and (4.81) into Eq. (4.79), we find

$$Q(0) = e^{-m_1}, \quad Q(y) = \binom{z}{y}\left(1 - e^{-\frac{m_1}{z}}\right)^y \left(e^{-\frac{m_1}{z}}\right)^{z-y} \quad y = 1, 2 \cdots \quad \dots (4.82)$$

Although the second equation of the last expression is defined only for $y = 1, 2\ldots$, substituting $y = 0$ and calculating, we find that $Q(0) = e^{-m_1}$, which is in agreement with the first equation. Therefore, it is possible to describe the distribution of number of contact places on fiber No. 1 by one collective expression

$$Q(y) = \binom{z}{y}\left(1 - e^{-\frac{m_1}{z}}\right)^y \left(e^{-\frac{m_1}{z}}\right)^{z-y} \quad y = 0, 1, \cdots, \qquad \dots (4.83)$$

where m_1 is the mean value of number of interactions on fiber No. 1 given by Eq. (4.31) and z is the maximum number of contact places on the fiber. The distribution depends on the orientation angles ϑ_1 and φ_1 of fiber No. 1 by means of $J(\vartheta_1, \varphi_1)$ expressed in Eq. (4.31).

Introducing the variable q and applying into Eq. (4.31), we get

$$q = 1 - e^{-\frac{m_1}{z}} = 1 - e^{-\frac{8\mu l}{z\pi d}J(\vartheta_1, \varphi_1)}, \qquad \dots (4.84)$$

and $Q(y)$ may be also written as follows

$$Q(y) = \binom{z}{y} q^y (1-q)^{z-y} \quad y = 0, 1, \cdots. \qquad \dots (4.85)$$

It is obvious from the last expression that the distribution of number of contacts on fiber No. 1 is binomial. Accordingly, the mean value of contact places on fiber No. 1 is

$$m_1^* = \sum_{y=0}^{z} y\, Q(y) = zq = z\left(1 - e^{-\frac{m_1}{z}}\right) = z\left(1 - e^{-\frac{8\mu l}{z\pi d}J(\vartheta_1,\varphi_1)}\right). \qquad \dots (4.86)$$

According to Eq. (4.86), the mean value of number of contacts on fiber No. 1 is a result of mutual obstruction of fibers. This is illustrated in Fig. 4.7.

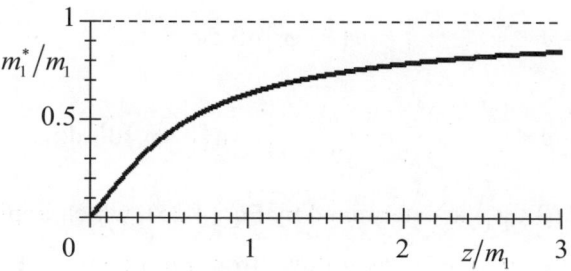

4.7 Relative reduction in mean value of number of contact places on fiber No. 1, according to the Eq. (4.86); $m_1^*/m_1 = (z/m_1)[1 - e^{-1/(z/m_1)}]$.

Note: Fibers will not "prevent" creating contact places if each contact place on fiber No. 1 is infinitely small. In this case each interaction is realized in successive contact places. The maximum number of contact places $z \rightarrow \infty$ occurs when the mean number of contact places on fiber No. 1

is $m_1^* = \lim\limits_{z \to \infty}\left[z\left(1 - e^{-m_1/z}\right)\right] = m_1$ and $q = \lim\limits_{z \to \infty}\left(1 - e^{-m_1/z}\right) = 0$. In this case, the

binomial distribution $Q(y)$ limits to Poisson's distribution $\left(m_1^y/y!\right)e^{-m_1}$.
This is identical with the results obtained from Eq. (4.32) for calculating the number of contact places on fiber No. 1.

Distribution of contact places $C(y)$ on fibers.[7] The probability of the randomly selected fiber No. 1 belonging to the elementary directional class limited by the interval $(\vartheta_1, \vartheta_1 + d\vartheta_1)$ and $(\varphi_1, \varphi_1 + d\varphi_1)$, is $w(\vartheta_1, \varphi_1)d\vartheta_1 d\varphi_1$. The probability $dC(y)$ of this selected fiber "fiber No. 1" belonging to the considered elementary class and at the same time a number of y contacting

places lie on it, is the product of $Q(y), \left[w(\vartheta_1, \varphi_1)\, d\vartheta_1\, d\varphi_1\right]$. By applying Eq. (4.84) we get

$$dC(y) = Q(y) \cdot w(\vartheta_1, \varphi_1)\, d\vartheta_1\, d\varphi_1 = \binom{z}{y} q^y (1-q)^{z-y} w(\vartheta_1, \varphi_1)\, d\vartheta_1\, d\varphi_1.$$

$$\dots (4.87)$$

---

7. The procedure of calculation is analogous to the derivation of Eq. (4.36).

The probability $C(y)$ of the randomly selected fiber having just y contact places is obtained by the integral of the previous expression. By applying Eqs. (4.84) and (4.85), we find the distribution of contact places $C(y)$ on the fiber in the following form

$$
\begin{aligned}
C(y) &= \iint_{\omega_1} dC(y) = \iint_{\omega_1} \binom{z}{y} q^y (1-q)^{z-y} \, w(\vartheta_1,\varphi_1) \, d\vartheta_1 d\varphi_1 \\
&= \iint_{\omega_1} \binom{z}{y} \left(1 - e^{-\frac{m_1}{z}}\right)^y \left(e^{-\frac{m_1}{z}}\right)^{z-y} w(\vartheta_1,\varphi_1) \, d\vartheta_1 d\varphi_1 \qquad \ldots (4.88) \\
&= \iint_{\omega_1} \binom{z}{y} \left(1 - e^{-\frac{8\mu l}{z\pi d}J(\vartheta_1,\varphi_1)}\right)^y \left(e^{-\frac{8\mu l}{z\pi d}J(\vartheta_1,\varphi_1)}\right)^{z-y} w(\vartheta_1,\varphi_1) \, d\vartheta_1 d\varphi_1 .
\end{aligned}
$$

The integral of $J(\vartheta_1, \varphi_1)$ is determined by Eq. (4.25), which implicates the function of $\sin\xi = \sqrt{1 - \cos^2\xi}$ as follows from Eq. (4.1).

The mean value m^* of contact places is given by $m^* = \sum_{y=0}^{z}\left[y\,C(y)\right]$. By applying Eqs. (4.83), (4.86), and (4.88), we find

$$
\begin{aligned}
m^* = \sum_{y=0}^{z}\left[y\,C(y)\right] &= \sum_{y=0}^{z}\left[y \overbrace{\iint_{\omega_1} \binom{z}{y} \left(1 - e^{-\frac{m_1}{z}}\right)^y \left(e^{-\frac{m_1}{z}}\right)^{z-y} w(\vartheta_1,\varphi_1)\,d\vartheta_1 d\varphi_1}^{Q(y)} \right] \\
&= \iint_{\omega_1} \overbrace{\sum_{y=0}^{z}\left[y\,Q(y)\right]}^{m_1^*} w(\vartheta_1,\varphi_1)\,d\vartheta_1 d\varphi_1 = z \iint_{\omega_1}\left(1 - e^{-\frac{8\mu l}{z\pi d}J(\vartheta_1,\varphi_1)}\right) w(\vartheta_1,\varphi_1)\,d\vartheta_1 d\varphi_1 .
\end{aligned}
$$

$$\ldots (4.89)$$

Distribution of contact places in case of spatial isotropic orientation. According to Eq. (4.43), the integral of $J(\vartheta_1, \varphi_1)$ takes a constant value of $\pi/4$ for spatial isotropic fiber orientation. Applying this result into Eq. (4.88), we can express the distribution $C(y)$ for studied case as follows

$$
\begin{aligned}
C(y) &= \iint_{\omega_1} \binom{z}{y} \left(1 - e^{-\frac{8\mu l\,\pi}{z\pi d\,4}}\right)^y \left(e^{-\frac{8\mu l\,\pi}{z\pi d\,4}}\right)^{z-y} w(\vartheta_1,\varphi_1)\,d\vartheta_1\,d\varphi_1 \\
&= \binom{z}{y}\left(1 - e^{-\frac{2\mu l}{zd}}\right)^y \left(e^{-\frac{2\mu l}{zd}}\right)^{z-y} \overbrace{\iint_{\omega_1} w(\vartheta_1,\varphi_1)\,d\vartheta_1\,d\varphi_1}^{=1} \qquad \ldots (4.90) \\
&= \binom{z}{y}\left(1 - e^{-\frac{2\mu l}{zd}}\right)^y \left(e^{-\frac{2\mu l}{zd}}\right)^{z-y} .
\end{aligned}
$$

By applying Eq. (4.43) into Eq. (4.89), we find the mean value of contact places on a fiber as follows

$$m^* = z \iint_{\omega_1} \left(1 - e^{-\frac{8\mu l}{z\pi d}\frac{\pi}{4}} \right) w(\vartheta_1, \varphi_1) \, d\vartheta_1 d\varphi_1 = z \left(1 - e^{-\frac{2\mu l}{zd}} \right) \overbrace{\iint_{\omega_1} w(\vartheta_1, \varphi_1) \, d\vartheta_1 d\varphi_1}^{=1}$$

$$= z \left(1 - e^{-\frac{2\mu l}{zd}} \right). \qquad \qquad \ldots (4.91)$$

In spatial isotropic fibrous assembly, the distribution of the number of contacts is binomial. (The value of m could be also written immediately as the mean value from binomial distribution expressed in Eq. (4.90)).

Distribution of contact places in case of plane isotropic orientation. According to Eq. (4.51), the integration of $J(\vartheta_1, \varphi_1) = J(\psi_1)$ for isotropic fiber orientation in plane leads to a constant value of $2/\pi$. Applying this value into Eq. (4.88), we find the distribution of number of contacts places on fibers as follows

$$C(y) = \iint_{\omega_1} \binom{z}{y} \left(1 - e^{-\frac{8\mu l}{z\pi d}\frac{2}{\pi}} \right)^y \left(e^{-\frac{8\mu l}{z\pi d}\frac{2}{\pi}} \right)^{z-y} w(\vartheta_1, \varphi_1) \, d\vartheta_1 d\varphi_1$$

$$= \binom{z}{y} \left(1 - e^{-\frac{16\mu l}{\pi^2 zd}} \right)^y \left(e^{-\frac{16\mu l}{\pi^2 zd}} \right)^{z-y} \overbrace{\iint_{\omega_1} w(\vartheta_1, \varphi_1) \, d\vartheta_1 d\varphi_1}^{=1}$$

$$= \binom{z}{y} \left(1 - e^{-\frac{16\mu l}{\pi^2 zd}} \right)^y \left(e^{-\frac{16\mu l}{\pi^2 zd}} \right)^{z-y}. \qquad \qquad \ldots (4.92)$$

By applying Eq. (4.51) into Eq. (4.89), we obtain the mean number of contact places on a fiber as follows

$$m^* = z \iint_{\omega_1} \left(1 - e^{-\frac{8\mu l}{z\pi d}\frac{2}{\pi}} \right) w(\vartheta_1, \varphi_1) \, d\vartheta_1 d\varphi_1$$

$$= z \left(1 - e^{-\frac{16\mu l}{\pi^2 zd}} \right) \overbrace{\iint_{\omega_1} w(\vartheta_1, \varphi_1) \, d\vartheta_1 d\varphi_1}^{=1} = z \left(1 - e^{-\frac{16\mu l}{\pi^2 zd}} \right). \qquad \ldots (4.93)$$

In isotropic fiber orientation in plane, the number of contact places on fibers is also binomial. (The value m could be also written immediately as the mean value from binomial distribution (4.92)).

Relative size of contact places. In Section 4.4, we have introduced the maximum number of contact places z on a fiber of length l. We assume that each contact place "occupies" a place of l/z. The contact of two fibers is a kind of interlacement of two fibers. The length occupied by one contact place is therefore proportional (to a certain degree) to the effective fiber diameter d. Generally; it is reasonable to express the "occupied" length of one contact place by proportional to equivalent fiber diameter. Now we introduce the relative size of contact place γ.

$$\gamma = \frac{l}{zd}, \quad \left(\frac{l}{z} = \gamma d\right). \qquad \ldots (4.94)$$

It is expected that the value of γ lies in the range of tenth or in some units (for example, in some special fiber arrangement as shown in Fig. 4.4) the maximum contact places on each fiber are $z = 2(l/d) = l/(0.5d)$, thus $\gamma = 0.5$.

Note: The previous equation can be simplified by introducing the variable γ, as for example the expression $8\mu l/(z\pi d) = 8\mu\gamma/\pi$.

Figure 4.8 illustrates an example (for $\mu = 0.5$) of the reduction of number of contacts due to mutual obstruction of fibers.

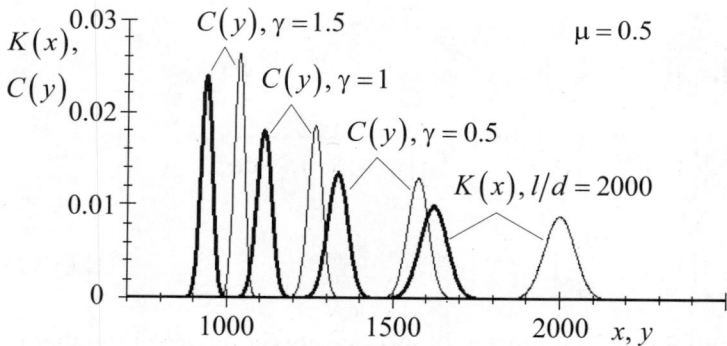

4.8 Distribution of number of contact places on a fiber for isotropic orientations.

——— spatial isotropy: $K(x)$ ...Equation (4.46), $C(y)$ ...Equation (4.90).
——— planar isotropy: $K(x)$ ...Equation (4.54), $C(y)$ ...Equation (4.92).

Note: Let us remind that when $z \to \infty$, i.e. $\gamma \to 0$ the behavior of $C(y)$ identifies with $K(x)$.

4.6   Modified parameters of fiber contacts

General definitions. We consider a fibrous assembly containing N fibers, where $N \to \infty$. The mean value of contact places per fiber is m^*. The number M of contact places in the fibrous assembly is

$$M = N m^*. \qquad \ldots (4.95)$$

It is known that two contact places create one contact so that the number n of contacts in the fibrous assembly is

$$n = \frac{M}{2} = \frac{N m^*}{2}. \qquad \qquad \text{... (4.96)}$$

The total volume of the fibrous assembly according to Eq. (4.15) is $V_c = N \pi d^2 l / (4\mu)$. The density of contacts in the fibrous assembly is

$$\upsilon = \frac{n}{V_c} = \frac{N m^*}{2} \frac{4\mu}{N \pi d^2 l} = \frac{2 m^* \mu}{\pi d^2 l}. \qquad \qquad \text{... (4.97)}$$

The mean distance between neighboring contact places $\bar{\delta}$ (see Fig. 4.3) is

$$\bar{\delta} = \frac{N l}{M} = \frac{N l}{N m^*} = \frac{l}{m^*}. \qquad \qquad \text{... (4.98)}$$

Modification in model of fiber contacts. Using Eqs. (4.89) and (4.94) in the set of Eqs. (4.95) to (4.98) we obtain the following expressions. The number M of contact places in the fibrous assembly is

$$M = N m^* = Nz \iint\limits_{\omega_1} \left(1 - e^{-\frac{8\mu l}{z\pi d} J(\vartheta_1, \varphi_1)} \right) w(\vartheta_1, \varphi_1) \, d\vartheta_1 d\varphi_1$$

$$= \frac{N l}{\gamma d} \iint\limits_{\omega_1} \left(1 - e^{-\frac{8\mu\gamma}{\pi} J(\vartheta_1, \varphi_1)} \right) w(\vartheta_1, \varphi_1) \, d\vartheta_1 d\varphi_1. \qquad \text{... (4.99)}$$

The number n of contacts in the fibrous assembly is

$$n = \frac{M}{2} = \frac{N l}{2\gamma d} \iint\limits_{\omega_1} \left(1 - e^{-\frac{8\mu\gamma}{\pi} J(\vartheta_1, \varphi_1)} \right) w(\vartheta_1, \varphi_1) \, d\vartheta_1 \, d\varphi_1. \qquad \text{... (4.100)}$$

The density υ of contacts is

$$\upsilon = \frac{2 m^* \mu}{\pi d^2 l} = \frac{2\mu}{\pi d^2 l} z \iint\limits_{\omega_1} \left(1 - e^{-\frac{8\mu l}{z\pi d} J(\vartheta_1, \varphi_1)} \right) w(\vartheta_1, \varphi_1) \, d\vartheta_1 d\varphi_1$$

$$= \frac{2\mu\gamma}{\pi d^3} \iint\limits_{\omega_1} \left(1 - e^{-\frac{8\mu l}{z\pi d} J(\vartheta_1, \varphi_1)} \right) w(\vartheta_1, \varphi_1) \, d\vartheta_1 d\varphi_1. \qquad \text{... (4.101)}$$

The mean distance $\bar{\delta}$ of neighboring contact places is

$$\bar{\delta} = \frac{l}{m^*} = \frac{l}{z} \frac{1}{\displaystyle\iint_{\omega_1}\left(1 - e^{-\frac{8\mu l}{z\pi d}J(\vartheta_1,\varphi_1)}\right) w(\vartheta_1,\varphi_1)\,d\vartheta_1 d\varphi_1}$$ ... (4.102)

$$= \frac{\gamma d}{\displaystyle\iint_{\omega_1}\left(1 - e^{-\frac{8\mu l}{z\pi d}J(\vartheta_1,\varphi_1)}\right) w(\vartheta_1,\varphi_1)\,d\vartheta_1 d\varphi_1}.$$

Spatial isotropic orientation. In this special case, if we substitute the **mean number of contact places on one fiber** m^* according to Eq. (4.91), and the expression γ according to Eq. (4.94), we obtain the following expressions from the set of Eqs. (4.95) to (4.98). The number M of contact places in the fibrous assembly is

$$M = N m^* = Nz\left(1 - e^{-\frac{2\mu l}{zd}}\right) = \frac{Nl}{\gamma d}\left(1 - e^{-2\mu\gamma}\right).$$ ... (4.103)

The number n of contacts in the fibrous assembly is

$$n = \frac{M}{2} = \frac{Nl}{2\gamma d}\left(1 - e^{-2\mu\gamma}\right).$$ ... (4.104)

The density υ of contacts is

$$\upsilon = \frac{2m^*\mu}{\pi d^2 l} = \frac{2\mu zd}{\pi d^3 l}\left(1 - e^{-\frac{2\mu l}{zd}}\right) = \frac{2\mu}{\pi d^3 \gamma}\left(1 - e^{-2\mu\gamma}\right),$$ ... (4.105)

and the mean distance $\bar{\delta}$ between contact places is

$$\bar{\delta} = \frac{l}{m^*} = \frac{l}{z\left[1 - e^{-\frac{2\mu l}{zd}}\right]} = \frac{\gamma d}{1 - e^{-2\mu\gamma}}.$$ ... (4.106)

Note: It is true that when $\gamma \to 0$, $\displaystyle\lim_{\gamma\to 0}\upsilon = \left[2\mu/(\pi d^3)\right]\overbrace{\lim_{\gamma\to 0}\left[\left(1 - e^{-2\mu\gamma}\right)/\gamma\right]}^{=2\mu} = 4\mu^2/(\pi d^3)$. In Section 4.2, the density of contacts has been derived according to van Wyk in Eq. (4.16). Here, for spatial isotropic orientation, it is the integral of I according to Eq. (4.44). From these two equations, we obtain $\upsilon = \left[16\mu^2/(\pi^2 d^3)\right]\pi/4 = 4\mu^2/(\pi d^3)$. As expected, the density of contacts shown in Eq. (4.105) limits to van Wyk's density of contacts when $\gamma \to 0$. Similarly, Eq. (4.106) is identical with the expression (4.19) for $\gamma \to 0$, as we substitute the value of integration I from Eq. (4.44) in it.

Isotropic orientation in plane. In this special case, if we substitute the mean number of contact places on one fiber m^* according to Eq. (4.93), and the expression γ according to Eq. (4.94), we obtain the following expressions from the set of Eqs. (4.95) to (4.98). The number M of contact places in the fibrous assembly is expressed as follows

$$M = N m^* = Nz\left(1-e^{-\frac{16\mu l}{\pi^2 zd}}\right) = \frac{Nl}{\gamma d}\left(1-e^{-\frac{16\mu\gamma}{\pi^2}}\right). \qquad \ldots (4.107)$$

The number n of contacts in the fibrous assembly is expressed as follows

$$n = \frac{M}{2} = \frac{Nl}{2\gamma d}\left(1-e^{-\frac{16\mu\gamma}{\pi^2}}\right). \qquad \ldots (4.108)$$

The density υ of contacts is expressed as follows

$$\upsilon = \frac{2m^*\mu}{\pi d^2 l} = \frac{2\mu dz}{\pi d^3 l}\left(1-e^{-\frac{16\mu l}{\pi^2 zd}}\right) = \frac{2\mu}{\pi d^3 \gamma}\left(1-e^{-\frac{16\mu\gamma}{\pi^2}}\right), \qquad \ldots (4.109)$$

and the mean distance $\bar{\delta}$ between contact places is expressed as follows

$$\bar{\delta} = \frac{l}{m^*} = \frac{l}{z\left[1-e^{-\frac{16\mu l}{\pi^2 zd}}\right]} = \frac{\gamma d}{1-e^{-\frac{16\mu\gamma}{\pi^2}}}. \qquad \ldots (4.110)$$

Table 4.3 shows some typical values for density of contacts υ and the mean distance $\bar{\delta}$ between contact places. Comparing these values with the values obtained from Table 4.2, we can conclude that the reduction in υ is a result of mutual "obstruction" of fibers. Obviously, the reduction of υ is accompanied by increasing in γ and decreasing in μ values.

Table 4.3 Values of υ and $\bar{\delta}$ for isotropic orientation.

Material. Polyester fibers, $t = 0.17$ tex, $\rho = 1360\,\mathrm{kg\,m^{-3}}$ ($d = 0.012616$ mm)							
	Spatial isotropic orientation				Plane isotropic orientation		
Packing density	$\gamma = 0.5$		$\gamma = 1$		$\gamma = 0.5$		$\gamma = 1$
	$\upsilon\,[\mathrm{mm^{-3}}]$	$\bar{\delta}$ [mm]	$\upsilon\,[\mathrm{mm^{-3}}]$	$\bar{\delta}$ [mm]	$\upsilon\,[\mathrm{mm^{-3}}]$	$\bar{\delta}$ [mm]	$\upsilon\,[\mathrm{mm^{-3}}]$ $\bar{\delta}$ [mm]
$\mu = 0.7$	223444	0.012530	167202	0.016745	192191	0.014568	150581 0.018594
$\mu = 0.5$	124746	0.016032	100204	0.019958	105642	0.018931	88041 0.022715
$\mu = 0.3$	49303	0.024338	42914	0.027962	41062	0.029222	36630 0.032758
$\mu = 0.1$	6034	0.066287	5747	0.069598	4937	0.081018	4745 0.084300
$\mu = 0.01$	63.09	0.633959	62.78	0.637129	51.19	0.781376	50.98 0.784543

4.7   References

1. van Wyk, C. M. (1946). Note on the compressibility of wool, *Journal of Textile Institute*, **37**(10), T285–T291.
2. Komori, T., and Makishima, K. (1977). Number of fiber-to-fiber contacts in general fiber assemblies, *Textile Research Journal*, **47**, 13–17.
3. Cheng, C. C., and Duckett, K. E. (1979). The direction distribution on cross-contact points in anisotropic fiber assemblies, *Textile Research Journal*, **49**, 379–384.
4. Taylor, D. S. (1956). The determination of contacts between the constituents of fiber assemblies, *Journal of Textile Institute*, **47**, T141–T146.
5. Stern, A. E. (1971). The effect of anisotropy in the randomness of fiber orientation of fiber-to-fiber contacts, *Journal of Textile Institute*, **62**, T353–T360.
6. Pan, N. (1993). A modified analysis of the microstructural characteristics of general fiber assemblies, *Textile Research Journal*, **63**(6), 336–345.
7. Komori, T., and Itoh, M. (1994). A modified theory of fiber contact in general fiber assemblies, *Textile Research Journal*, **64**(9), 519–528.

Compression behavior of fibrous assemblies

5.1 General relations and modeling strategy[1]

Introduction. The fiber materials often experience compression. Examples include compression of fibers in yarn due to twist, thermal calendaring of fibrous webs for nonwoven production, etc. These examples inform us that the fiber materials experience compression during manufacturing. But there are many other examples that tell us that the fiber materials also experience compression during transportation and application. For example, the fibers are usually transported in a heavily compressed state in the forms of bales, the fiberglass nonwovens are often transported in a compressed form to lower the transportation cost. The fibrous materials in the form of seats, beddings, geotextiles, filters, to name a few, experience significant compression during their usage.

In order to understand the compression behavior of fiber materials, it is generally required to find out the relation between the stress and strain tensors[2]. Nevertheless, this approach is extremely complicated for fiber materials. It is therefore seen that the problem of compression is mostly solved under the theory of uniaxial deformation. Many earlier studies [1–10] were dealt with the theoretical and experimental behavior of uniaxial compression of fibrous materials.

Note: Some terms and quantities in relation to the mechanics of fibrous materials are introduced in Appendix 3.

Uniaxial deformation. Let us take a non-deformable rigid box of dimensions a and b as shown in Fig. 5.1a; this box is filled with "free"

---

1. This chapter presents a general relationship on the compression of fiber materials. For this, a set of general symbols for different functions are used. The following convention is followed for the symbols of such general functions: if a variable z is a function of variables x and y then we write $z = z(x, y)$. If – in an alternative way – z is a function of other variables u and v then we write $z = z'(u,v)$; the superscript $'$ (or sometimes used $''$, etc.) is only a graphical symbol (not derivative symbols) which says that the second function of the same variable $z = z'(u,v)$ takes other expression than that taken by the first function $z = z(x, y)$.

2. More generally, the solution should also include the rheological relationships.

fiber material up to the height c_0. Let us consider that the fiber packing density in this structure takes a very small value μ_0.

Note: Here, the quantities related to the non-compressed "free" fiber material are expressed with the subscript 0. But, the quantities related to the compressed fiber material are expressed without this superscript.

Let us apply a pressure p (black arrow) onto this fiber material so that it gets compressed (shown in Fig. 5.1b). Consequently, the height of the column of fiber material decreases to a smaller value c, but the non-deformable rigid box maintains the constant dimensions a and b. The length $\lambda = c_0 - c$ represents the whole trajectory of movement. Let us assume that the resulting fiber packing density in the deformed structure be μ.

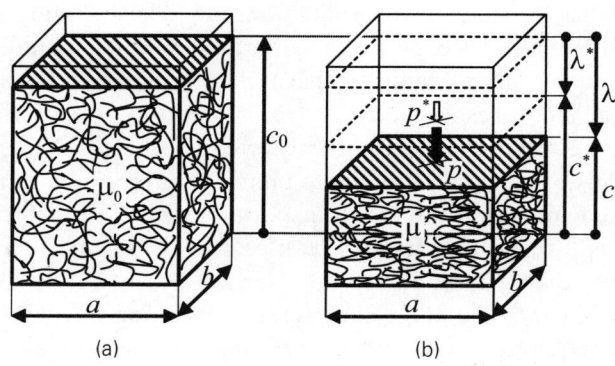

(a)   (b)

5.1 Uniaxial compression.

While the fiber material is being compressed, it takes in-between-states as shown in Fig. 5.1b. Consider, in a general position, the actual value of packing density is $\mu^* \in \langle \mu_0, \mu \rangle$, the corresponding pressure is $p^* \in \langle 0, p \rangle$ (white arrow), the vertical coordinate is $c^* \in \langle c, c_0 \rangle$, and the trajectory of movement is $\lambda^* \in \langle 0, \lambda \rangle$, where

$$\lambda^* = c_0 - c^*, \quad \lambda = c_0 - c. \qquad \ldots (5.1)$$

The volume of air gaps among the fibers is reduced by the process of compression, but we assume that the fiber volume V stays roughly the same as in the non-deformable rigid box. (We think about a reasonably moderate compression, not about hard "briquetting"). Then, the following equations are valid to write

$$V = abc_0\mu_0 = abc^*\mu^* = abc\mu, \quad c^* = c_0 \mu_0/\mu^*, \quad c = c_0 \mu_0/\mu. \qquad \ldots (5.2)$$

The following derivatives are resulting from Eqs. (5.1) and (5.2)

$$\frac{d\lambda^*}{d\mu^*} = \frac{d\lambda^*}{dc^*}\frac{dc^*}{d\mu^*} = (-1)\left(-c_0\mu_0/\mu^{*2}\right) = \frac{c_0\mu_0}{\mu^{*2}}. \qquad \dots (5.3)$$

Generally, the pressure is an increasing function of packing density, so that

$$p^* = p^*(\mu^*), \quad 0 = p^*(\mu_0), \quad p = p^*(\mu). \qquad \dots (5.4)$$

Work done. Definitely, a specific amount of work is done during the process of compression. According to Fig. 5.1 and Eqs. (5.2) and (5.3), it can be said that the immediate working force is p^*ab, and the elemental increment of work done is

$$dA = (p^*ab)\, d\lambda^* = p^*(\mu^*)\frac{abc_0\mu_0}{\mu^{*2}}\, d\mu^* = V\frac{p^*(\mu^*)}{\mu^{*2}}\, d\mu^*, \qquad \dots (5.5)$$

and the whole work done is

$$A = \int_{\mu^*=\mu_0}^{\mu^*=\mu} dA = V\int_{\mu_0}^{\mu}\frac{p^*(\mu^*)}{\mu^{*2}}\, d\mu^*. \qquad \dots (5.6)$$

Finally, the derivative of work done with respect to packing density[3] is possible to write by using Eqs. (5.4) and (5.6) as follows

$$\frac{dA}{d\mu} = V\frac{d}{d\mu}\left[\int_{\mu_0}^{\mu}\frac{p^*(\mu^*)}{\mu^{*2}}\, d\mu^*\right] = V\frac{p^*(\mu)}{\mu^2} = V\frac{p}{\mu^2}. \qquad \dots (5.7)$$

As shown in the last expression as well as illustrated graphically in Fig. 5.1, the pressure p is a desired function of packing density μ.

Model structure. It appears that the aforesaid relations do not use any information about the internal arrangement of fibers in the compressed material. However, the solution of compression problem must take the (idealized) structural images of fiber arrangement into consideration.

Figure 5.2 illustrates one general fiber (its segments) in the non-deformable rigid box. We assume that the corrugated fibers are lying on planes α, perpendicular to the direction of pressure vector. The fibers follow

---

3. Let us remember that the general mathematical formula $d\left[\int_k^y f(x)\, dx\right]/dy = f(y)$

is valid, when the quantity y stays as the upper limit of the integral.

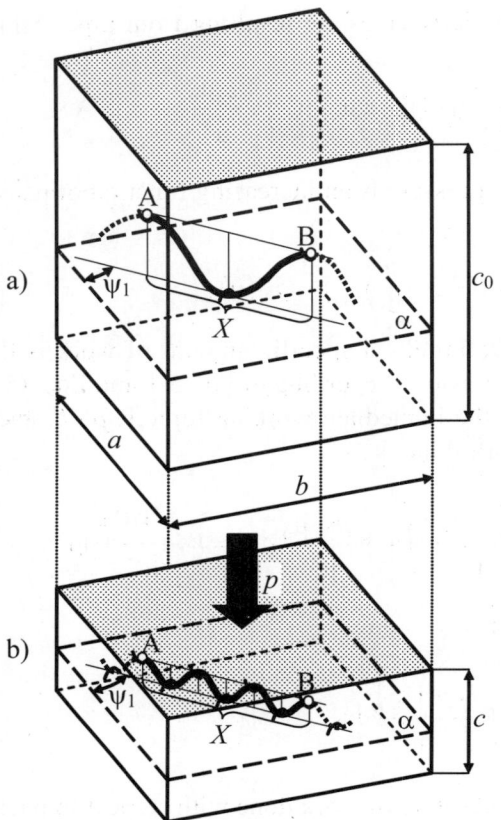

5.2 Fiber in a compressed material.

(a) Non-compressed state; (b) Compressed state.

(roughly) planar orientation with probability density function $f(\psi_1)$ of angle $\psi_1 \in (-\pi/2, \pi/2)$, so that we can use Eq. (4.47) for the expression of the integral $J(\psi_1)$. Because of the idea of planar orientation, we also assume that each directional angle ψ_1 remains still the same, i.e., this is independent of the "level of compression" given by the value of packing density μ (see Figures 5.2a and 5.2b).

We assume that the total fiber volume V stays the same as in the non-deformable rigid box and we also assume that the equivalent fiber diameter d, determined by Eq. (1.6), stays permanently the same. Then the total fiber length can be expressed as follows

$$L = \frac{V}{\pi d^2/4} = \frac{4V}{\pi d^2}.$$
... (5.8)

Evidently, this is a constant, too.

The length of the fibers (fiber segments) lying only in the direction ψ_1 (i.e., in the elemental angular class ranging from ψ_1 to $\psi_1 + d\psi_1$) is then

$$dL = L f\left(\psi_1\right)d\psi_1 = \frac{4V}{\pi d^2} f\left(\psi_1\right)d\psi_1 . \qquad \ldots (5.9)$$

Further, we assume that the compression of fibrous materials results in bending deformation of fibers only. Each fiber is bending during the process of compression as an impact effect of the other surrounding fibers. The configuration of the bent fibers (fiber crimp) has a random character in reality; however, we assume this phenomenon as a regular crimp in each fiber.

Because of uniaxial compression (The cross-wise deformation of the fibrous material in the rigid box is assumed to be non-existing) and the constant value of total length L, we can assume that the length AB of each fiber segment and the projected length X are the same as they are in the non-compressed as well as in the compressed material (see Figs. 5.2a and 5.2b).

The general fiber segment introduced in Fig. 5.2 is shown with more details in Fig. 5.3. The fiber segment in the non-compressed state (shown in Fig. 5.3a) has X/h_0 (two here) number of segments of length δ_0, where the projected length of one segment is h_0. But, the same fiber portion in a compressed state (shown in Fig. 5.3b) has X/h number of segments of length δ, where the projected length of one segment is h. The length of fiber segment is still the same $AB = \left(X/h_0\right)\delta_0 = \left(X/h\right)\delta$. From this equality, the following relations are evident

$$h_0/\delta_0 = h/\delta, \quad h = \left(h_0/\delta_0\right)\delta, \quad \delta - h = \delta\left(1 - h_0/\delta_0\right) \qquad \ldots (5.10)$$

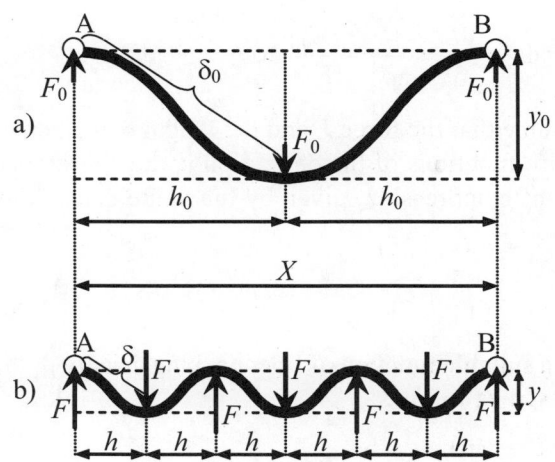

5.3 Fiber portion.
(a) Non-compressed state; (b) Compressed state.

Let us note that h_0/δ_0 is a parameter that characterizes the initial state of the fibrous assembly so that the "horizontal" lengths h and δ are mutually proportional and independent to the "level of compression" which is, for example, characterized by the value of packing density μ.

The forces F are acting on the fiber at the points of fiber-to-fiber contacts as shown in Fig. 5.3b.

Note: At the initial state as shown in Fig. 5.3a, very small forces F_0 can also act, because the initial fiber is crimped a little. However, it is the "natural" crimp of the fibers or the forces F_0 which is compensated by the internal friction of a real fibrous assembly. Therefore, the real outer pressure is equal to zero at the initial state.

Strategy of model creation. The current model is based on the assumption that the work done is proportional to the deformation energy required to compress the fibers in accordance with Eq. (5.6). The deformation energy can be determined by using the previous relations and following the strategy mentioned hereunder.

(1) The number m_1 (or m_1^*) of fiber-to-fiber contacts on one fiber of length l was derived earlier (Equation (4.49) or (4.86)). These equations can be expressed by a general formula $m_1 = l/\delta(\mu,\psi_1)$, so that the length δ of one fiber segment is a function of μ and ψ_1 as shown below

$$\delta = l/m_1 = \delta(\mu,\psi_1).\qquad\qquad\text{... (5.11)}$$

Then, the following equation is also valid for the initial length δ_0

$$\delta_0 = \delta(\mu_0, \psi_1).\qquad\qquad\text{... (5.12)}$$

Using Eq. (5.9) the number of fiber segments lying in the direction of angle ψ_1 is obtained as follows

$$dN = \frac{dL}{\delta} = \frac{4V}{\pi d^2}\frac{f(\psi_1)}{\delta}d\psi_1.\qquad\qquad\text{... (5.13)}$$

(2) We assume that the force F and the length δ of fiber segment shown in Fig. 5.3b are functions of the deflection y, the "horizontal" distance h, and the state of compression, given by the value ξ, as shown below

$$F = F(y, h, \xi),\qquad\qquad\text{... (5.14)}$$

$$\delta = \delta'(y,h,\xi),\qquad\qquad\text{... (5.15)}$$

where ξ is a suitable function of fiber packing density μ. Mathematically, this is expressed as follows

$$\xi = \xi(\mu),\qquad\qquad\text{... (5.16)}$$

$$\xi_0 = \xi(\mu_0).\qquad\qquad\text{... (5.17)}$$

The deflection y can be explicitly expressed from Eq. (5.15) in the form of a general function as shown below

$$y = y\,(\delta,\,h,\,\xi).$$ ... (5.18)

The "regularly" deformed fiber as shown in Fig. 5.3b evokes an idea of "regular" (infinity long) beam, which is deformed by the application of a force acting at the middle between two neighboring supports as shown in Fig. 5.4. The increasing force F (white arrow) results in increase in deflection η (thinner fiber line) from the starting value zero to the final value y. The elemental increment of energy between the supports (two fiber segments) due to the elemental increase in deflection η is $F\,d\eta$, so that the whole deformation energy in one fiber segment is $E_\delta = \dfrac{1}{2}\displaystyle\int_0^y F\,d\eta$.

This expression can be written as follows by applying the function expressed in Eq. (5.14) using η in place of y, further the function expressed in Eq. (5.18) and then Eq. (5.10)

$$\left.\begin{aligned}
E_\delta &= E_\delta'\left(y,h,\xi\right) = \frac{1}{2}\int_0^y F\left(\eta,h,\xi\right)d\eta, \\
E_\delta &= E_\delta''(\delta,h,\xi) = E_\delta'\left[y(\delta,h,\xi),h,\xi\right], \\
E_\delta &= E_\delta\left(\delta,\xi\right) = E_\delta''\left[\delta,\left(h_0/\delta_0\right)\delta,\xi\right].
\end{aligned}\right\} \qquad \text{... (5.19)}$$

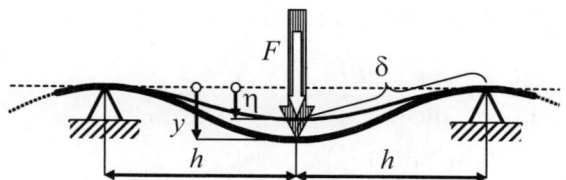

5.4 Regular fiber as an infinity long beam.

(3) It is possible to obtain an expression for the deformation energy in all dN segments having direction defined by the angle ψ_1 by using Eqs. (5.13) and (5.19) as follows

$$dE = E_\delta\,dN = E_\delta\left(\delta,\xi\right)\frac{4V}{\pi d^2}\frac{f\left(\psi_1\right)}{\delta}d\psi_1 = \frac{4V}{\pi d^2}\frac{E_\delta\left(\delta,\xi\right)}{\delta}f\left(\psi_1\right)d\psi_1.$$ ... (5.20)

Finally, the whole deformation energy (from all fiber directions) is expressed as follows

$$E = E\left(\delta,\xi\right) = \int_{\psi_1=-\pi/2}^{\psi_1=\pi/2} dE.$$ ... (5.21)

The deformation energy at the initial state, according to Eqs. (5.12) and (5.17), is expressed below

$$E_0 = E(\delta_0, \xi_0).$$ ... (5.22)

(Because δ_0 and ξ_0 are not the functions but the initial parameters, the energy E_0 is a parameter, too).

So, the increment of the deformation energy, in consequence of compression, as shown in Fig. 5.1, is expressed as follows

$$\Delta E = E - E_0 = E(\delta, \xi) - E_0.$$ ... (5.23)

(4) The variables δ and ξ are the functions of μ according to Eqs. (5.11) and (5.16) so that the derivative of ΔE with respect to μ is

$$\frac{d\Delta E}{d\mu} = \frac{dE(\delta, \xi)}{d\mu}.$$ ... (5.24)

(5) The increment of deformation energy is equal to the work done in the case of so-called conservative system. Such theoretical system is not really applicable to fibrous assemblies, because the dissipation of energy by mechanical straining of such materials is often significant. Let us therefore introduce a more general assumption that the increment of deformation energy ΔE is proportional to the work done A in our case. Using C as the coefficient of proportionality the relation $\Delta E = CA$ is valid. After differentiating this expression with respect to packing density μ and applying Eqs. (5.7) and (5.24) we obtain

$$\frac{d\Delta E}{d\mu} = C\frac{dA}{d\mu}, \quad \frac{dE(\delta, \xi)}{d\mu} = CV\frac{p}{\mu^2},$$

$$p = \frac{\mu^2}{CV}\frac{dE(\delta, \xi)}{d\mu}.$$ ... (5.25)

The last equation states that the pressure p is a function of packing density μ.

5.2   Model of compression according to van Wyk[4]

Length and number of fiber segments. The (mean) number of contact places m_1 on a fiber of length l is described by the expression $m_1 = l[8\mu/(\pi d)]J(\psi_1)$ according to Eq. (4.49)[5] in Section 4.3. Beside the fiber length l, this variable depends on the packing density μ, the equivalent fiber diameter d, and the angle ψ_1 which is expressed in the integral $J(\psi_1)$ given by Eq. (4.47). In accordance with Eq. (5.11), thelength of fiber

---

4.   Here, we use our own way for the derivation of the traditional results of van Wyk.

5.   This equation corresponds to the idea of van Wyk; see Section 4.1.

segment δ is expressed as follows

$$\delta = \frac{l}{m_1} = \frac{\pi d}{8\mu J(\psi_1)}$$

$$\qquad \text{... (5.26)}$$

Regular beam. The following relations specify the force F and the length of fiber segment δ in terms of deflection of a regular beam

$$F = F(y,h) = \frac{y}{h^3} k_F,$$

$$\qquad \text{... (5.27)}$$

$$\delta = \delta'(y,h) = h\left[1+\left(\frac{y}{h}\right)^2 q\right],$$

$$\qquad \text{... (5.28)}$$

where k_F and q are two material parameters.

Notes: (1) The last two equations were originally derived for the infinitely long beam with regularly distributed supports where the forces were acting at the center of the neighboring supports. These equations were determined from the so-called three-moment (Clapeyron) theorem, using the assumptions of Hook's law and small deformation. (The traditional problems are solved in many teaching books of technical mechanics for mechanical engineering).

(2) In this special case, the variables F and δ are the functions of the deflection y and the distance h only. (Generally, they are the function of $\xi(\mu)$ as shown in Eqs. (5.14) and (5.15)).

It is possible to rearrange Eq. (5.28) as follows in order to find an explicit expression for the deflection y, similar to what is shown in Eq. (5.18)

$$y = h\sqrt{\frac{1}{q}\left(\frac{\delta}{h}-1\right)}.$$

$$\qquad \text{...(5.29)}$$

Deformation energy in one segment. Applying Eqs. (5.10), (5.19), (5.27), and (5.29) the deformation energy in one fiber segment is expressed below

$$E_\delta = E_\delta'(y,h) = \frac{1}{2}\int_0^y F(\eta,h)\,\mathrm{d}\eta = \frac{1}{2}\int_0^y \frac{\eta}{h^3} k_F\,\mathrm{d}\eta = \frac{k_F}{2h^3}\int_0^y \eta\,\mathrm{d}\eta = \frac{k_F y^2}{4h^3},$$

$$E_\delta = E_\delta''(\delta,h) = E_\delta'\left[y(\delta,h),h\right] = \frac{k_F}{4h^3}\left[h\sqrt{\frac{1}{q}\left(\frac{\delta}{h}-1\right)}\right]^2$$

$$= \frac{k_F}{4h^3} h^2 \frac{1}{q}\left(\frac{\delta}{h}-1\right) = \frac{k_F}{4q}\frac{\delta-h}{h^2} = \frac{k_F}{4q}\frac{\delta\left(1-\dfrac{h}{\delta}\right)}{h^2},$$

$$E_\delta = E_\delta\left(\delta\right) = E_\delta''\left[\delta, h = \left(h_0/\delta_0\right)\delta\right] = \frac{k_F}{4q} \frac{\delta\left(1 - \dfrac{\left(h_0/\delta_0\right)\delta}{\delta}\right)}{\left[\left(h_0/\delta_0\right)\delta\right]^2} = \frac{k_F}{4q} \frac{1 - h_0/\delta_0}{\left(h_0/\delta_0\right)^2 \delta}.$$

$$\ldots (5.30)$$

Increment of the deformation energy. Using Eqs. (5.20) and (5.30) the following expression is valid to write for the deformation energy in all fiber segments having the direction ψ_1

$$\begin{aligned} dE &= \frac{4V}{\pi d^2} \frac{E_\delta\left(\delta\right)}{\delta} f\left(\psi_1\right) d\psi_1 = \frac{4V}{\pi d^2} \frac{\dfrac{k_F}{4q} \dfrac{1 - h_0/\delta_0}{\left(h_0/\delta_0\right)^2 \delta}}{\delta} f\left(\psi_1\right) d\psi_1 \\ &= \frac{k_F V}{\pi d^2 q} \frac{1 - h_0/\delta_0}{\left(h_0/\delta_0\right)^2 \delta^2} f\left(\psi_1\right) d\psi_1. \end{aligned}$$

$$\ldots (5.31)$$

The whole deformation energy is given by the general expression shown in Eq. (5.21). Using Eq. (5.31) we obtain the following expression for E in this case

$$E = E\left(\delta\right) = \int_{\psi_1 = -\pi/2}^{\psi_1 = \pi/2} dE = \frac{k_F V}{\pi d^2 q} \frac{1 - h_0/\delta_0}{\left(h_0/\delta_0\right)^2} \int_{-\pi/2}^{\pi/2} \frac{1}{\delta^2} f\left(\psi_1\right) d\psi_1 . \qquad \ldots (5.32)$$

(As δ is a function of ψ_1 as shown in Eq. (5.26), the ratio $1/\delta^2$ cannot be taken out of the integral). The following relation expresses the deformation energy at the initial stage according to Eqs. (5.22) and (5.32)

$$E_0 = \frac{k_F V}{\pi d^2 q} \frac{1 - h_0/\delta_0}{\left(h_0/\delta_0\right)^2} \int_{-\pi/2}^{\pi/2} \frac{1}{\delta_0^2} f\left(\psi_1\right) d\psi_1 . \qquad \ldots (5.33)$$

We obtain the increment of deformation energy by substituting the expressions mentioned in Eqs. (5.32) and (5.33) to Eq. (5.23) as shown below

$$\Delta E = E\left(\delta\right) - E_0 = \frac{k_F V}{\pi d^2 q} \frac{1 - h_0/\delta_0}{\left(h_0/\delta_0\right)^2} \int_{-\pi/2}^{\pi/2} \left(\frac{1}{\delta^2} - \frac{1}{\delta_0^2}\right) f\left(\psi_1\right) d\psi_1 . \qquad \ldots (5.34)$$

Using Eqs. (5.24), (5.32) and (5.26), the following derivative is valid to write

$$\frac{d\Delta E}{d\mu} = \frac{dE(\delta)}{d\mu} = \frac{k_F V}{\pi d^2 q} \frac{1 - h_0/\delta_0}{\left(h_0/\delta_0\right)^2} \int_{-\pi/2}^{\pi/2} \frac{d}{d\mu}\left(\frac{1}{\delta^2}\right) f(\psi_1) d\psi_1$$

$$= \frac{k_F V}{\pi d^2 q} \frac{1 - h_0/\delta_0}{\left(h_0/\delta_0\right)^2} \int_{-\pi/2}^{\pi/2} \frac{d}{d\mu}\left(\frac{64\mu^2 J^2(\psi_1)}{\pi^2 d^2}\right) f(\psi_1) d\psi_1$$

$$= \frac{k_F V}{\pi d^2 q} \frac{1 - h_0/\delta_0}{\left(h_0/\delta_0\right)^2} \int_{-\pi/2}^{\pi/2} \frac{128 J^2(\psi_1)}{\pi^2 d^2} \mu f(\psi_1) d\psi_1 \qquad \text{... (5.35)}$$

$$= \frac{128 k_F V}{\pi^3 d^4 q} \frac{1 - h_0/\delta_0}{\left(h_0/\delta_0\right)^2} \mu \int_{-\pi/2}^{\pi/2} J^2(\psi_1) f(\psi_1) d\psi_1.$$

Pressure. Finally, applying Eq. (5.35) into Eq. (5.25) we find the expression for the pressure p as shown below

$$p = \frac{\mu^2}{CV} \frac{dE(\delta)}{d\mu} = \frac{\mu^2}{CV} \frac{128 k_F V}{\pi^3 d^4 q} \frac{1 - h_0/\delta_0}{\left(h_0/\delta_0\right)^2} \mu \int_{-\pi/2}^{\pi/2} J^2(\psi_1) f(\psi_1) d\psi_1$$

$$= \frac{128 k_F}{C\pi^3 d^4 q} \frac{1 - h_0/\delta_0}{\left(h_0/\delta_0\right)^2} \left[\int_{-\pi/2}^{\pi/2} J^2(\psi_1) f(\psi_1) d\psi_1\right] \mu^3. \qquad \text{... (5.36)}$$

Let us now introduce a common parameter k_p as follows

$$k_p = \frac{128 k_F}{C\pi^3 d^4 q} \frac{1 - h_0/\delta_0}{\left(h_0/\delta_0\right)^2} \int_{-\pi/2}^{\pi/2} J^2(\psi_1) f(\psi_1) d\psi_1, \qquad \text{... (5.37)}$$

so that

$$p = k_p \mu^3. \qquad \text{... (5.38)}$$

(Let us remember that the parameter k_p is independent of packing density μ). The last expression is known as the well-known result of van Wyk [1].

As a special case of planar isotropic orientation, it is valid to write $f(\psi_1) = 1/\pi$ in accordance with Eq. (3.26), and $J(\psi_1) = 2/\pi$ in accordance with Eq. (4.51), respectively. Then, the following expression is obtained for the parameter k_p in accordance with Eq. (5.37)

$$k_p = \frac{128 k_F}{\pi^3 d^4 q} \frac{1 - h_0/\delta_0}{\left(h_0/\delta_0\right)^2} \int_{-\pi/2}^{\pi/2} \frac{4}{\pi^2} \frac{1}{\pi} d\psi_1 = \frac{512 k_F}{\pi^5 d^4 q} \frac{1 - h_0/\delta_0}{\left(h_0/\delta_0\right)^2}. \qquad \text{... (5.39)}$$

Equation (5.38) was experimentally verified by many researchers [1–4] mainly by compressing the fibers in the bales. The experimental results were found to be in satisfactory agreement with the theoretical results when the packing density was low, especially around 0.2 or 0.3. But, for moderate values of packing density (e.g. when the value of packing density was around 0.5 which is typical for common yarns), this equation was not found too precise and at high compression the equation was found to be quite false. Also, there are difficulties for extremely small compression where μ-values are very near to the initial value μ_0 of "free" fiber materials[6]. Summarily, there are two problems encountered with Eq. (5.38): (1) problem at very high pressure and (2) problem at very low pressure.

Problem at very high pressure. The behavior of the resulting function expressed in Eq. (5.38) is shown in Fig. 5.5a. It can be seen that the packing density is increasing with the increase in pressure, and when $p = k_p$ the corresponding packing density is equal to one. Then, at $p > k_p$ the corresponding packing density $\mu > 1$, which is logically nonsense, evidently. The obvious question is why did we obtain such result? It appears that we did not think about the effect of mutual "obstruction" experienced by the fibers inside the fibrous assembly. Our model fibers were mechanically understood as infinitely thin "beams" having point contacts with "supports" (fiber-to-fiber contacts). Such a volume-free structure is possible to be compressed to the thickness $c = 0$, as shown in Fig. 5.1b, so that the total volume is limiting to zero. But, we still geometrically assumed the constant volume V of fibers during the whole process of compression. Therefore, the packing density must be limited to infinity (see later on).

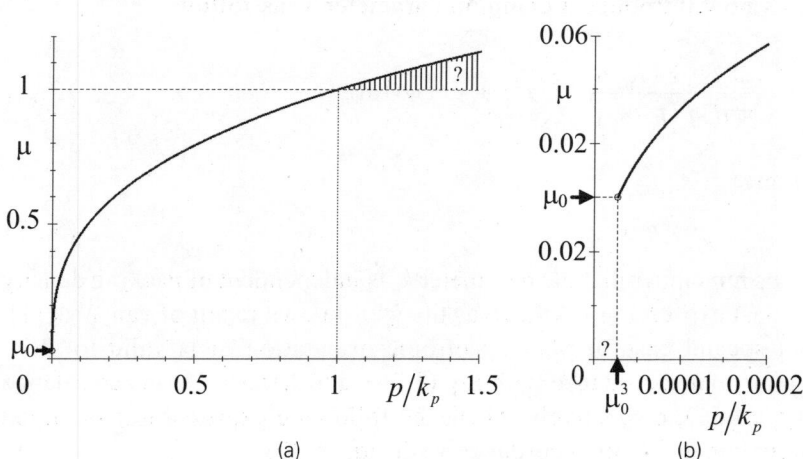

5.5 Behavior of function in Eq. (5.38) at $\mu_0 = 0.03$.

(a) Complete behavior; (b) Initial behavior.

Problem at very low pressure. The initial behavior of the function expressed in Eq. (5.38) is shown in Fig. 5.5b. When the pressure p is

6.   Typically, $\mu_0 \in (0.01, 0.03)$.

equal to zero at the initial stage, the packing density is equal to μ_0 (see Fig. 5.1), the resulting function expressed in Eq. (5.38) displays that the pressure is equal to $k_p\mu_0^3$ (shown in Fig. 5.5b). This quantity is very small in reality, but it is higher than zero; the second expression in Eq. (5.4) is not valid. Why did we obtain such result? It is explained as a note after Eq. (5.10). It is recommended by van Wyk [1] that the following correction – purely empirical – is required to be done in Eq. (5.38)

$$p = k_p\left(\mu^3 - \mu_0^3\right). \qquad\qquad \text{... (5.40)}$$

Note: Nevertheless, it is sufficient to work with relatively easy Eq. (5.38) for a dominant majority of practical cases.

5.3   Empirical modification of van Wyk's model

The negligence of mutual "obstruction" of fibers in a fibrous assembly is probably the dominant reason why van Wyk's model is not enough precise when the pressure is high. The free fiber segments between the neighboring contact places, surrounded by air only, cannot "obstruct" other fibers, naturally. But, this obstruction must be realized only at the vicinity of fiber-to-fiber contacts.

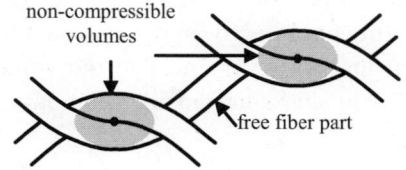

non-compressible volumes

free fiber part

5.6 Non-compressible region around fiber-to-fiber contacts.

Non-compressible region. The traditional concept interprets fiber-to-fiber contacts as contact points (black points shown in Fig. 5.6); then the whole fiber length is free for bending deformation. Nevertheless, in reality, each fiber-to-fiber contact occupies an area of contact. The fibrous material is compressed at the surrounding of the contact area and such surrounding creates a no-more-compressible region, something as a non-compressible "solid" inside the fibrous assembly – see gray color region in Fig. 5.6. The more deformable fiber material is created only by free fiber segments lying outside the mentioned non-compressible regions.

Empirical idea of modification. Wyk's Eq. (5.38) can be rearranged by using the definition of packing density according to Eq. (1.22) as follows

$$p = k_p\,\mu^3 = k_p\frac{V^3}{V_c^3}, \qquad\qquad \text{... (5.41)}$$

where the common parameter k_p and the total volume of fibers V are considered as suitable constants. It is evident that the increasing pressure p is the function of the decreasing total volume V_c only. (If the pressure is infinitely high then the total volume must limit to an impossible value equal to zero). In spite of them, let us empirically assume that van Wyk's equation could be right, but only for a deformable region; it is the total volume V_c of fibrous assembly minus the total volume of all non-compressible volumes W_c. Thus we obtain

$$p = k_p \frac{V^3}{\left(V_c - W_c\right)^3}. \qquad \qquad \dots (5.42)$$

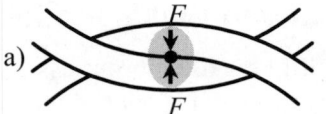 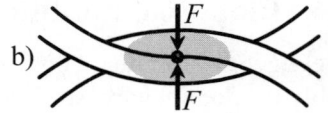

5.7 Size of non-compressible volumes.

(a) Slightly compressed fibers; (b) Heavily compressed fibers.

Fiber volume in non-compressible region. Let us take that one non-compressible region occupies a total volume W_1. The fiber volume inside the region is $W_{f,1}$ so that the packing density inside the region is $\mu_s = W_{f,1}/W_1$. (We can expect that μ_s is very near to the value 1. The air gaps between fibers are probably very small inside the non-compressible region). We can also write

$$W_1 = W_{f,1}/\mu_s. \qquad \qquad \dots (5.43)$$

The size W_1 of non-compressible space can be probably different as shown in Fig. 5.7. If the packing density μ of a fibrous assembly is small, then the forces F in the region of each fiber-to-fiber contact are also small, fibers are only slightly compressed and the generated non-compressible region is created from smaller volume of fibrous material $W_{f,1}$ so that it is small – see Fig. 5.7a. On the other hand, at high value of packing density μ, the fibrous assembly is highly compressed, the forces F in each fiber-to-fiber contact are high, the fibers are heavily compressed and therefore, the generated non-compressible volume is created from higher volume of fibrous material $W_{f,1}$ so that it is large – see Fig. 5.7b. Therefore, there exists an increasing function $W_{f,1} = f(\mu)$ between the packing density μ and the fiber volume $W_{f,1}$ in one non-compressible region.

Unfortunately, we do not exactly know the behavior of the mentioned function. We can only empirically suggest the following function

$$W_{f,1} = f(\mu) = K\mu^{a}, \qquad \qquad \ldots (5.44)$$

where K and a are two suitable parameters. Such function can describe a convex bow, a concave bow, and a straight line as shown

Total volume of non-compressible regions. Based on van Wyk's idea, the density of contacts υ (number of fiber-to-fiber contacts per unit volume of the fibrous assembly) was derived and expressed by Eq. (4.18) in Section 4.2. The total number of contacts in the whole fibrous assembly is consequently υV_c and because there is a non-compressible region existing around each contact, this is also equal to the number of non-compressible regions. The total volume of all non-compressible regions ("solids") is possible to express by using Eqs. (4.18), (5.43) and (5.44) as follows

$$W_c = \upsilon V_c W_1 = \upsilon V_c W_{f,1}/\mu_s = (k_\upsilon \mu^2) V_c (K\mu^a)/\mu_s = K\frac{k_\upsilon \mu^{2+a} V_c}{\mu_s}. \qquad \ldots (5.45)$$

Limit state. The limit state refers to a most theoretically compressed fibrous assembly. In such state it is valid to write that

(1) The total volume of fibrous assembly is minimum; $V_c = V_{c,\,min}$.
(2) The packing density of fibrous assembly is maximum (near to 1);

$$\mu = \mu_m, \quad \mu_m = V/V_{c,min}.$$

(3) The non-compressible regions fully occupy the total volume of the fibrous assembly; $W_c = V_{c,min}$.

    Note: Let us imagine that the non-compressible regions do not fully occupy the total volume of fibrous assembly. Then, $W_c < V_{c,min}$, so that the deformable volume $(V_{c,min} - W_c) > 0$, and the fibrous assembly can be further compressed. However, it is not the limit state as it was assumed to be.

(4) The packing density of the fibrous assembly is the same as the packing density of the non-compressible regions; $\mu_m = \mu_s$. (Fibrous assembly is created only from non-compressible regions. This is analogous to the wall created from bricks).

Applying the quantities of the limit state to general Eq. (5.45) the parameter K can be evaluated as follows

$$V_{c,min} = K\frac{k_\upsilon \mu_m^{2+a} V_{c,min}}{\mu_m}, \quad K = \frac{1}{k_\upsilon \mu_m^{1+a}}. \qquad \ldots (5.46)$$

Substituting K from Eq. (5.46) to Eq. (5.45) the following equation is obtained

$$W_c = \frac{1}{k_\upsilon \mu_m^{1+a}} \frac{k_\upsilon \mu^{2+a} V_c}{\mu_s} = V_c \frac{\mu^{2+a}}{\mu_m^{1+a} \mu_s} . \qquad \ldots (5.47)$$

Pressure. In the limit case, the packing density inside the non-compressible region follows the point (4). In a general case, the packing density inside the non-compressible region need not to be precisely equal to μ_m, but, for simplification, let us assume that the relation $\mu_s = \mu_m$ is valid independent to the level of compression. Using this equality in Eq. (5.47) we obtain

$$W_c = V_c \frac{\mu^{2+a}}{\mu_m^{1+a} \mu_m} = V_c \left(\mu/\mu_m\right)^{2+a} . \qquad \ldots (5.48)$$

Finally, let us use the last equation in our modified idea expressed by Eq. (5.42) and then we obtain

$$p = k_p \frac{V^3}{\left[V_c - V_c\left(\mu/\mu_m\right)^{2+a}\right]^3} = k_p \frac{\mu^3}{\left[1-\left(\mu/\mu_m\right)^{2+a}\right]^3} . \qquad \ldots (5.49)$$

This equation uses three parameters: k_p, μ_m and a. Usually, μ_m is a quantity whose numerical value is equal to, if not near to, one and a – based on our experimental experience – can be chosen to be near to one, too. The behavior of the modified function expressed in Eq. (5.49) and its comparison with original van Wyk's Eq. (5.38) is illustrated in Fig. 5.8.

Let us note that at smaller values of packing density, for example, 0.2 or 0.3, the modified relation is practically the same as the traditional van Wyk's expression, in pursuance of our empirical experience. Nevertheless,

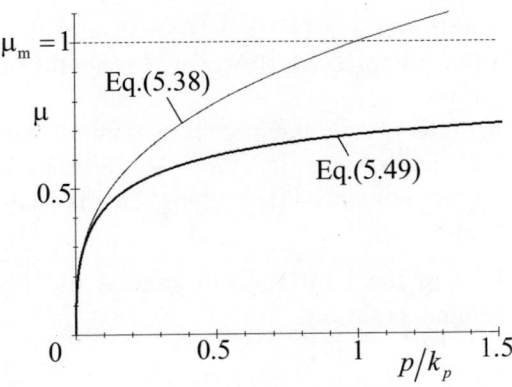

5.8 Original equation of Wyk and modified equation; $\mu_m = 1$, $a = 1$.

at higher values of packing density, the difference is very significant. The packing density limits to the value μ_m when the pressure limits to infinity.

The previous relation expressed in Eq. (5.40) is easy to use when we know the packing density μ of a fibrous assembly and we want to calculate the corresponding pressure p. But the solution of the inverse function is much more difficult. If $a = 1$ then the rearrangement of Eq. (5.49), resulting in an explicit value for μ, is analytically possible based on the solution of the cubic equation according to the well-known Cardano's formulas. So we obtain

$$\frac{\mu}{\mu_m} = \left\{ 1 + \left[\sqrt{\left(\frac{x}{3}\right)^3 + \left(\frac{x}{2}\right)^2} - \frac{x}{2} \right]^{1/3} - \left[\sqrt{\left(\frac{x}{3}\right)^3 + \left(\frac{x}{2}\right)^2} + \frac{x}{2} \right]^{1/3} \right\}, \qquad \ldots (5.50)$$

where $x = \dfrac{\mu_m^3 k_p}{p}$.

If a is another quantity then μ must be solved numerically from Eq. (5.49). Both possibilities are more or less unpractical.

Approximation. Often, in practice, we need to know the behavior of μ as a function of p in a relatively small interval around the value of a packing density $\mu = \mu^*$ only. (For example, the traditional yarns have an average packing density around $\mu^* \cong 0.45$) Then the following approximation is good to use

$$b = 3 \left[1 + (1+a)(\mu^*/\mu_m)^{2+a} \right] \Big/ \left[1 - (\mu^*/\mu_m)^{2+a} \right], \qquad \ldots (5.51)$$

$$c = 1 \Big/ \left\{ \left[1 - (\mu^*/\mu_m)^{2+a} \right]^3 (\mu^*)^{b-3} \right\}, \qquad \ldots (5.52)$$

and then the approximated equation around μ^* takes the following form

$$p = k_p c \mu^b. \qquad \ldots (5.53)$$

Note: The parameters b and c are derived based on two assumptions: the values of the first derivative of the original Eq. (5.49) and the approximation Eq. (5.53) must be the same at $\mu = \mu^*$.

The approximated result according to Eq. (5.53) is compared with the original result according to Eq. (5.49). This comparison is shown in Fig. 5.9. The thick line corresponds to the original result and the thin lines correspond to approximated results.

Note: Let us note that at $\mu^* = 0$ the parameters b and c take the values $b = 3$ and $c = 1$, in accordance with Eqs. (5.51) and (5.52), respectively. Thus the expression $p = k_p \mu^3$ accords to Eq. (5.53) and this expression is identical with the original van Wyk's Eq. (5.38).

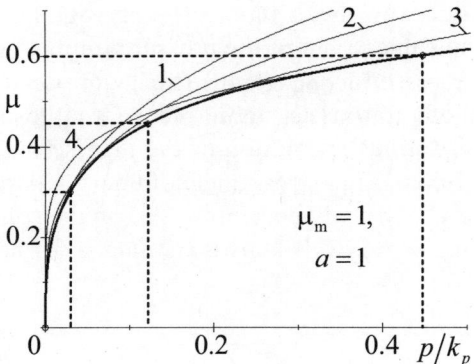

5.9 Comparison of original (━━) and approximated (───) results.
1...$\mu^* = 0$; 2...$\mu^* = 0.3$; 3...$\mu^* = 0.45$; 4...$\mu^* = 0.6$.

Problem at very low pressure. The problem at very low pressure is also actual in this model, because at $\mu = \mu_0$, the pressure according to Eq. (5.49) is very negligible, but it is higher than zero. So as to obtain precisely the zero value for $\mu = \mu_0$ we need (empirically) to correct Eq. (5.49) in the following manner

$$p = k_p \left[\varphi(\mu) - \varphi(\mu_0) \right],$$ ... (5.54)

where

$$\varphi(\mu) = \frac{\mu^3}{\left[1 - (\mu/\mu_m)^{2+a} \right]^3}, \quad \varphi(\mu_0) = \frac{\mu_0^3}{\left[1 - (\mu_0/\mu_m)^{2+a} \right]^3}.$$ ... (5.55)

Note: Nevertheless, it is sufficient to work with the relatively easy Eq. (5.49) for a dominant majority of practical cases.

5.4   An alternative model of compression

The aforesaid empirical modification of van Wyk's model is relatively easy and this brings satisfactory results in many applications. However, the following theoretical model makes it possible to better understand the compression behavior of fibrous assembly in terms of its internal structure.

This model follows the general ideal concept described in Section 5.1. Nevertheless, alternative ideas are also used.

Length and number of fiber segments. The modified probability of fiber-to-fiber contact, following mutual "obstruction" of fibers, was solved in Section 4.4. The (mean) number of contact places m_1^* on a fiber of length

l is described by the expression $m_1^* = z \left(1 - e^{-\frac{8\mu l}{z\pi d} J(\vartheta_1, \varphi_1)} \right)$ according to

Eq. (4.86), where $l/z = \gamma d$ according to Eq. (4.94). Here, z is the maximum possible contact places on a fiber of length l, γd expresses the length of the fiber segment that is "covered" by one contact (the length occupied by one contact place is equal to γ times fiber diameter d), and the integral $J(\vartheta_1, \varphi_1)$ is reduced to the integral $J(\psi_1)$, $\psi_1 \in (-\pi/2, \pi/2)$ according to Eq. (4.47) for planar orientation. Using all these expressions the following expression is valid to write for m_1^*

$$m_1^* = \frac{l}{\gamma d}\left(1 - e^{\frac{-\frac{8\mu l}{l}J(\psi_1)}{\gamma d}\pi d}\right) = \frac{l}{\gamma d}\left(1 - e^{-\frac{8\mu\gamma}{\cdot\pi}J(\psi_1)}\right). \qquad \ldots (5.56)$$

According to Eq. (5.11) the length of fiber segment δ is expressed as follows

$$\delta = \frac{l}{m_1^*} = \frac{\gamma d}{1 - e^{-\frac{8\mu\gamma}{\pi}J(\psi_1)}}, \quad 1 - \frac{\gamma d}{\delta} = e^{-\frac{8\mu\gamma}{\pi}J(\psi_1)}, \qquad \ldots (5.57)$$

$$\delta_0 = \frac{\gamma d}{1 - e^{-\frac{8\mu_0\gamma}{\pi}J(\psi_1)}}, \quad 1 - \frac{\gamma d}{\delta_0} = e^{-\frac{8\mu_0\gamma}{\pi}J(\psi_1)}. \qquad \ldots (5.58)$$

(δ_0 is the length of fiber segment at the initial position, that is, before compression, when $\mu = \mu_0$).

Note: Let us denote $x = -\frac{8\mu\gamma}{\pi}J(\psi_1)$, so that $\gamma = -\frac{x\pi}{8\mu J(\psi_1)}$. Then from

Eq. (5.57) $\delta = \frac{l}{m_1^*} = \frac{-\frac{x\pi}{8\mu J(\psi_1)}d}{1 - e^x} = \frac{\pi d}{8\mu J(\psi_1)}\frac{x}{e^x - 1}$ and $\lim_{\gamma \to 0}\delta = \frac{\pi d}{8\mu J(\psi_1)} \times$

$\lim_{x \to 0}\frac{x}{e^x - 1} = \frac{\pi d}{8\mu J(\psi_1)}$. The last expression is identical with Eq. (5.26).

Regular beam. On the place of traditional infinitely long beam shown in Fig. 5.4 an alternative concept can be used as follows.

Let us imagine two mutually clenched fibers as shown in Fig. 5.10. The segment AB = u on fiber No. 1 is firmly gripped by fiber No. 2 so that the bending deformation is not (or no more) possible in this segment. On the other hand, the "covered" length CD, onto which no other fiber can make any contact with fiber No. 1, is CD = γd. (Compare this with the hypothetical dotted fibers at the closest vicinity illustrated in Fig. 5.10). The ratio $u/(\gamma d) = \xi$ is perhaps smaller than one, according to the image and this ratio is probably starting from zero and increasing with the increase

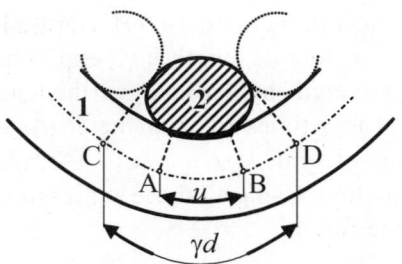

5.10 Mutually clenched fibers in the contact area.

in packing density of the fibrous assembly[7]. (At the initial stage, that is, at $\mu = \mu_0$, we imagine the gripped length is reduced to a point). Thus

$$u = \xi \gamma d, \quad \xi = \xi(\mu) \leq 1, \qquad \qquad ... (5.59)$$

and especially

$$\xi_0 = \xi(\mu_0). \qquad \qquad (5.60)$$

Simplifying the previous image we can suggest an alternative scheme of regular beam in Fig. 5.11 in lieu of Fig. 5.4.

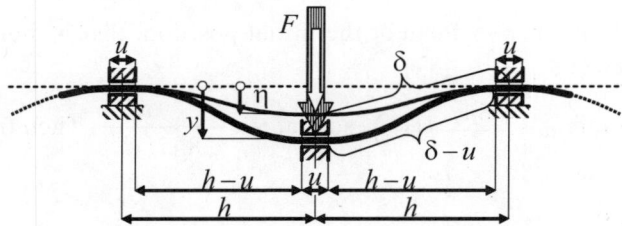

5.11 Regular fiber as an infinity long beam with regularly distributed grips.

Instead of exact contacts between the beam and the supports and the exact action of the force, the new "fiber beam" has a firm and straight support and force-grips[8] along the width u. The fiber segments inside the grips of length u are considered to be straight. The segments outside the grips of length u are bent and we assume that Eqs. (5.27) and (5.28) are valid analogically. Nevertheless, in place of earlier h we must use $h - u$ and in place of δ we must use $\delta - u$. Then, we obtain

$$F = F(y, h, \xi) = \frac{y}{(h-u)^3} k_F = \frac{y}{(h-\xi\gamma d)^3} k_F, \qquad \qquad ... (5.61)$$

---

7.   The function $\xi(\mu)$ will be discussed later on.
8.   The grip substitutes clinching of our "fiber beam" with fibers from surroundings.

$$\delta - u = (h-u)\left[1+\left(\frac{y}{h-u}\right)^2 q\right],$$

$$\delta = \delta'(y,h,\xi) = (h-\xi\gamma d)\left[1+\left(\frac{y}{h-\xi\gamma d}\right)^2 q\right]+\xi\gamma d, \qquad \ldots (5.62)$$

where y is deflection, and k_F and q are two material parameters. The last two equations for the force F and the length δ of fiber segment are the model versions of Eqs. (5.14) and (5.15).

It is possible to rearrange Eq. (5.62) to get an explicit value of deflection y, similar to Eq. (5.18). Thus

$$y = y(\delta,h,\xi) = \sqrt{\frac{1}{q}\left(\frac{\delta-\xi\gamma d}{h-\xi\gamma d}-1\right)}\,(h-\xi\gamma d). \qquad \ldots (5.63)$$

Deformation energy in one segment. Applying Eqs. (5.10), (5.19), (5.61), and (5.63) the deformation energy in one fiber segment is expressed as follows

$$E_\delta = E'_\delta(y,h,\xi) = \frac{1}{2}\int_0^y F(\eta,h,\xi)\,d\eta = \frac{1}{2}\int_0^y \frac{\eta}{(h-\xi\gamma d)^3}k_F\,d\eta$$

$$= \frac{k_F}{2(h-\xi\gamma d)^3}\int_0^y \eta\,d\eta = \frac{k_F y^2}{4(h-\xi\gamma d)^3}$$

$$E_\delta = E''_\delta(\delta,h,\xi) = E'_\delta\left[y(\delta,h,\xi),h,\xi\right]$$

$$= \frac{k_F}{4(h-\xi\gamma d)^3}\left(\sqrt{\frac{1}{q}\left(\frac{\delta-\xi\gamma d}{h-\xi\gamma d}-1\right)}\,(h-\xi\gamma d)\right)^2$$

$$= \frac{k_F}{4(h-\xi\gamma d)^3}(h-\xi\gamma d)^2 \frac{1}{q}\left(\frac{\delta-\xi\gamma d}{h-\xi\gamma d}-1\right) = \frac{k_F}{4q}\frac{(\delta-\xi\gamma d)-(h-\xi\gamma d)}{(h-\xi\gamma d)^2}$$

$$= \frac{k_F}{4q}\frac{\delta-h}{(h-\xi\gamma d)^2},$$

$$E_\delta = E_\delta(\delta,\xi) = E''_\delta\left[\delta, h=(h_0/\delta_0)\delta,\xi\right] = \frac{k_F}{4q}\frac{\delta-(h_0/\delta_0)\delta}{\left[(h_0/\delta_0)\delta-\xi\gamma d\right]^2}$$

$$= \frac{k_F}{4q}\frac{\delta(1-h_0/\delta_0)}{\left[(h_0/\delta_0)\delta-\xi\gamma d\right]^2}. \qquad \ldots (5.64)$$

Increment of deformation energy. Using Eqs. (5.20) and (5.64) the following expression is valid to write for the deformation energy in all fiber segments having direction ψ_1

$$dE = \frac{4V}{\pi d^2} \frac{E_\delta(\delta,\xi)}{\delta} f(\psi_1) d\psi_1 = \frac{4V}{\pi d^2} \frac{\dfrac{k_F}{4q} \dfrac{\delta(1-h_0/\delta_0)}{\left[(h_0/\delta_0)\delta - \xi\gamma d\right]^2}}{\delta} f(\psi_1) d\psi_1$$

$$= \frac{k_F V}{q\pi d^2} \frac{1-h_0/\delta_0}{\left[(h_0/\delta_0)\delta - \xi\gamma d\right]^2} f(\psi_1) d\psi_1. \qquad \ldots (5.65)$$

The total deformation energy is generally expressed by Eq. (5.21). Using Eq. (5.65) we obtain the following expression in this case

$$E = E(\delta,\xi) = \int_{\psi_1=-\pi/2}^{\psi_1=\pi/2} dE = \frac{k_F V}{q\pi d^2} \int_{-\pi/2}^{\pi/2} \frac{1-h_0/\delta_0}{\left[(h_0/\delta_0)\delta - \xi\gamma d\right]^2} f(\psi_1) d\psi_1 \quad \ldots (5.66)$$

If $\mu = \mu_0$, i.e. $\delta = \delta_0$ according to Eq. (5.58) and $\xi = \xi_0$ according to Eq. (5.60), respectively, then the initial value of the deformation energy is

$$E_0 = \int_{\psi_1=-\pi/2}^{\psi_1=\pi/2} dE = \frac{k_F V}{q\pi d^2} \int_{-\pi/2}^{\pi/2} \frac{1-h_0/\delta_0}{\left[(h_0/\delta_0)\delta_0 - \xi_0\gamma d\right]^2} f(\psi_1) d\psi_1$$

$$= \frac{k_F V}{q\pi d^2} \int_{-\pi/2}^{\pi/2} \frac{1-h_0/\delta_0}{\left[h_0 - \xi_0\gamma d\right]^2} f(\psi_1) d\psi_1. \qquad \ldots (5.67)$$

We obtain the increment of deformation energy by using the expressions mentioned in Eqs. (5.66) and (5.67) in Eq. (5.23) as follows

$$\Delta E = E(\delta,\xi) - E_0 = \frac{k_F V}{q\pi d^2} \int_{-\pi/2}^{\pi/2} \left(\frac{1-h_0/\delta_0}{\left[(h_0/\delta_0)\delta - \xi\gamma d\right]^2} - \frac{1-h_0/\delta_0}{\left[h_0 - \xi_0\gamma d\right]^2} \right) f(\psi_1) d\psi_1.$$

$$\ldots (5.68)$$

Derivatives. The derivative of the deformation energy E with respect to μ is necessary to know for the determination of pressure according to Eq. (5.25). The following expression is valid according to Eq. (A4.10) in Appendix 4.

$$\frac{dE(\delta,\xi)}{d\mu} = \frac{16k_F V}{q\pi^2 d^4} \int_{-\pi/2}^{\pi/2} \left\{ J(\psi_1) \frac{(1-h_0/\delta_0)}{(h_0/\delta_0)^2} \frac{d}{\delta} \frac{1-\frac{\gamma d}{\delta}\left(1-\frac{\pi}{8J(\psi_1)} \frac{1}{\delta} \frac{d\xi}{h_0} \frac{d\xi}{d\mu}\right)}{\left(1-\xi\frac{\gamma d}{\delta}\frac{\delta_0}{h_0}\right)^3} \right\} f(\psi_1) d\psi_1$$

... (5.69)

Pressure. Using the last expression in Eq. (5.25) we obtain the following expression for the pressure p as a function of packing density μ

$$p = \frac{\mu^2}{CV} \frac{dE(\delta,\xi)}{d\mu}$$

$$= \frac{16k_F \mu^2}{Cq\pi^2 d^4} \int_{-\pi/2}^{\pi/2} \left\{ J(\psi_1) \frac{(1-h_0/\delta_0)}{(h_0/\delta_0)^2} \frac{d}{\delta} \frac{1-\frac{\gamma d}{\delta}\left(1-\frac{\pi}{8J(\psi_1)} \frac{1}{\delta} \frac{d\xi}{h_0} \frac{d\xi}{d\mu}\right)}{\left(1-\xi\frac{\gamma d}{\delta}\frac{\delta_0}{h_0}\right)^3} \right\} f(\psi_1) d\psi_1$$

... (5.70)

Limit case. Here, the limit case denotes the theoretical maximum compression. In this situation, the following statements are valid to write: (1) the packing density is maximum, $\mu \to \mu_m$, (2) the length of the fiber segment is minimum, $\delta \to \delta_m$, (3) the distance h is minimum, $h \to h_m$, the quantity ξ is maximum, $\xi = \xi_m$. According to Eqs. (5.57), (5.10) and (5.59) it is valid to write

$$\delta_m = \frac{\gamma d}{1-e^{-\frac{8\mu_m \gamma}{\pi} J(\psi_1)}},$$

... (5.71)

$$h_0/\delta_0 = h_m/\delta_m, \quad h_m = (h_0/\delta_0)\delta_m,$$

... (5.72)

$$\xi_m = \xi(\mu_m).$$

... (5.73)

It is natural to expect that the pressure is limited to infinity when the packing density reaches to its maximum value; $\lim\limits_{\mu \to \mu_m} p(\mu) = \infty$. Such a result can be obtained from Eq. (5.70) – independent of fiber orientation – when the denominator of the last fraction in Eq. (5.70) is limiting to zero. Thus

$$\lim_{\mu \to \mu_m} \left(1 - \xi \frac{\gamma d}{\delta} \frac{\delta_0}{h_0}\right) = 1 - \xi_m \frac{\gamma d}{\delta_m} \frac{\delta_0}{h_0} = 0, \qquad \frac{h_0}{\delta_0} = \xi_m \frac{\gamma d}{\delta_m},$$

$$1 - \xi \frac{\gamma d}{\delta} \frac{\delta_0}{h_0} = 1 - \xi \frac{\gamma d}{\delta} \frac{\delta_m}{\gamma d \xi_m} = 1 - \frac{\xi}{\xi_m} \frac{\delta_m}{\delta},$$

$$\frac{1}{\dfrac{\delta \; h_0}{d \; \delta_0}} = \frac{1}{\dfrac{\delta}{d} \xi_m \dfrac{\gamma d}{\delta_m}} = \frac{1}{\gamma \xi_m} \frac{\delta_m}{\delta}. \qquad \qquad \text{... (5.74)}$$

Applying these relations to Eq. (5.70), the expression for the pressure is obtained as follows

$$p = \frac{16 k_F \mu^2}{C q \pi^2 d^4} \int_{-\pi/2}^{\pi/2} \left\{ J(\psi_1) \frac{\left(1 - \dfrac{h_0}{\delta_0}\right)}{\left(\dfrac{h_0}{\delta_0}\right)^2} \frac{d}{\delta} \frac{1 - \dfrac{\gamma d}{\delta}\left(1 - \dfrac{\pi}{8 J(\psi_1) \gamma} \dfrac{\delta_m}{\delta} \dfrac{d\xi/d\mu}{\xi_m}\right)}{\left(1 - \dfrac{\xi}{\xi_m} \dfrac{\delta_m}{\delta}\right)^3} \right\} f(\psi_1) \, d\psi_1$$

$$\text{... (5.75)}$$

Value (γ). It is valid to write the following expression from Eqs. (5.71) and (5.74)

$$\gamma d = \frac{h_0}{\delta_0 \xi_m} \delta_m = \frac{h_0}{\delta_0 \xi_m} \frac{\gamma d}{1 - e^{-\frac{8\mu_m \gamma}{\pi} J(\psi_1)}}, \qquad e^{-\frac{8\mu_m \gamma}{\pi} J(\psi_1)} = 1 - \frac{h_0}{\delta_0 \xi_m},$$

$$\frac{8\mu_m \gamma}{\pi} J(\psi_1) = \ln\left(\frac{1}{1 - \dfrac{h_0}{\delta_0 \xi_m}}\right), \qquad \gamma = \frac{\pi}{8\mu_m J(\psi_1)} \ln\left(\frac{1}{1 - \dfrac{h_0}{\delta_0 \xi_m}}\right). \qquad \text{... (5.76)}$$

It is valid that $\gamma = 0$ when (a) $\mu_m \to \infty$ or (b) $h_0/(\delta_0 \xi_m) \to 0$; but, both are not real.

Nevertheless, let us assume – in contrary to reality – that the value $\gamma = 0$ because the limit value of packing density $\mu_m \to \infty$. According to the note mentioned after Eq. (5.58) it is valid $\lim_{\gamma \to 0} \delta = \dfrac{\pi d}{8\mu J(\psi_1)}$ and especially

$$\delta_m = \lim_{\mu = \mu_m \to \infty}\left[\lim_{\gamma \to 0} \delta\right] = \lim_{\mu = \mu_m \to \infty}\left[\frac{\pi d}{8\mu J(\psi_1)}\right] = 0. \quad \text{Further, the expression}$$

$\xi_m \dfrac{\gamma d}{\delta_m} \to \xi_m \dfrac{0d}{0}$ is the indefinite expression now; its value is equal to the

initial parameter h_0/δ_0 according to Eq. (5.74). Applying these relations into Eq. (5.75) we obtain

$$p = \frac{16k_F\mu^2}{Cq\pi^2 d^4} \int_{-\pi/2}^{\pi/2} \left\{ J(\psi_1)\frac{1-h_0/\delta_0}{(h_0/\delta_0)^2}\frac{d}{\frac{\pi d}{8\mu J(\psi_1)}} \frac{1-\dfrac{0d}{\pi d}\left(1-\dfrac{\pi d}{8\mu J(\psi_1)}\dfrac{h_0}{\delta_0}\dfrac{\frac{\pi d}{8\mu J(\psi_1)}\frac{d\xi}{d\mu}}{}\right)}{\left(1-\dfrac{\xi}{\xi_m}\dfrac{0}{\frac{\pi d}{8\mu J(\psi_1)}}\right)^3} \right\} f(\psi_1)d\psi_1$$

$$= \frac{128k_F}{Cq\pi^3 d^4}\frac{1-h_0/\delta_0}{(h_0/\delta_0)^2}\left[\int_{-\pi/2}^{\pi/2} J^2(\psi_1)f(\psi_1)d\psi_1\right]\mu^3 = k_p\mu^3. \qquad \ldots (5.77)$$

This result is identical with that obtained from Eqs. (5.36) to (5.38), describing the traditional van Wyk's model.

Case of planar isotropic orientation. As a special case of planar isotropic orientation of fibers it is valid that $f(\psi_1) = 1/\pi$ according to Eq. (3.26), and $J(\psi_1) = 2/\pi$ according to Eq. (4.51). According to Eq. (5.57) it is valid to write

$$\delta = \frac{\gamma d}{1-e^{-\frac{8\mu\gamma}{\pi}\frac{2}{\pi}}} = \frac{\gamma d}{1-e^{-\frac{16\mu\gamma}{\pi^2}}}, \quad \frac{\gamma d}{\delta} = 1-e^{-\frac{16\mu\gamma}{\pi^2}}, \qquad \ldots (5.78)$$

and according to Eq. (5.71) the limit (minimum) value of δ can be expressed as

$$\delta_m = \frac{\gamma d}{1-e^{-\frac{8\mu_m\gamma}{\pi}\frac{2}{\pi}}} = \frac{\gamma d}{1-e^{-\frac{16\mu_m\gamma}{\pi^2}}}, \quad \frac{\gamma d}{\delta_m} = 1-e^{-\frac{16\mu_m\gamma}{\pi^2}}, \qquad \ldots (5.79)$$

The following equation for pressure p is valid to write from Eq. (5.75)

$$p = \frac{16k_F\mu^2}{Cq\pi^2 d^4} \int_{-\pi/2}^{\pi/2} \left\{ \frac{2}{\pi}\frac{\left(1-\dfrac{h_0}{\delta_0}\right)}{\left(\dfrac{h_0}{\delta_0}\right)^2}\frac{d}{\delta}\frac{1-\dfrac{\gamma d}{\delta}\left(1-\dfrac{\pi^2}{16\gamma}\dfrac{\delta_m}{\delta}\dfrac{d\xi/d\mu}{\xi_m}\right)}{\left(1-\dfrac{\xi}{\xi_m}\dfrac{\delta_m}{\delta}\right)^3} \right\}\frac{1}{\pi}d\psi_1,$$

$$p = \frac{32k_F\mu^2}{Cq\pi^3 d^4} \frac{\left(1 - \dfrac{h_0}{\delta_0}\right)}{\left(\dfrac{h_0}{\delta_0}\right)^2} \frac{d}{\delta} \frac{1 - \dfrac{\gamma d}{\delta}\left(1 - \dfrac{\pi^2}{16\gamma}\dfrac{\delta_m}{\delta}\dfrac{d\xi/d\mu}{\xi_m}\right)}{\left(1 - \dfrac{\xi}{\xi_m}\dfrac{\delta_m}{\delta}\right)^3}$$

$$= \left[\frac{512k_F}{Cq\pi^5 d^4}\frac{1 - h_0/\delta_0}{(h_0/\delta_0)^2}\right]\frac{\pi^2}{16}\frac{d}{\delta}\frac{1 - \dfrac{\gamma d}{\delta}\left(1 - \dfrac{\pi^2}{16\gamma}\dfrac{\delta_m}{\delta}\dfrac{d\xi/d\mu}{\xi_m}\right)}{\left(1 - \dfrac{\xi}{\xi_m}\dfrac{\delta_m}{\delta}\right)^3}\mu^2,$$

$$p = k_p\frac{\pi^2}{16}\frac{d}{\delta}\frac{1 - \dfrac{\gamma d}{\delta}\left(1 - \dfrac{\pi^2}{16\gamma}\dfrac{\delta_m}{\delta}\dfrac{d\xi/d\mu}{\xi_m}\right)}{\left(1 - \dfrac{\xi}{\xi_m}\dfrac{\delta_m}{\delta}\right)^3}\mu^2. \qquad \ldots (5.80)$$

Especially, for the non-real case ($\gamma = 0$, $\mu_m = \infty$), mentioned earlier, Eq. (5.77) is expressed as follows for the planar isotropic orientation

$$p = \frac{128k_F}{Cq\pi^3 d^4}\frac{1 - h_0/\delta_0}{(h_0/\delta_0)^2}\left[\int_{-\pi/2}^{\pi/2}\left(\frac{2}{\pi}\right)^2\frac{1}{\pi}d\psi_1\right]\mu^3 = \left[\frac{512k_F}{Cq\pi^5 d^4}\frac{1 - h_0/\delta_0}{(h_0/\delta_0)^2}\right]\mu^3 = k_p\mu^3.$$

$$\ldots (5.81)$$

Note: In the last two equations, the symbol k_p for planar isotropic orientation was used in accordance with the expression mentioned in Eq. (5.39).

Force in fiber-to-fiber contact. The force F in one fiber-to-fiber contact, shown in Fig. 5.3 b or Fig. 5.11, was introduced by Eq. (5.61). Applying Eq. (5.63) in Eq. (5.61) we obtain the square of the force as follows

$$F^2 = y^2\frac{k_F^2}{(h - \xi\gamma d)^6} = \left[\frac{1}{q}\left(\frac{\delta - \xi\gamma d}{h - \xi\gamma d} - 1\right)(h - \xi\gamma d)^2\right]\frac{k_F^2}{(h - \xi\gamma d)^6}$$

$$= k_F^2\frac{\dfrac{\delta - \xi\gamma d - h + \xi\gamma d}{h - \xi\gamma d}}{q(h - \xi\gamma d)^4} = k_F^2\frac{\delta - h}{q(h - \xi\gamma d)^5} = k_F^2\frac{\left(1 - \dfrac{h}{\delta}\right)\delta}{q\left(\dfrac{h}{\delta} - \xi\dfrac{\gamma d}{\delta}\right)^5\delta^5}$$

$$= k_F^2\frac{1 - \dfrac{h}{\delta}}{q\left(\dfrac{h}{\delta} - \xi\dfrac{\gamma d}{\delta}\right)^5\delta^4}. \qquad \ldots (5.82)$$

Substituting the ratio h/δ by the ratio h_0/δ_0 according to Eq. (5.10), we can write

$$F^2 = k_F^2 \frac{1 - \dfrac{h_0}{\delta_0}}{q\left(\dfrac{h_0}{\delta_0} - \xi\dfrac{\gamma d}{\delta}\right)^5 \delta^4} = k_F^2 \frac{1 - \dfrac{h_0}{\delta_0}}{q\left(\dfrac{h_0}{\delta_0}\right)^5 \left(1 - \xi\dfrac{\gamma d}{\delta}\dfrac{\delta_0}{h_0}\right)^5 \delta^4} =$$

$$= \frac{k_F^2}{qd^4}\left(\frac{d}{\delta}\right)^4 \frac{1 - \dfrac{h_0}{\delta_0}}{\left(\dfrac{h_0}{\delta_0}\right)^5 \left(1 - \xi\dfrac{\gamma d}{\delta}\dfrac{\delta_0}{h_0}\right)^5}. \qquad \ldots (5.83)$$

Finally, we apply the second expression from Eq. (5.74) in the last equation and we obtain

$$F^2 = \frac{k_F^2}{qd^4}\left(\frac{d}{\delta}\right)^4 \frac{1 - \dfrac{h_0}{\delta_0}}{\left(\dfrac{h_0}{\delta_0}\right)^5 \left(1 - \dfrac{\xi}{\xi_m}\dfrac{\delta_m}{\delta}\right)^5},$$

$$F = \frac{k_F}{\sqrt{q}\, d^2} \frac{\sqrt{1 - \dfrac{h_0}{\delta_0}}}{\left(\dfrac{h_0}{\delta_0}\right)^{5/2}}\left(\frac{d}{\delta}\right)^2 \frac{1}{\left(1 - \dfrac{\xi}{\xi_m}\dfrac{\delta_m}{\delta}\right)^{5/2}}. \qquad \ldots (5.84)$$

Function $\xi(\mu)$ from Hertzian contact mechanics. The size of a small contact surface between two mutually compressed round bodies is solved in the traditional theory, often called under the term "Hertzian contact mechanics[9]. This theory is found to be very useful in tracking the contact surfaces, finding out the pressure between the teeth of the wheels, and solving similar other problems in the field of mechanical engineering. The mentioned theory was derived by using a lot of simplified assumptions like Hook's law is valid, contact surface is "small", i.e. near to "point contact", etc. The fundamental result of Hertz's theory defines the linear dimension of contact surface (e.g., the length u resulting from the contact

---

9.   The theory of Hertzian contact mechanics is described in different books on
      contact mechanics in mechanical engineering.

of our fibers – see Fig. 5.10) as a function of applied force F, stated below

$$u = C_F \sqrt[3]{F} , \qquad \qquad \dots (5.85)$$

where the parameter C_F depends on the curvature of the contacting surfaces, stress moduli, etc.

Applying Eqs. (5.59) and (5.84) into Eq. (5.85) the following expressions are obtained

$$\xi \gamma d = C_F \left[\frac{k_F}{\sqrt{q}\, d^2} \frac{\sqrt{1 - \dfrac{h_0}{\delta_0}}}{\left(\dfrac{h_0}{\delta_0}\right)^{5/2}} \left(\frac{d}{\delta}\right)^2 \frac{1}{\left(1 - \dfrac{\xi}{\xi_m}\dfrac{\delta_m}{\delta}\right)^{5/2}} \right]^{1/3}$$

$$= C_F \frac{k_F^{1/3}}{q^{1/6}\, d^{2/3}} \frac{(1 - h_0/\delta_0)^{1/6}}{(h_0/\delta_0)^{5/6}} \left(\frac{d}{\delta}\right)^{2/3} \frac{1}{\left(1 - \dfrac{\xi}{\xi_m}\dfrac{\delta_m}{\delta}\right)^{5/6}} ,$$

$$\frac{\xi}{\xi_m} = C_F \frac{k_F^{1/3}}{q^{1/6}\, d^{5/3}\xi_m} \frac{(1 - h_0/\delta_0)^{1/6}}{(h_0/\delta_0)^{5/6}} \frac{1}{\gamma} \left(\frac{d}{\delta}\right)^{2/3} \frac{1}{\left(1 - \dfrac{\xi}{\xi_m}\dfrac{\delta_m}{\delta}\right)^{5/6}} ,$$

$$\frac{\xi}{\xi_m}\left(1 - \frac{\xi}{\xi_m}\frac{\delta_m}{\delta}\right)^{5/6} = C_F \frac{k_F^{1/3}}{q^{1/6}\, d^{5/3}\xi_m} \frac{(1 - h_0/\delta_0)^{1/6}}{(h_0/\delta_0)^{5/6}} \frac{1}{\gamma} \left(\frac{d}{\delta}\right)^{2/3} \qquad \dots (5.86)$$

For each given value of packing density (this is present in the expression for the quantity δ) the corresponding value of ξ/ξ_m can be found out by a suitable numerical way.

Numerical determination of ξ/ξ_m. For a given value of packing density let us write

$$C_F \frac{k_F^{1/3}}{q^{1/6}\, d^{5/3}\xi_m} \frac{(1 - h_0/\delta_0)^{1/6}}{(h_0/\delta_0)^{5/6}} \frac{1}{\gamma} \left(\frac{d}{\delta}\right)^{2/3} = Q \dots \text{parameter,} \qquad \dots (5.87)$$

and also

$$\frac{\delta_m}{\delta} = c \dots \text{parameter,} \qquad \qquad \dots (5.88)$$

$$\frac{\xi}{\xi_m} = x \dots \text{obtained value.} \qquad \qquad \dots (5.89)$$

Then we obtain

$$x(1-xc)^{5/6} = Q \qquad \qquad \text{... (5.90)}$$

Let us express the function of the left-hand side of the last expression by y as follows

$$x(1-xc)^{5/6} = y \qquad \qquad \text{... (5.91)}$$

The behavior of this function is illustrated in Fig. 5.12. For $x = 0$ and $x = 1/c$ the value of y is $y = 0$. The maximum of such function, i.e. the point (x^*, y^*), corresponds to the following expression

$$\frac{dy}{dx} = 0 = \left(1 - x^*c\right)^{5/6} + x^* \frac{5}{6} \frac{-c}{\left(1 - x^*c\right)^{1/6}}, \quad 1 - x^*c = \frac{5}{6}x^*c,$$

$$x^* = \frac{6}{11c} \cong \frac{0.5454}{c}, \qquad \qquad \text{... (5.92)}$$

$$y^* = x^*\left(1 - x^*c\right)^{5/6} = \frac{6}{11c}\left(1 - \frac{6}{11}\right)^{5/6} \cong \frac{0.2828}{c}. \qquad \qquad \text{... (5.93)}$$

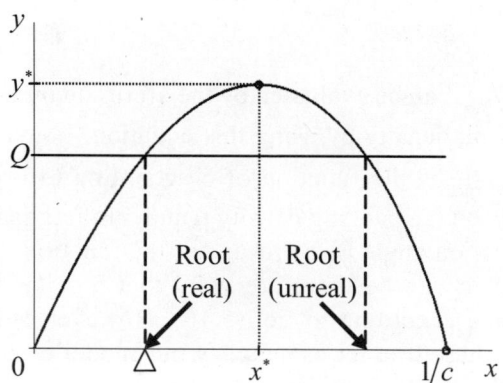

5.12 Behavior of the function expressed in Eq. (5.91).

Equation (5.90) can be considered as a special case of Eq. (5.91), where the variable y is just equal to the value of the parameter Q. There are two roots of this equation, one corresponds to when $Q < y^*$ and the other corresponds to when $Q = y^*$, and this equation has no solution when $Q > y^*$ – see Fig. 5.12. If the two roots are existing then the smaller root (lower than the value x^*) gives the physical real value, while the second root (higher than the value x^*) is not real[10]. Therefore, if $Q \leq y^*$ then we must find the true root in the interval $(0, x^*\rangle$ (e.g. using the algorithm of "interval halving"). The finally obtained value $x = \xi/\xi_m$ (shown by symbol $\triangle$ in Fig. 5.12) is the solution of Eq. (5.86).

Enlargement and empirical generalization of $\xi(\mu)/\xi_m$. The quantity Q according to Eq. (5.87) has the character of a parameter for only one given value of the packing density μ, which is present in the expression for δ – see Eq. (5.57) and/or Eq. (5.78). Therefore, let us introduce the parameter K at the first instance

$$K = C_F \frac{k_F^{1/3}}{q^{1/6} d^{5/3} \xi_m} \frac{\left(1 - h_0/\delta_0\right)^{1/6}}{\left(h_0/\delta_0\right)^{5/6}}, \qquad \ldots (5.94)$$

so that

$$Q = K \frac{1}{\gamma} \left(\frac{d}{\delta}\right)^{2/3}. \qquad \ldots (5.95)$$

Note that the defined parameter K is a constant which is independent of the value of δ, i.e. independent of the value of packing density and independent of the value of γ, too.

Using Eq. (5.94) in Eq. (5.86) we can write

$$\frac{\xi}{\xi_m} \left(1 - \frac{\xi}{\xi_m} \frac{\delta_m}{\delta}\right)^{5/6} = K \frac{1}{\gamma} \left(\frac{d}{\delta}\right)^{2/3}. \qquad \ldots (5.96)$$

The quantity ξ/ξ_m can be evaluated by the aforesaid numerical way for all values of packing density by using this equation.

The variable ξ/ξ_m is the function of δ according to Eq. (5.96). The variable δ depends on the packing density μ and – in full generality – also on the fiber orientation angle ψ_1 by means of the function $J(\psi_1)$; see Eq. (5.57). In general, it can be therefore valid that $\xi = \xi(\mu, \psi_1)$, not only $\xi = \xi(\mu)$ as assumed according to Eq. (5.16). However, such concept is too complicated. Therefore, let us simplify our model by introducing an assumption that the quantity δ expressed in Eq. (5.96) always corresponds to the case of planar isotropy of fiber orientation as expressed in Eq. (5.78). Then the earlier introduced expression $\xi = \xi(\mu)$ is right.

Let us illustrate the derived relation for isotropic planar orientation (Equations (5.78) and (5.79) are valid). Figure 5.13 corresponds to the parameters $\mu_m = 1$, $\gamma = 0.5$. The thick lines represent Eq. (5.96) when $K = 0.1$ – curve A, $K = 0.2$ – curve B, and $K = 0.3$ – curve C.

---

10. The value of the second root is decreasing with the increase in packing density, which is logically nonsense.

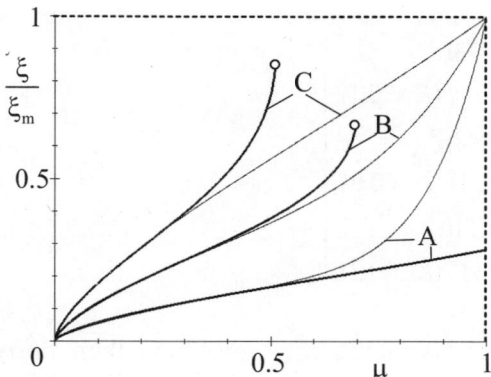

5.13 Example of original function ξ/ξ_m and its approximation.

o...the point where $Q = y^*$.

Note: The value of the parameter K is difficult to determine from the definition as expressed by Eq. (5.94), because a lot of unknown components are present there. We interpret the parameter K as a general material parameter, beside μ_m and γ.

The increasing character of these curves was logically expected and the behavior of their first "flat" part is well acceptable. Nevertheless, the markedly curved convex bows and the self ends (o) in the final part of curves B and C, as well as too small value of ξ/ξ_m when $\mu = \mu_m = 1$ corresponding to curve A probably have no physical interpretation. The earlier mentioned phenomenon is probably due to the effects of non-validity of the Hertz's Eq. (5.85) for too large contact surfaces, that is, too different from the idea of "point contacts". The "right-hand side" curves must be defined for all values of $\mu \in (0, \mu_m)$ and evidently they must give the value $\xi/\xi_m = 1$ (i.e. $\xi = \xi_m$) when $\mu = \mu_m = 1$. The "left-hand side" curves could follow the function expressed by Eq. (5.96) for smaller values of μ. Such curves could be expressed by the following empirical approximation

$$\xi/\xi_m = a_1\mu^{b_1} + (1-a_1)\mu^{b_2}, \quad \frac{d\xi/d\mu}{\xi_m} = a_1 b_1 \mu^{b_1-1} + (1-a_1)b_2\mu^{b_2-1}, \quad \dots \ (5.97)$$

Where the parameters $a_1 \in (0, 1)$, $b_1 \in (0, 1)$, and $b_2 > 0$.

Note: The first addition component follows the behavior of the first part of the original curve according to Eq. (5.96). On the other hand, the second addition component is not found legitimate; this must be "creatively" found based on experimental experience at this moment.

The behavior of the suitable approximated functions are demonstrated by the thin lines in Fig. 5.13, when the following relations are used

$$\left.\begin{aligned}
\xi/\xi_m &= 0.27\mu^{0.7} + 0.73\mu^{8} \\
&\quad \text{for the curve A } (K = 0.1), \\
\xi/\xi_m &= 0.57\mu^{0.7} + 0.43\mu^{5} \\
&\quad \text{for the curve B } (K = 0.2), \\
\xi/\xi_m &= 0.89\mu^{0.7} + 0.11\mu^{3} \\
&\quad \text{for the curve C } (K = 0.3).
\end{aligned}\right\}\qquad \dots (5.98)$$

Applying these approximated equations (and their derivatives) to Eq. (5.80) we obtain the functions whose behavior is illustrated in Fig. 5.14. Curves A, B, and C denote the approximated curves according to Eq. (5.98) when the marking is considered to be the same.

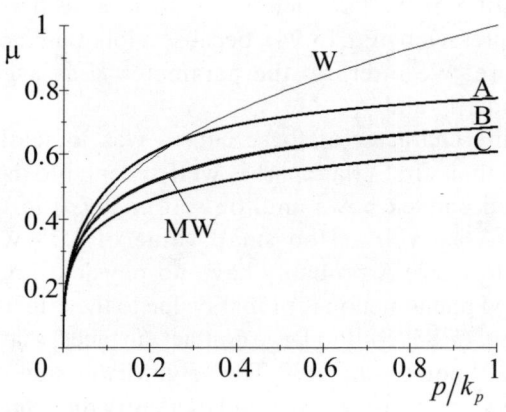

5.14 Packing density as the function of pressure.

A, B, C: (5.80) with (5.98). W: (5.38). MW: (5.49) by $\mu_m = 1$, $a = 1$.

Moreover, the behavior of the earlier derived functions is displayed by the thin lines in Fig. 5.14. The classical result of van Wyk's theory, given by Eq. (5.38), is marked by symbol W. The result of modified van Wyk's model, given by Eq. (5.49) where $\mu_m = 1$ and $a = 1$, is marked by symbol MW. It can be seen that its behavior is very much same as the behavior of the curve B.

Let us discuss more about the second example of isotropic planar orientation (Equations (5.78) and (5.79) are still valid) with $\mu_m = 1$ and $\gamma = 1$. The thick lines shown in Fig. 5.15 represent Eq. (5.96) when $K = 0.3$ – curve D, $K = 0.45$ – curve E, and $K = 0.57$ – curve F. The thin lines correspond to the approximated functions shown below

$$\xi/\xi_m = 0.35\mu^{0.6} + 0.65\mu^8$$
$$\text{for the curve D } (K = 0.3),$$
$$\xi/\xi_m = 0.58\mu^{0.65} + 0.42\mu^5$$
$$\text{for the curve E } (K = 0.45),$$
$$\xi/\xi_m = 0.82\mu^{0.7} + 0.18\mu^9$$
$$\text{for the curve F } (K = 0.57).$$

$$\dots (5.99)$$

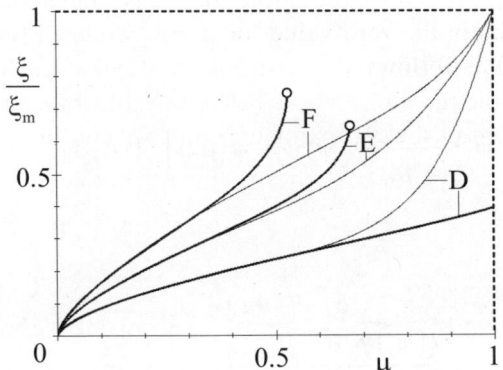

5.15 Example of original function ξ/ξ_m and its approximation.

o...the point where $Q = y^*$.

Applying these approximated expressions (and their derivatives) to Eq. (5.80) we obtain the functions whose behaviors are illustrated in Fig. 5.16. The curves D, E, and F follow the approximated curves according to Eq. (5.99) with the markings carry the same meaning.

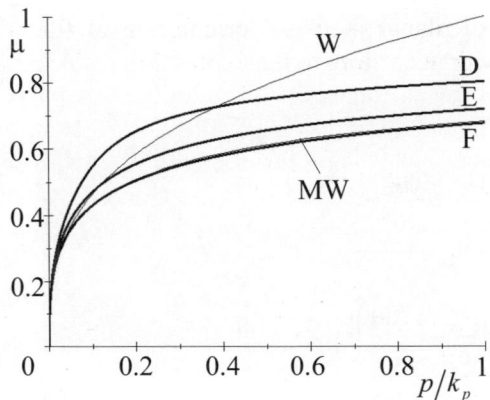

5.16 Packing density as the function of pressure.

D, E, F: (5.80) with (5.99). W: (5.38). MW: (5.49) by $\mu_m = 1$, $a = 1$.

Also in the previous example, the thin curves represent the classical van Wyk's function shown in Eq. (5.38) – curve W, and the modified van Wyk's function shown in Eq. (5.49) when $\mu_m = 1$ and $a = 1$ – curve MW.

Also, it is possible here to show practically the same behavior of the thick curve F (when $K = 0.57$) and the earlier derived thin curve MW.

Problem at very low pressure. There exists a problem at very low pressure in this model, too. At $\mu = \mu_0$ it is valid that $\delta = \delta_0$ according to Eq. (5.58) and $\xi = \xi_0$ according to Eq. (5.60). The pressure obtained according to Eq. (5.75) is very negligible, but it is higher than zero. In order to precisely obtain the zero value for $\mu = \mu_0$ we need (empirically) to correct Eq. (5.75) as follows

$$p = \frac{16 k_F \mu^2}{Cq\pi^2 d^4} \int_{-\pi/2}^{\pi/2} J(\psi_1) \frac{1 - h_0/\delta_0}{(h_0/\delta_0)^2} \left[\psi(\mu) - \psi(\mu_0) \right] f(\psi_1) d\psi_1, \qquad \dots (5.100)$$

where

$$\psi(\mu) = \frac{d}{\delta} \frac{1 - \dfrac{\gamma d}{\delta} \left(1 - \dfrac{\pi}{8J(\psi_1)\gamma} \dfrac{\delta_m}{\delta} \dfrac{d\xi/d\mu}{\xi_m} \right)}{\left(1 - \dfrac{\xi}{\xi_m} \dfrac{\delta_m}{\delta} \right)^3},$$

$$\psi(\mu_0) = \frac{d}{\delta_0} \frac{1 - \dfrac{\gamma d}{\delta_0} \left(1 - \dfrac{\pi}{8J(\psi_1)\gamma} \dfrac{\delta_m}{\delta_0} \dfrac{(d\xi/d\mu)_{\mu=\mu_0}}{\xi_m} \right)}{\left(1 - \dfrac{\xi_0}{\xi_m} \dfrac{\delta_m}{\delta_0} \right)^3} \qquad \dots (5.101)$$

Note: As a special case of planar isotropic orientation of fibers, the function ψ changes its behavior according to the expression resulting from Eq. (5.80) as follows

$$p = k_p \frac{\pi^2}{16} \left[\psi(\mu) - \psi(\mu_0) \right] \mu^2, \qquad \dots (5.102)$$

where

$$\psi(\mu) = \frac{d}{\delta} \frac{1 - \dfrac{\gamma d}{\delta} \left(1 - \dfrac{\pi^2}{16\gamma} \dfrac{\delta_m}{\delta} \dfrac{d\xi/d\mu}{\xi_m} \right)}{\left(1 - \dfrac{\xi}{\xi_m} \dfrac{\delta_m}{\delta} \right)^3},$$

$$\psi(\mu_0) = \frac{d}{\delta_0} \frac{1 - \dfrac{\gamma d}{\delta_0}\left(1 - \dfrac{\pi^2}{16\gamma}\dfrac{\delta_m}{\delta_0}\dfrac{(d\xi/d\mu)_{\mu=\mu_0}}{\xi_m}\right)}{\left(1 - \dfrac{\xi}{\xi_m}\dfrac{\delta_m}{\delta_0}\right)^3} \qquad \text{... (5.103)}$$

Note: Nevertheless, it is sufficient to work with Eq. (5.75) or (5.80) for a dominant majority of the practical cases in this model.

Final notes. The described model determines the relation between pressure and packing density in accordance with suitable choices of

(a) the maximum of packing density μ_m (usually, $\mu_m \cong 1$),
(b) the value γ characterizing the "covered length" on the fiber; usually $\gamma \in (0.5, 1.5)$,
(c) the aggregate material parameter K,
(d) the multiplying parameter k_p and
(e) the probability density function $f(\psi_1)$ of fiber orientation.

Then the process of determination of the relation between pressure and packing density can be stated as follows:

1. At first, we derive ξ/ξ_m as a function of μ from Eq. (5.96), applying Eq. (5.78) and (5.79).
2. Then, we determine the approximation function shown in Eq. (5.97).
3. Applying it into Eq. (5.80), or more generally to Eq. (5.75), we obtain the relation between pressure and packing density.

Some combinations of parameters lead to the relation which is practically the same as the modified van Wyk's model (e.g., the curves B and F in Fig. 5.14 and Fig. 5.16), another parameters lead to another relations.

The advantage of this theory lies in deeper analysis of structural phenomena. Briefly speaking, it is physically more correct than the earlier concepts. On the other hand, the weak point of this theory lies in the determination of the approximated function shown in Eq. (5.97), namely the determination of second addition component of it. The used Hertz Eq. (5.85) is not valid for higher values of packing density and we have only a few of experimental experience in the field of high values of packing density. Therefore, the open question for future research is "How to generalize the Hertz's theory for high values of pressure?"

5.5   Experimental results of Baljasov

There exists hardly any literature reporting the relation between pressure and packing density from extremely small to extremely high values. One of such rare work is due to Baljasov [2]. He compressed the fiber materials in a rigid metal box whose length was 60 mm and width was 50 mm. Every time just 20g of fiber material was put inside the box and this material was compressed. He used a tensile testing equipment from the textile laboratory for measurement at smaller values of pressure and employed a pressing machine from the engineering laboratory for measurement at high values of pressure.

The primary measured quantity was the height of the fiber material in the rigid box at a given value of pressure. The area of the box multiplied by the measured height was equal to the total volume V_c of the tested fiber material. Baljasov published the values of these volumes together with the pressure values in his book [2].

We calculated the fiber volume V from the known relation $V = m/\rho$, where the mass of the fiber material was $m = 20$g and the value for the fiber density ρ was taken from Table 1.1. In this way, we determined the actual values of for the packing density $\mu = V/V_c$ for all the pressure values.

Baljasov [2] investigated four different types of fiber materials. They were (a) cotton, fibers 108F[11] of staple length 31/32 mm, (b) viscose fibers of 0.17 tex fineness and 38/40 mm length, (c) merino wool 64's, middle length 67.7 mm, and (d) polyester fibers[12] of 0.21 tex fineness and 38/40 mm length. Baljasov studied two types of fiber directional organization for each material. He put in the rigid box either chaotically organized fibers (roughly isotropic orientation) or roughly parallel organized fibers (significant preferential direction).

The experimental results of Baljasov [2] represents the points (✕ and ☐) in the semi-logarithmic graphs, from (a) to (d), in Fig. 5.17. It is shown that the different types of fiber materials, the orientation does not play too significant (systematic) role.

Also, three types of theoretical curves are displayed in Fig. 5.17. The thin curves marked by number 1 correspond to the original van Wyk's model – Section 5.2, the thin curves marked by number 2 correspond to the empirically modified van Wyk's model – Section 5.3, and the thick curves marked by number 3 correspond to the alternative model – Section ·5.4 (Curves 2 and 3 are practically identical which was already mentioned in Fig. 5.16, curve F).

It appears that the experimentally found trends are in agreement with the behavior of the curves 2 and 3, while the behavior of the curve 1 is markedly different at higher values of packing density. It means that the empirically modified van Wyk's model as well as the alternative model

---

11.   Former Soviet system of description of cotton variety.
12.   Former Soviet polyester fibers "Lavsan".

can describe this compression or the used fibrous material was quite good. However, another experimental research in the field of high values of pressure and packing density is required to be studied in future.

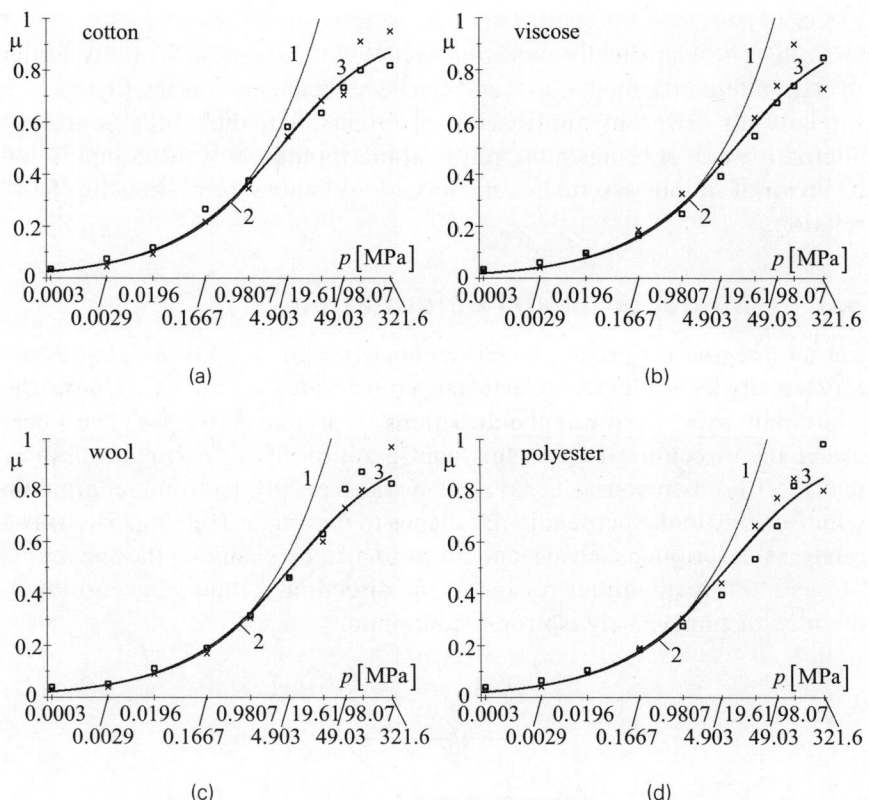

(a)   (b)

(c)   (d)

5.17 Dependence of packing density on pressure – comparison between theoretical and experimental results.

Experimental points: ×...chaotic organization of fibers,
                       □...roughly parallel organization of fibers
Material: **(a)** Cotton, ρ = 1520kgm⁻³; (b) viscose, k_p = 45 MPa; (c) wool,
   ρ = 1320 kg m⁻³; (d) polyester, ρ = 1360 kg m⁻³.

Theoretical curves: cotton k_p = 18MPa, viscose k_p = 45 Mpa, wool k_p = 28 MPa, polyester k_p = 33 MPa.

1... Original van Wyk's model – Equation (5.38).
2... Empirically modified van Wyk's model – Equation (5.49), μ_m = 1, a = 1.
3... Alternative model – Equation (5.80) with Eqs. (5.78) and (5.79), μ_m = 1, γ = 1,
    K = 0.57, Approximated function in Eq. (5.99) (curve F).

Note: Many attempts were made to solve the relation between pressure and packing density as a master's research work at the Technical university of Liberec (Haňáčková [11], Gurová [12], Pavelka [13]). Unfortunately, the technical equipment available in the laboratory did not allow to achieve a higher value of packing density than $\mu \cong 0.45$, so that the differences among the curves 1, 2, and 3 in the measured area were too small (see also Fig. 5.17).

Note: The empirically modified van Wyk's model is formally easier than the alternative model, so that it can be recommended as the first variant for solving different application problems. On the other hand, the alternative model brings more physical interpretation of the compression behavior of fibrous assemblies and has more chances for finding the "best" relation.

5.6   Model of biaxial deformation

Let us imagine a fibrous assembly consisting of roughly parallel fibers located at the system of Cartesian coordinates $x_1, x_2, x_3,$, where the coordinate axes determine the directions of principal stresses. The fibers prefer the direction of x_3. In this configuration, it is possible to assume that the fibrous material behaves as a transversally isotropic continuum with isotropy in the perpendicular planes to the axis x_3 (see Fig. 5.18). The relations describing such system are valid also by changing the subscripts "1" and "2" by quantities related to the directions x_1 and x_2, according to the idea of transversely isotropic continuum.

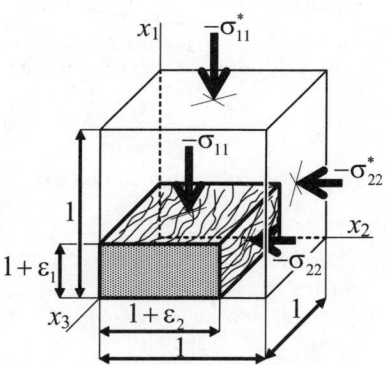

5.18 Biaxial compressing of fibrous assembly.

Basic relations. Let us imagine the initial fibrous assembly in the form of a unit cube as shown in Fig. 5.18. The normal forces $-\sigma_{11}^*, -\sigma_{22}^*$ act on the unit area of the initial fibrous cube.

Note: Traditionally, the vectors of positive values $\sigma_{11}^*, \sigma_{22}^*$ direct outside from the body (tensile loads). Nevertheless, the vectors of forces direct inside of the body (pressure) as shown in Fig. 5.18. Therefore, the negative symbols $-\sigma_{11}$, $-\sigma_{22}$ are used there.

Generally, the tensile forces σ_{11}^*, σ_{22}^* act on the unit area of the starting fibrous cube so that they are also called as engineering or nominal (fictive) stresses at the same time.

In consequence of acting forces, the initial unit dimensions of the starting cube are changed (deformed) to new dimensions $1 + \varepsilon_1$ and $1 + \varepsilon_2$ as shown in Fig. 5.18 (The values of ε_1 and ε_2 are negative for compression). Only the dimension in the direction of x_3- axis stays equal to one[13].

After deformation the forces σ_{11}^*, σ_{22}^* act on the real areas $1(1+\varepsilon_1)$ and $1(1+\varepsilon_2)$. The following expressions are then valid for Cauchy's (real) stresses

$$\sigma_{11} = \frac{\sigma_{11}^*}{1(1+\varepsilon_2)} = \frac{\sigma_{11}^*}{1+\varepsilon_2}, \quad \sigma_{22} = \frac{\sigma_{22}^*}{1(1+\varepsilon_1)} = \frac{\sigma_{22}^*}{1+\varepsilon_1}. \qquad \ldots (5.104)$$

All the time we assume that the volume V of fibers stays the same after compression of the initial cube (Only the volume of air is decreasing due to compression). Then the starting value of the packing density is

$$\mu_0 = V/(1\cdot1\cdot1) = V, \qquad \ldots (5.105)$$

and the packing density after compression is

$$\mu = \frac{V}{1(1+\varepsilon_1)(1+\varepsilon_2)} = \frac{\mu_0}{(1+\varepsilon_1)(1+\varepsilon_2)}. \qquad \ldots (5.106)$$

Let us characterize the levels of deformation by the following quantities

$$\mu_1 = \frac{\mu_0}{1+\varepsilon_1}, \quad \mu_2 = \frac{\mu_0}{1+\varepsilon_2}, \text{ i.e. } 1+\varepsilon_1 = \mu_0/\mu_1, \quad 1+\varepsilon_2 = \mu_0/\mu_2 . \quad \ldots (5.107)$$

Note: While μ and μ_0 have the logical sense of packing densities, the quantities μ_1 and μ_2, determined by Eq. (5.107), do not have this sense. They can only be thought as suitable quantities expressing the deformation in another way.

The following expression is valid from Eqs. (5.106) and (5.107)

$$\mu_1\mu_2 = \frac{\mu_0}{1+\varepsilon_1}\frac{\mu_0}{1+\varepsilon_2} = \mu\mu_0 . \qquad \ldots (5.108)$$

---

13. It is possible to obtain, for example, by placing the initial cube between two rigid plates. However, this dimension will not probably much change from the starting value 1 in case of a roughly parallel fiber bundle.

The derivatives of μ, μ_1 and μ_2 are derived using Eqs. from (5.106) to (5.108)

$$\frac{d\mu_1}{d\varepsilon_1} = \frac{d}{d\varepsilon_1}\left(\frac{\mu_0}{1+\varepsilon_1}\right) = \frac{-\mu_0}{\left(1+\varepsilon_1\right)^2} = \frac{-\mu_1^2}{\mu_0}, \qquad \frac{d\mu_2}{d\varepsilon_2} = \frac{d}{d\varepsilon_2}\left(\frac{\mu_0}{1+\varepsilon_2}\right) =$$

$$= \frac{-\mu_0}{\left(1+\varepsilon_2\right)^2} = \frac{-\mu_2^2}{\mu_0} \qquad \qquad \text{... (5.109)}$$

$$\left.\begin{aligned}
\frac{\partial\mu}{\partial\varepsilon_1} &= \frac{d}{d\varepsilon_1}\left[\frac{\mu_0}{\left(1+\varepsilon_1\right)\left(1+\varepsilon_2\right)}\right] = \frac{-\mu_0}{\left(1+\varepsilon_1\right)^2\left(1+\varepsilon_2\right)} = \frac{-\mu\mu_1}{\mu_0}, \\
\frac{\partial\mu}{\partial\varepsilon_2} &= \frac{d}{d\varepsilon_2}\left[\frac{\mu_0}{\left(1+\varepsilon_1\right)\left(1+\varepsilon_2\right)}\right] = \frac{-\mu_0}{\left(1+\varepsilon_1\right)\left(1+\varepsilon_2\right)^2} = \frac{-\mu\mu_2}{\mu_0}.
\end{aligned}\right\} \qquad \text{... (5.110)}$$

Idea similar to conservative system. The deformation energy E depends only on the final values of deformations and each increment dA of the work done is fully "saved" as the increment dE of the deformation energy into the deformed body; this is the known theoretical idea, comes under the conservative system. In our case, according to Fig. 5.18, we assume:

(a) The deformation energy is a function of the strain values ε_1, ε_2 only. We can write $E = E(\varepsilon_1, \varepsilon_2)$.

(b) According to the idea of conservative system we assume that the elemental increment of deformation energy is proportional[14] to the elemental increment of work done,

$$dE = C\,dA, \qquad \qquad \text{... (5.111)}$$

where $C \leq 1$ is a suitable constant of fiber material.

The elemental increment of deformation energy is the total differential of the function $E = E(\varepsilon_1, \varepsilon_2)$. Thus

$$dE = \frac{\partial E}{\partial\varepsilon_1}d\varepsilon_1 + \frac{\partial E}{\partial\varepsilon_2}d\varepsilon_2. \qquad \qquad \text{... (5.112)}$$

The elemental increment of the work done is easy to derive with a view to Fig. 5.19. The two forces (engineering stresses) $\sigma_{11}^*, \sigma_{22}^*$ act on the fibrous body in a general moment. In consequence of the force σ_{11}^* the body extends its strain ε_1 to the elemental increment $d\varepsilon_1$. Similarly, in consequence of

---

14. A part of work done is usually dissipated in the form of thermal energy due to fiber-to-fiber friction, etc., so that $C < 1$. Only for the conservative system it is valid that $C = 1$. Our assumption, given by Equation (5.111), bears then a little "looser" sense than that meant by the strict conservative system.

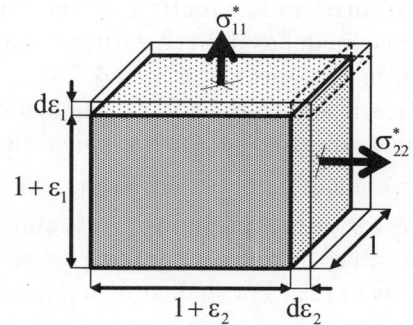

5.19 Elemental increments of strains.

the force σ_{22}^*, the body extends its strain ε_2 to the elemental increment $d\varepsilon_2$. Then the increment of the work done is

$$dA = \sigma_{11}^* d\varepsilon_1 + \sigma_{22}^* d\varepsilon_2. \qquad \ldots (5.113)$$

Applying Eqs. (5.112) and (5.113) in Eq. (5.111) we obtain

$$\frac{\partial E}{\partial \varepsilon_1} d\varepsilon_1 + \frac{\partial E}{\partial \varepsilon_2} d\varepsilon_2 = C\left(\sigma_{11}^* d\varepsilon_1 + \sigma_{22}^* d\varepsilon_2\right). \qquad \ldots (5.114)$$

The last equation is valid for all couples of values ε_1, ε_2, so that the following two equations must be right

$$\left.\begin{aligned}\frac{\partial E}{\partial \varepsilon_1} d\varepsilon_1 = C\sigma_{11}^* d\varepsilon_1, \quad \sigma_{11}^* = \frac{1}{C}\frac{\partial E}{\partial \varepsilon_1}, \\ \frac{\partial E}{\partial \varepsilon_2} d\varepsilon_2 = C\sigma_{22}^* d\varepsilon_2, \quad \sigma_{22}^* = \frac{1}{C}\frac{\partial E}{\partial \varepsilon_2}.\end{aligned}\right\} \qquad \ldots (5.115)$$

Transverse isotropy. The assumption of transverse isotropy of our fibrous assembly was introduced at the beginning of this chapter. Under this assumption the following relation is valid

$$E\left(\varepsilon_1, \varepsilon_2\right) = E\left(\varepsilon_2, \varepsilon_1\right) \qquad \ldots (5.116)$$

for all couples ε_1, ε_2.

Uniaxial deformation. The uniaxial deformation, solved in the previous chapters, is a special case of biaxial deformation. Consider that the fibrous material is deformed only in the direction of x_1-axis as shown in Fig. 5.18. Then the following relations must be valid according to Eqs. (5.104), (5.106) and (5.107)

$$\varepsilon_2 = 0, \quad \mu_2 = \mu_0, \quad \mu_1 = \mu, \quad \sigma_{11} = \sigma_{11}^* = -p(\mu), \qquad \ldots (5.117)$$

where the pressure $p(\mu)$ as a function of the packing density μ corresponds to a suitable model as derived earlier. (Some of the resulting equations are reported in Sections 5.2, 5.3, and 5.4).

For the first time, Hearle and El-Behery [14] studied experimentally the ratio ω of Cauchy's (real) stresses, i.e. the transverse stress σ_{22} divided by the stress σ_{11} in the direction of deformation; $\omega = \sigma_{22}/\sigma_{11}$. (They measured also the transverse stress σ_{22} experimentally). This ratio, except at the area of very small pressure values, is roughly speaking constant. Similar results were obtained by Gurová [12]. She studied experimentally five different materials and evaluated the ratio ω as an experimental function of packing density μ. One example is illustrated in Fig. 5.20. It is shown that the behavior of the studied relation is very flat over the value around $\mu \cong 0.05$, so that it can be approximated by a constant in a rough way

$$\sigma_{22}/\sigma_{11} = \omega \ldots \text{constant.} \qquad \ldots (5.118)$$

Similar behaviors are also shown by other materials. Table 5.1 illustrates the estimated values of ω.

Table 5.1 Estimated values of ω according to experimental results of Gurová [12].

Type	Fibers in the carded fiber layers		Estimated value ω for about $\mu > 0.05$
	Fineness [dtex]	Length [mm]	
Polyester	6.7	80	0.57
Polypropylene	6.7	60	0.40
Polypropylene	17	85	0.32
Polypropylene	70	90	0.65
Kevlar	2.4	40	0.30

In accordance with our experimental experience, let us assume that the ratio ω according to Eq. (5.118) must be constant in our theoretical model.

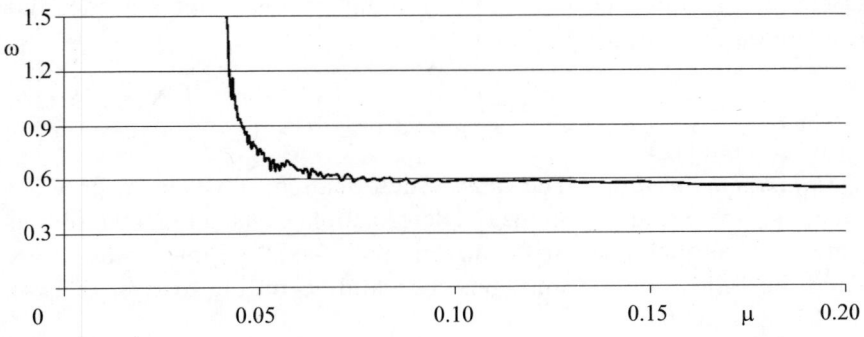

5.20 Experimental behavior of ω as a function of packing density μ, according to Gurová [12]. Material: Polyester fibers, 6.7 dtex, 80 mm.

Hypothesis of deformation energy. It is necessary to introduce a hypothesis of deformation energy in order to solve the problem of biaxial deformation. The following linear relation seems to be probably the easiest

$$E = \alpha F(\mu_1) + \alpha F(\mu_2) + \beta F(\mu), \qquad \ldots (5.119)$$

where it is valid that

$$\alpha + \beta = 1. \qquad \ldots (5.120)$$

(The summation character of the expression given in Eq. (5.119) partly evokes the deformation energy according to Hooke's law). The only one suitable function F occurs with three arguments $-\mu_1$, μ_2 and μ – in the formula according to Eq. (5.119).

Engineering (nominal) stresses. For a future rearrangement let us call the derivative of the function F with respect to a general argument x as follows

$$dF(x)/dx = f(x). \qquad \ldots (5.121)$$

The expressions for the engineering stresses can be found from Eqs. (5.115) and (5.119) by using Eqs. (5.109), (5.110), and (5.121) as follows

$$\left.\begin{array}{l} \sigma_{11}^* = \dfrac{1}{C}\dfrac{\partial}{\partial \varepsilon_1}\left[\alpha F(\mu_1) + \alpha F(\mu_2) + \beta F(\mu)\right] = \dfrac{1}{C}\left[\alpha f(\mu_1)\dfrac{-\mu_1^2}{\mu_0} + \beta f(\mu)\dfrac{-\mu\mu_1}{\mu_0}\right], \\[4mm] \sigma_{22}^* = \dfrac{1}{C}\dfrac{\partial}{\partial \varepsilon_2}\left[\alpha F(\mu_1) + \alpha F(\mu_2) + \beta F(\mu)\right] = \dfrac{1}{C}\left[\alpha f(\mu_2)\dfrac{-\mu_2^2}{\mu_0} + \beta f(\mu)\dfrac{-\mu\mu_2}{\mu_0}\right]. \end{array}\right\}$$
$$\ldots (5.122)$$

The initial (undeformed) cube resembling the fibrous material is the special case of this biaxial deformation where $\mu_1 = \mu_2 = \mu = \mu_0$ and $\sigma_{11}^* = \sigma_{22}^* = 0$. Then, according to Eqs. (5.122) and (5.120), it is valid

$$0 = \dfrac{1}{C}\left[\alpha f(\mu_0)\dfrac{-\mu_0^2}{\mu_0} + \beta f(\mu_0)\dfrac{-\mu_0\mu_0}{\mu_0}\right] = \dfrac{-\mu_0}{C}f(\mu_0), \quad f(\mu_0) = 0. \ \ldots (5.123)$$

The expressions given in Eqs. (5.117) and (5.123) are valid as a special relation mentioned in Eq. (5.22) in the case of uniaxial deformation (in the direction x_1), then

$$\left.\begin{array}{l} \sigma_{11}^* = \dfrac{1}{C}\left[\alpha f(\mu)\dfrac{-\mu^2}{\mu_0} + \beta f(\mu)\dfrac{-\mu^2}{\mu_0}\right] = \dfrac{1}{C}f(\mu)\dfrac{-\mu^2}{\mu_0}, \\[4mm] \sigma_{22}^* = \dfrac{1}{C}\left[\alpha f(\mu_0)\dfrac{-\mu_0^2}{\mu_0} + \beta f(\mu)\dfrac{-\mu\mu_0}{\mu_0}\right] = \dfrac{1}{C}\beta f(\mu)(-\mu). \end{array}\right\} \quad \ldots (5.124)$$

Cauchy's (real) stresses. Equation (5.104) formulates the Cauchy's (real) stresses. Applying Eqs. (5.122), and (5.107), and (5.108) we obtain the following expressions

$$
\left.
\begin{aligned}
\sigma_{11} &= \frac{\sigma_{11}^{*}\mu_{2}}{\mu_{0}} = \frac{1}{C}\left[\alpha f(\mu_{1})\frac{-\mu_{1}^{2}\mu_{2}}{\mu_{0}^{2}} + \beta f(\mu)\frac{-\mu\mu_{1}\mu_{2}}{\mu_{0}^{2}}\right] = \\
&= \frac{1}{C}\left[\alpha f(\mu_{1})\frac{-\mu_{1}\mu}{\mu_{0}} + \beta f(\mu)\frac{-\mu^{2}}{\mu_{0}}\right], \\
\sigma_{22} &= \frac{\sigma_{22}^{*}\mu_{1}}{\mu_{0}} = \frac{1}{C}\left[\alpha f(\mu_{2})\frac{-\mu_{2}^{2}\mu_{1}}{\mu_{0}^{2}} + \beta f(\mu)\frac{-\mu\mu_{2}\mu_{1}}{\mu_{0}^{2}}\right] = \\
&= \frac{1}{C}\left[\alpha f(\mu_{2})\frac{-\mu_{2}\mu}{\mu_{0}} + \beta f(\mu)\frac{-\mu^{2}}{\mu_{0}}\right].
\end{aligned}
\right\} \quad \ldots (5.125)
$$

As a special case of uniaxial deformation, applying the set of conditions according to Eq. (5.117) and Eq. (5.23), Eq. (5.125) takes the following shape

$$
\left.
\begin{aligned}
\sigma_{11} &= \frac{1}{C}\left[\alpha f(\mu)\frac{-\mu\mu}{\mu_{0}} + \beta f(\mu)\frac{-\mu^{2}}{\mu_{0}}\right] = \frac{1}{C}f(\mu)\frac{-\mu^{2}}{\mu_{0}}, \\
\sigma_{22} &= \frac{1}{C}\left[\alpha f(\mu_{0})\frac{-\mu_{0}\mu}{\mu_{0}} + \beta f(\mu)\frac{-\mu^{2}}{\mu_{0}}\right] = \frac{1}{C}\beta f(\mu)\frac{-\mu^{2}}{\mu_{0}}.
\end{aligned}
\right\} \quad \ldots (5.126)
$$

Note: Comparing Eq. (5.124) with Eq. (5.126) we can see that $\sigma_{11}^{*} = \sigma_{11}$ in the case of uniaxial deformation. Nevertheless, it was already found in Eq. (5.117).

The ratio ω defined according to Eq. (5.118) takes the following expression

$$
\omega = \frac{\sigma_{22}}{\sigma_{11}} = \frac{\dfrac{1}{C}\beta f(\mu)\dfrac{-\mu^{2}}{\mu_{0}}}{\dfrac{1}{C}f(\mu)\dfrac{-\mu^{2}}{\mu_{0}}} = \beta \ldots \text{constant.} \quad \ldots (5.127)
$$

The last equation expresses the logical meaning of the parameter β and currently fulfills the earlier assumed condition according to Eq. (5.118).

The parameter α also has a logical meaning. For uniaxial deformation, the following relation is valid from Eq. (5.127)

$$\frac{\sigma_{11} - \sigma_{22}}{\sigma_{11}} = 1 - \beta = \alpha .$$ ... (5.128)

However, it is valid that $(\sigma_{11} - \sigma_{22})/2 = \tau_{max}$, where τ_{max} is the maximum shear stress – remember the stress (Mohr's) circle. Thus,

$$2\tau_{max}/\sigma_{11} = \alpha .$$ ... (5.129)

The logical meaning of the parameter α is now evident from the last equation.

Homogenous stress. In the case of homogenous stress the following relations are valid

$$\sigma_{11} = \sigma_{22} = \sigma, \text{ so that } \mu_1 = \mu_2 = \sqrt{\mu\mu_0} .$$ ... (5.130)

(Equations (5.107) and (5.108) were used for rearrangement). Then, equation for the homogenous stress takes the following expression which is derived from the expressions (5.125) by application of the relations mentioned in Eq. (5.130)

$$\sigma = \frac{1}{C} \left[\alpha f\left(\sqrt{\mu\mu_0}\right) \frac{-\sqrt{\mu\mu_0}\,\mu}{\mu_0} + \beta f(\mu) \frac{-\mu^2}{\mu_0} \right] =$$

$$= \frac{-\mu}{C} \left[\alpha f\left(\sqrt{\mu\mu_0}\right) \sqrt{\frac{\mu}{\mu_0}} + \beta f(\mu) \frac{\mu}{\mu_0} \right] .$$ ... (5.131)

Determination of the function f. The relation $\sigma_{11} = -p(\mu)$ was introduced in Eq. (5.117) for uniaxial deformation; $p(\mu)$ expresses the pressure as a function of packing density μ, studied in more details in Sections 5.2, 5.3 or 5.4. Comparing this relation with the first expression in Eq. (5.126) we obtain the following relation

$$\sigma_{11} = \frac{1}{C} f(\mu) \frac{-\mu^2}{\mu_0} = -p(\mu), \quad f(\mu) = C \frac{\mu_0}{\mu^2} p(\mu) .$$ ... (5.132)

It is valid that $f(\mu_0) = 0$ according to Eq. (5.123) so that from Eq. (5.132) we get $0 = f(\mu_0) = \frac{C}{\mu_0} p(\mu_0)$, i.e. $p(\mu_0) = 0$. We can use the following expressions for pressure:

(a) Equation (5.40) in the case of traditional van Wyk's model according to Section 5.2 or

(b) Equation (5.54) with Eq. (5.55) in the case of modified van Wyk's model mentioned in Section 5.3 or

(c) Equation (5.100) with Eq. (5.101) in the case of alternative model mentioned in Section 5.4. In the special case of planar isotropic orientation of fibers the relevant expressions are mentioned in Eqs. (5.102) and (5.103).

Application of modified van Wyk's model. Let us illustrate the described procedure in case (b), i.e. application of modified van Wyk's model. Using Eq. (5.55) in Eq. (5.132) we obtain

$$f(\mu) = C\frac{\mu_0}{\mu^2} k_p \left[\varphi(\mu) - \varphi(\mu_0) \right], \qquad \ldots (5.133)$$

where $\varphi(\mu)$ and $\varphi(\mu_0)$ are defined by Eqs. (5.55). It is also valid

$$f(\mu_1) = C\frac{\mu_0}{\mu_1^2} k_p \left[\varphi(\mu_1) - \varphi(\mu_0) \right],$$

$$f(\mu_2) = C\frac{\mu_0}{\mu_2^2} k_p \left[\varphi(\mu_2) - \varphi(\mu_0) \right]. \qquad \ldots (5.134)$$

Engineering stresses: We rearrange the expression for the engineering (nominal) stresses according to Eq. (5.122) by using the last two expressions as follows

$$\sigma_{11}^* = \frac{1}{C} \left\{ \alpha C\frac{\mu_0}{\mu_1^2} k_p \left[\varphi(\mu_1) - \varphi(\mu_0) \right] \frac{-\mu_1^2}{\mu_0} + \beta C\frac{\mu_0}{\mu^2} k_p \left[\varphi(\mu) - \varphi(\mu_0) \right] \frac{-\mu\mu_1}{\mu_0} \right\}$$

$$= -\alpha k_p \left[\varphi(\mu_1) - \varphi(\mu_0) \right] - \beta \frac{\mu_1}{\mu} k_p \left[\varphi(\mu) - \varphi(\mu_0) \right],$$

$$\sigma_{11}^* = -k_p \left[\alpha \varphi(\mu_1) + \beta \varphi(\mu) \frac{\mu_1}{\mu} - \left(\alpha + \beta \frac{\mu_1}{\mu} \right) \varphi(\mu_0) \right],$$

$$\sigma_{22}^* = -k_p \left[\alpha \varphi(\mu_2) + \beta \varphi(\mu) \frac{\mu_2}{\mu} - \left(\alpha + \beta \frac{\mu_2}{\mu} \right) \varphi(\mu_0) \right]. \qquad \ldots (5.135)$$

Note: Because of the transverse isotropy we can obtain the expression for σ_{22}^* also by replacing the subscript 1 by 2 in the expression for σ_{11}^*.

Applying Eq. (5.133) in Eq. (5.24) we can obtain the expression for the engineering (nominal) stresses for the special case of uniaxial deformation (in the direction x_1) as follows

$$\sigma_{11}^* = \frac{1}{C}C\frac{\mu_0}{\mu^2}k_p\left[\phi(\mu)-\phi(\mu_0)\right]\frac{-\mu^2}{\mu_0} = -k_p\left[\phi(\mu)-\phi(\mu_0)\right],$$

$$\sigma_{22}^* = \frac{1}{C}\beta C\frac{\mu_0}{\mu^2}k_p\left[\phi(\mu)-\phi(\mu_0)\right](-\mu) = -k_p\beta\frac{\mu_0}{\mu}\left[\phi(\mu)-\phi(\mu_0)\right].$$

$$\dots (5.136)$$

Cauchy's stresses: According to Eqs. (5.104) and (5.107) it is valid $\sigma_{11} = \sigma_{11}^* \mu_2/\mu_0$ and $\sigma_{22} = \sigma_{22}^* \mu_1/\mu_0$. Applying Eqs. (5.135) and Eq. (5.108) in these two relations we obtain the following expressions

$$\sigma_{11} = \sigma_{11}^* \frac{\mu_2}{\mu_0} = -k_p\left[\alpha\phi(\mu_1)+\beta\phi(\mu)\frac{\mu_1}{\mu}-\left(\alpha+\beta\frac{\mu_1}{\mu}\right)\phi(\mu_0)\right]\frac{\mu_2}{\mu_0}$$

$$= -k_p\left[\alpha\phi(\mu_1)\frac{\mu_2}{\mu_0}+\beta\phi(\mu)\frac{\mu_1}{\mu}\frac{\mu_2}{\mu_0}-\left(\alpha\frac{\mu_2}{\mu_0}+\beta\frac{\mu_1}{\mu}\frac{\mu_2}{\mu_0}\right)\phi(\mu_0)\right],$$

$$\sigma_{11} = -k_p\left[\alpha\phi(\mu_1)\frac{\mu}{\mu_1}+\beta\phi(\mu)-\left(\alpha\frac{\mu}{\mu_1}+\beta\right)\phi(\mu_0)\right],$$

$$\sigma_{22} = -k_p\left[\alpha\phi(\mu_2)\frac{\mu}{\mu_2}+\beta\phi(\mu)-\left(\alpha\frac{\mu}{\mu_2}+\beta\right)\phi(\mu_0)\right].$$

$$\dots (5.137)$$

Note: Because of the transverse isotropy we obtain the expression for σ_{22} by replacing the subscript 1 by 2 in the expression for σ_{11}.

For the special case of uniaxial deformation (in the direction x_1) we need to use Eq. (5.117) in Eqs. (5.137). Thus

$$\sigma_{11} = -k_p\left[\alpha\phi(\mu)\frac{\mu}{\mu}+\beta\phi(\mu)-\left(\alpha\frac{\mu}{\mu}+\beta\right)\phi(\mu_0)\right] = -k_p\left[\phi(\mu)-\phi(\mu_0)\right],$$

$$\sigma_{22} = -k_p\left[\alpha\phi(\mu_0)\frac{\mu}{\mu_0}+\beta\phi(\mu)-\left(\alpha\frac{\mu}{\mu_0}+\beta\right)\phi(\mu_0)\right] = -k_p\beta\left[\phi(\mu)-\phi(\mu_0)\right].$$

$$\dots (5.138)$$

Homogenous stress: The general expression for homogenous stress describes the expression mentioned in Eq. (5.131) by applying the conditions in accordance with Eq. (5.130). Now, Eq. (5.133) is valid, so that Eq. (5.131) can be rearranged as follows

$$\sigma = \frac{-\mu}{C} \left[\alpha C \frac{\mu_0}{\left(\sqrt{\mu\mu_0}\right)^2} k_p \left[\varphi\left(\sqrt{\mu\mu_0}\right) - \varphi(\mu_0) \right] \sqrt{\frac{\mu}{\mu_0}} + \beta C \frac{\mu_0}{\mu^2} k_p \left[\varphi(\mu) - \varphi(\mu_0) \right] \right]$$

$$= -k_p \left[\alpha \left[\varphi\left(\sqrt{\mu\mu_0}\right) - \varphi(\mu_0) \right] \sqrt{\frac{\mu}{\mu_0}} + \beta \left[\varphi(\mu) - \varphi(\mu_0) \right] \right]$$

$$= -k_p \left[\alpha \varphi\left(\sqrt{\mu\mu_0}\right) \sqrt{\frac{\mu}{\mu_0}} + \beta \varphi(\mu) - \left(\alpha \sqrt{\frac{\mu}{\mu_0}} + \beta \right) \varphi(\mu_0) \right]. \qquad \ldots (5.139)$$

Note: The function φ expressed in Eqs. from (5.133) to (5.139) describes Eq. (5.55) for the modified van Wyk's model that we are using now.

Graphical illustrations of derived equations. The expression derived for stresses relate to the values μ_1, μ_2 and μ, which are the functions of strains ε_1 and ε_2 according to Eqs. (5.106) and (5.107); μ_0 expresses the initial value of packing density. From Eq. (5.106) we can write $(1+\varepsilon_1)(1+\varepsilon_2) = \mu_0/\mu$, so that $\ln(1+\varepsilon_1)/\ln(\mu_0/\mu) + \ln(1+\varepsilon_1)/\ln(\mu_0/\mu) = 1$. Let us denote

$$g_1 = \frac{\ln(1+\varepsilon_1)}{\ln(\mu_0/\mu)} = \frac{\ln(\mu_0/\mu_1)}{\ln(\mu_0/\mu)}, \quad g_2 = \frac{\ln(1+\varepsilon_2)}{\ln(\mu_0/\mu)} = \frac{\ln(\mu_0/\mu_2)}{\ln(\mu_0/\mu)}, \quad g_1 + g_2 = 1.$$

$$\ldots (5.140)$$

If we characterize the deformations in the axial directions x_1, x_2[15] by the quantities g_1, g_2 then, for a given value of packing density μ, the scale on the abscissa (X-axis) can be designed as shown in all the graphs in Figs. 5.21 and 5.22. It can be seen that the linear scale for g_1 increases from 0 to 1 from left to right whereas the linear scale for g_2 increases from 0 to 1 from right to left. So, both values g_1, g_2 are given by one point on the abscissa.

We can express the values $1 + \varepsilon_1$, $1 + \varepsilon_2$ from Eq. (5.140). Thus

$$1+\varepsilon_1 = (\mu_0/\mu)^{g_1}, \quad 1+\varepsilon_2 = (\mu_0/\mu)^{g_2} \qquad \ldots (5.141)$$

For a given value of packing density μ the nonlinear scale for $1 + \varepsilon_1$ is increasing from right to left while the nonlinear scale for $1 + \varepsilon_2$ is increasing from left to right.

---

15.   See Fig. 5.18.

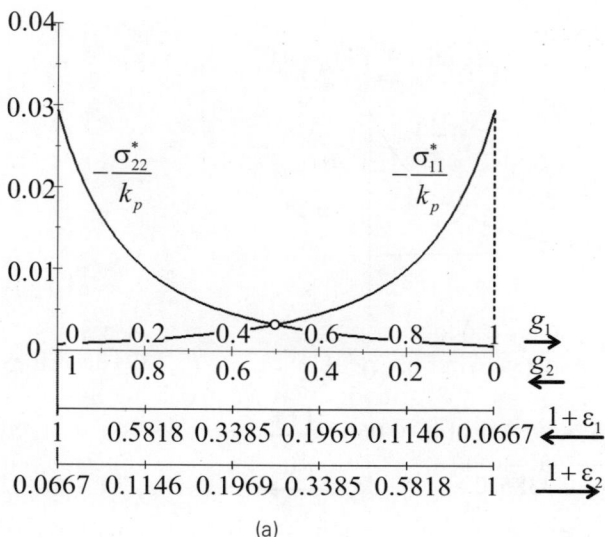

(a)

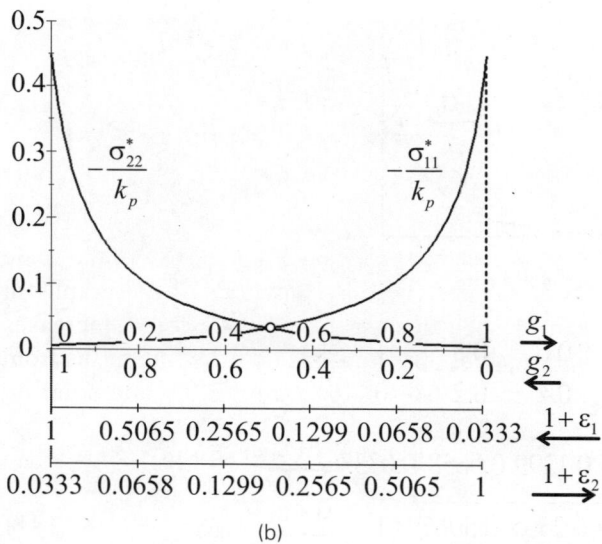

(b)

5.21 Behavior of engineering stresses (pressures), according to Eqs. (5.135) and (5.55). Parameters used: $\mu_m = 1$, $a = 1$, $\beta = 0.4$, $\mu_0 = 0.02$;

(a) $\mu = 0.3$ ($\mu_0/\mu = 0.0667$) , (b) $\mu = 0.6$ ($\mu_0/\mu = 0.0333$) .

Note: Note that the product of the corresponding values of $1 + \varepsilon_1$ and $1 + \varepsilon_2$ always gives the identical value μ_0/μ .

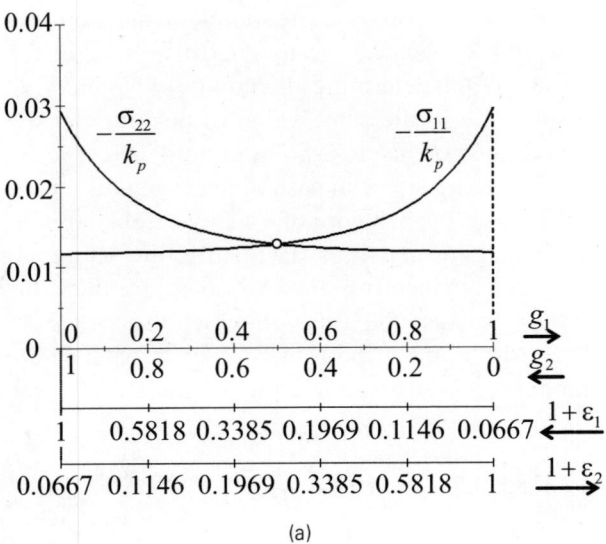

(a)

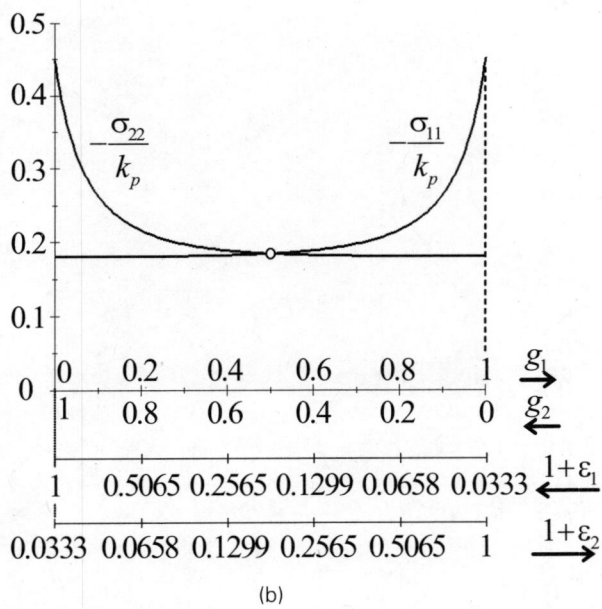

(b)

5.22 Behavior of Cauchy's stresses (pressures) according to Eqs. (5.137) and (5.55).

Parameters used: $\mu_m = 1$, $a = 1$, $\beta = 0.4$, $\mu_0 = 0.02$;

(a) $\mu = 0.3$ $(\mu_0/\mu = 0.0667)$, (b) $\mu = 0.6$ $(\mu_0/\mu = 0.0333)$.

Figure 5.21 characterizes the behavior of engineering stresses by two values of packing densities; in Fig. 5.21a $\mu = 0.3$ and in Fig. 5.21b $\mu = 0.6$

(As a matter of fact the displayed curves correspond to the nominal pressures divided by parameter k_p because we use negative sign in the figures). The two curves in one graph determine all couples of engineering stresses (pressures) corresponding to the same value of packing density according to Eqs. (5.135) and (5.55). The cross point of both the curves in each graph expresses the engineering stress in case of homogenous stress.

Similarly, Fig. 5.22 characterizes the behavior of Cauchy's (real) stresses by the same two values of packing densities. Evidently, the values of Cauchy's stresses are higher than engineering stresses (except for the value σ_{11} at $\varepsilon_2 = 0$ and σ_{22} at $\varepsilon_1 = 0$), because the areas on which the forces are acting are diminished. The cross point of both the curves in each figure expresses the Cauchy's homogenous stress, corresponding to Eq. (5.139).

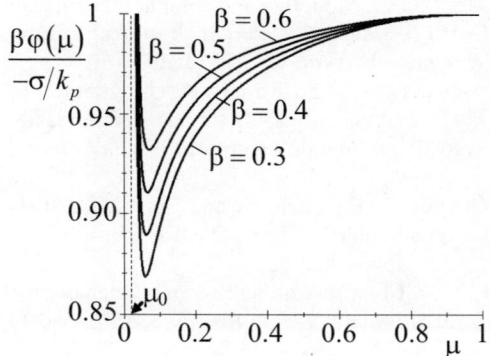

5.23 Size of addend $\beta\varphi(\mu)$ in relation to the whole value of homogenous stress (pressure), according the Eq. (5.139) with (5.55).
Parameters: $\mu_m = 1$, $a = 1$, $\mu_0 = 0.02$.

There are three addition components inside the square brackets in Eq. (5.139) for homogenous (Cauchy's) stress. The first and the third addition components are very often relatively small in relation to the second addition component $\beta\varphi(\mu)$. It is shown in Fig. 5.23. We can see that the addition component $\beta\varphi(\mu)$ represents 95% or more of the whole homogenous stress (pressure) if the packing density is higher than 0.2 or 0.3. Therefore, the following expression for homogenous stress can be estimated and used for higher values of packing densities

$$\sigma \doteq -k_p \beta\varphi(\mu). \qquad \qquad \dots (5.142)$$

Note: Comparing Eq. (5.49) with Eq. (5.142) it is shown that the expression for uniaxial compression can be roughly applied also for the homogenous compression, but with another (smaller) parameter, i.e. $k_p\beta$ in place of k_p only.

5.7   References

1. van Wyk, C. M. (1946). Note on the compressibility of wool, *Journal of Textile Institute*, **37**(10), T285–T291..
2. Baljasov, P. D. (1976). *Compression of Textile Fibers in Mass and Technology of Textile Manufacture*, Legkaya promyshlennost, Moscow.
3. Dunlop, J. I. (1974). Characterizing the compression properties of fibre masses, *Journal of Textile Institute*, **65**, 532–536.
4. Dunlop, J. I. (1983). On the compression characteristics of fiber masses, *Journal of Textile Institute*, **74**, 92–97.
5. Schoppee, M. M. (1998). A Poisson model of nonwoven fiber assemblies in compression at high stress, *Textile Research Journal*, **68**, 371–384.
6. Beil, N. B., and Roberts, W. W., Jr. (2002) Modeling and computer simulation of the compressional behavior of fiber assemblies, Part I: comparison to van wyk's theory, *Textile Research Journal*, **72**, 341–351.
7. Beil, N. B., and Roberts, W. W., Jr., (2002). Modeling and computer simulation of the compressional behavior of fiber assemblies, Part II: hysteresis, crimp, and orientation effects, *Textile Research Journal*, **72**, 375–382.
8. Parikh, D. V., Calamari, T. A., Sawhney, A. P. S., Robert, K. Q., Kimmel, L., Glynn, E., Jirsak, O., Mackova, I., and Saunders, T. (2002). Compression behavior of perpendicular-laid nonwovens containing cotton, *Textile Research Journal*, **72**, 550–554.
9. Parikh, D. V., Calamari, T. A., Goynes, W. R., Chen, Y., and Jirsak, O. (2004). Compressibility of cotton blend perpendicular-laid nonwoven, *Textile Research Journal*, **74**, 7–12.
10. Das, D., and Pourdeyhimi, B. (2010). Compression and recovery behavior of highloft nonwovens, *Indian Journal of Fiber & Textile Research*, **35**, 303–309.
11. Haňáčková, A. (2004). Compression of fiber material, M.Sc. Thesis, TU Liberec (Czech).
12. Gurová, M. (2008). Uniaxial compression of fibrous material, M.Sc. Thesis, TU Liberec (Czech).
13. Pavelka, M. (2008). Non-woven fabrics and foams compression, M.Sc. Thesis, TU Liberec (Czech).
14. Hearle, J. W. S., and EL-Behery, H. M. A. (1960). The transmission of transverse stresses in fiber assemblies, *Journal of Textile Institute*, **51**, T164–T171.

6

Mechanics of parallel fiber bundles

6.1 Mechanics of simplest ideal parallel fiber bundle

Introduction. There exist different types of fibrous assemblies such as slivers, rovings, filament yarns, and staple yarns, as well as some systems of yarns such as warp and weft sets in multiaxial textiles, etc. Although all of them are different from one another, but they share a common resemblance, that is, they pose an image or generate an idea of parallel bundles created from linear structural units. We, however, prefer the term "parallel fiber bundle" here, but the derived results can be appropriately applied to all other types of parallel bundles.

Naturally, the real fiber bundles are much more complicated than the ideal parallel fiber bundles discussed here as the real bundles are not quite parallel to one another, the constituent fibers are not quite straight, the fibers affect mutually by means of fiber-to-fiber friction through fiber-to-fiber contacts, etc. Nevertheless, the derived results create a base for deeper understanding of different mechanical behaviors of various real bundles.

Note: Some useful terms and quantities of mechanics in relation to this chapter are described in Appendix 3.

One fiber. Let us imagine one straight fiber which is clamped between two jaws A and B of a tensile tester (real or imaginary) as shown in Fig. 6.1a. Because of the movement of the bottom jaw from the original position B to a new position B', the original (gauge) length h is extended to a new length $h(1+\varepsilon)$, where ε denotes the fiber strain. Before break, the fiber is tensioned by the force F according to an increasing force–strain function $F = F(\varepsilon)$ of the fiber. The maximum value of the force F, i.e. fiber breaking force F^*, corresponds to the breaking strain a; then $F^* = F(a)$. After break, when $\varepsilon > a$, the force $F = 0$.

Ideal fiber bundle. In a similar manner, let us consider a bundle consisting of n fibers clamped between two jaws A and B of the tensile tester (real or imaginary) as shown in Fig. 6.1b. This fiber bundle would be termed as ideal fiber bundle if it fulfills the following assumptions:

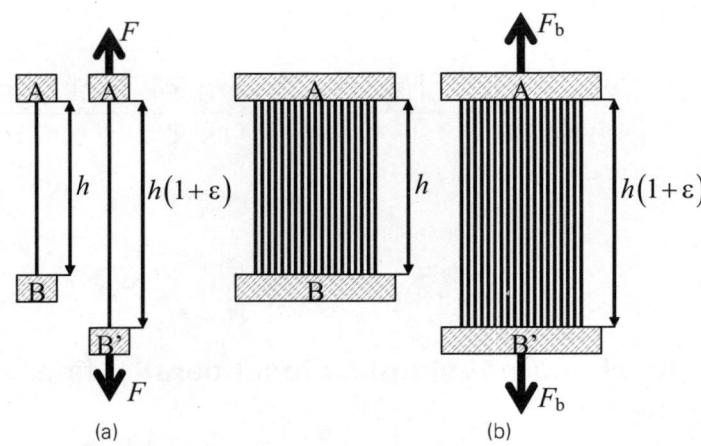

6.1 Parallel fiber bundle between jaws. (a) One fiber. (b) Set of fibers.

1. All fibers are mutually independent.
2. Each fiber is
   (a) straight and
   (b) clamped between two jaws such that it is parallel to the jaw-axis (i.e. parallel fiber bundle).

   Simplest ideal fiber bundle. Let us think about the simplest ideal fiber bundle, which satisfies the following additional assumption:
3. Each fiber shows
   (a) same fiber density ρ,
   (b) same fineness t,
   (c) same continuously increasing force–strain relation $F = F(\varepsilon)$,
   (d) same breaking force F^*, and
   (e) same breaking strain a.

The fiber cross-sectional area, according to Eq. (1.5), is $s = t/\rho$. In this case, the bundle fineness[1] T can be expressed as follows

$$T = nt. \qquad \qquad \qquad \dots (6.1)$$

While extension of the original (gauge) length h to a new length $h(1+\varepsilon)$, the force $F_b = F_b(\varepsilon)$ influences the bundle. The maximum value of F_b, that is, the bundle breaking force F_b^*, corresponds to the bundle breaking strain a_b, which is the same as fiber breaking strain; $F_b^* = F_b(a)$. While breaking of the bundle, all fibers are broken at the same moment; if $\varepsilon > a$ then $F_b = 0$.

---

1. Equation (6.1) follows Eq. (3.65) where $k_n = 1$. In case of a parallel bundle, each fiber sectional area s^* is equal to its cross-sectional area s, then the mean fiber sectional area $\overline{s^*} = s$, and therefore, according to Eq. (3.17), $k_n = 1$.

The following equations are then evidently valid

$$F_b(\varepsilon) = nF(\varepsilon), \quad a_b = a, \quad F_b^* = nF^* = nF(a). \quad \dots (6.2)$$

The bundle force per one fiber F_f and the bundle breaking force per one fiber F_f^* are

$$F_f = F_b(\varepsilon)/n = F(\varepsilon), \quad F_f^* = F_b^*/n = F^* = F(a). \quad \dots (6.3)$$

The following equations determine the bundle specific stress σ_b and the bundle specific strength (tenacity) σ_b^*

$$\sigma_b(\varepsilon) = \frac{F_b(\varepsilon)}{T} = \frac{nF(\varepsilon)}{nt} = \frac{F(\varepsilon)}{t} = \sigma(\varepsilon),$$

$$\sigma_b^* = \frac{F_b^*}{T} = \frac{nF^*}{nt} = \frac{F^*}{t} = \sigma^*. \quad \dots (6.4)$$

(Here, Eqs. (1.21), (6.1) and (6.3) are used).
The total cross-sectional area S of all n fibers in the bundle is

$$S = ns. \quad \dots (6.5)$$

Using the foregone equations the following expressions are valid for the bundle stress $\sigma_b'(\varepsilon)$ and the bundle strength $\sigma_b'^*$

$$\sigma_b'(\varepsilon) = \frac{F_b(\varepsilon)}{S} = \frac{nF(\varepsilon)}{ns} = \frac{F(\varepsilon)}{s} = \sigma'(\varepsilon),$$

$$\sigma_b'^* = \frac{F_b^*}{S} = \frac{nF^*}{ns} = \frac{F^*}{s} = \sigma'^*. \quad \dots (6.6)$$

6.2   Mechanics of bi-component parallel fiber bundle

Let us now change our earlier assumption number 3 and take the following alternative assumptions:
3*. In an ideal fiber bundle,

(I) there are two components (for example, cotton and polyester are the two components in a cotton-polyester fiber bundle),

(II) each fiber of the same component exhibits
   (a) same fiber density ρ,
   (b) same fineness t,

(c)   same continuously increasing force–strain relation $F = F(\varepsilon)$,
(d)   same breaking force F^* and
(e)   same breaking strain a.

(III) the properties of fibers between components are generally different.

Note: Hamburger [1] is known to solve the mechanical properties of such type of bundle for the first time.

Table 6.1 Symbols used for first and second components.

Quantity	First component		Second component
Fiber density	ρ_1		ρ_2
Fiber fineness	t_1		t_2
Force–strain function of fiber	$F_1(\varepsilon)$		$F_2(\varepsilon)$
Specific stress of fiber	$\sigma_1(\varepsilon)$		$\sigma_2(\varepsilon)$
Stress of fiber	$\sigma_1'(\varepsilon)$		$\sigma_2'(\varepsilon)$
Breaking strain of fiber	a_1	$\leq$	a_2
Breaking force of fiber	F_1^*		F_2^*
Specific strength of fiber	σ_1^*		σ_2^*
Strength of fiber	$\sigma_1'^*$		$\sigma_2'^*$
Number of fibers in bundle	n_1		n_2
Mass fraction in bundle	g_1		g_2
Mass(+) of component in bundle	m_1		m_2

(+) This corresponds to the (gauge) length h between jaws A and B shown in Fig. 6.1b.

Initial quantities. We introduce a convention for displaying the same quantities but for different components. The quantities related to the component showing smaller value of breaking strain are displayed with subscript 1. But, the quantities of the other component showing higher value of breaking strain are displayed with subscript 2. Table 6.1 lists the symbols used for different quantities for different components.

According to Eq. (1.5) it is valid that

$$s_1 = t_1/\rho_1, \quad s_2 = t_2/\rho_2 . \qquad \ldots (6.7)$$

Using Eq. (1.21) the specific stresses can be expressed as follows

$$\left.\begin{array}{l} \sigma_1(\varepsilon) = F_1(\varepsilon)/t_1, \\ \sigma_2(\varepsilon) = F_2(\varepsilon)/t_2, \end{array}\right\} \qquad \ldots (6.8)$$

while the stresses can be written as

$$\sigma_1'(\varepsilon) = F_1(\varepsilon)/s_1, \quad \sigma_2'(\varepsilon) = F_2(\varepsilon)/s_2. \qquad \ldots (6.9)$$

The following expressions are valid to write for fiber breaking forces, fiber specific strengths (tenacities) and fiber strengths.

$$F_1^* = F_1(a_1), \ F_2^* = F_2(a_2).$$ ... (6.10)[2]

$$\sigma_1^* = \sigma_1(a_1) = F_1^*/t_1, \ \sigma_2^* = \sigma_2(a_2) = F_2^*/t_2.$$ ... (6.11)

$$\sigma_1'^* = \sigma_1'(a_1) = F_1^*/s_1, \ \sigma_2'^* = \sigma_2'(a_2) = F_2^*/s_2.$$ ...(6.12)

The total number n of fibers in the bundle is evidently

$$n = n_1 + n_2.$$ ... (6.13)

The total mass of the bundle m (between jaws) is

$$m = m_1 + m_2.$$ ... (6.14)

The following summation of the mass fraction is valid in accordance with Eq. (1.38)

$$g_1 + g_2 = 1.$$ ... (6.15)

Based on the definition of mass fraction, according to Eq. (1.37), we can write

$$m_1 = g_1 m, \ m_2 = g_2 m.$$ ...(6.16)

The total fineness (count) T of the bundle with mass m and (gauge) length h is

$$T = m/h.$$ ... (6.17)

In the bundle, the total length of fibers of the first component is $n_1 h$ and the total length of fibers of the second component is $n_2 h$. Using the definition of fineness and Eqs. (6.16) and (6.17) it is valid to write that

$$\left. \begin{array}{l} t_1 = \dfrac{m_1}{n_1 h}, \ n_1 = \dfrac{m_1}{t_1 h} = \dfrac{g_1 m}{t_1 h} = g_1 \dfrac{T}{t_1}, \\[3mm] t_2 = \dfrac{m_2}{n_2 h}, \ n_2 = \dfrac{m_2}{t_2 h} = \dfrac{g_2 m}{t_2 h} = g_2 \dfrac{T}{t_2}. \end{array} \right\}$$ ... (6.18)

Forces in fibers. The force–strain functions of one fiber form the first and the second components are schematically illustrated in Fig. 6.2. The end point of function $F_1(\varepsilon)$ characterizes the breaking strain a_1 and the breaking force F_1^* of the fiber from the first component. Similarly, the end point of function $F_2(\varepsilon)$ characterizes the breaking strain a_2 ($a_2 \geq a_1$) and the breaking force F_2^* of the fiber from the second component. Further, the force $F_2(a_1)$ corresponds to the fiber of the second component at the strain value $\varepsilon = a_1$.

---

2. We think that a fiber is not broken at the value of breaking strain (a_1 and/or a_2), but it shows the maximum force, i.e. the breaking force at this value of strain. However, a fiber is shown to be broken at each and every higher than this value of strain.

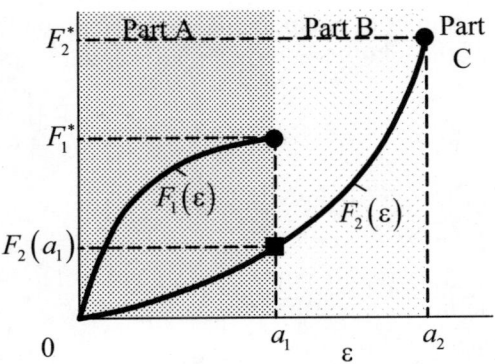

6.2 Force–strain functions of fibers form first and second component.

Force and specific stress in bundle. Let us divide the strain area into three parts as shown in Fig. 6.2. The strain values $\varepsilon \in \langle 0, a_1 \rangle$ correspond to part A. No one fiber is broken in this interval given for the strain. The strain $\varepsilon \in (a_1, a_2 \rangle$ falls in part B. All the fibers of the first component are broken in this interval, but each fiber of the second component is able to carry the force. In part C, the strain $\varepsilon > a_2$ and evidently, all fibers are broken.

In part A, each of n_1 fibers of the first component carries the tensile force $F_1(\varepsilon)$ and each of n_2 fibers of the second component carries the tensile force $F_2(\varepsilon)$. Using Eqs. (6.8) and (6.18), the bundle force $F_b(\varepsilon)$ and the bundle specific stress $\sigma_b(\varepsilon)$ can be expressed as follows

$$\left. \begin{array}{l} F_b(\varepsilon) = n_1 F_1(\varepsilon) + n_2 F_2(\varepsilon) = T\left[g_1 \dfrac{F_1(\varepsilon)}{t_1} + g_2 \dfrac{F_2(\varepsilon)}{t_2} \right], \\[4mm] \sigma_b(\varepsilon) = \dfrac{F_b(\varepsilon)}{T} = g_1 \dfrac{F_1(\varepsilon)}{t_1} + g_2 \dfrac{F_2(\varepsilon)}{t_2} = g_1 \sigma_1(\varepsilon) + g_2 \sigma_2(\varepsilon). \end{array} \right\} \varepsilon \in \langle 0, a_1 \rangle \ \dots (6.19)$$

In part B each of n_1 fibers of the first component is broken and each of n_2 fibers of the second component carries the force $F_2(\varepsilon)$. Now, using Eqs. (6.8) and (6.18), the bundle force $F_b(\varepsilon)$ and the bundle specific stress $\sigma_b(\varepsilon)$ can be expressed as follows

$$\left. \begin{array}{l} F_b(\varepsilon) = n_1 0 + n_2 F_2(\varepsilon) = T g_2 \dfrac{F_2(\varepsilon)}{t_2}, \\[4mm] \sigma_b(\varepsilon) = \dfrac{F_b(\varepsilon)}{T} = g_2 \dfrac{F_2(\varepsilon)}{t_2} = g_2 \sigma_2(\varepsilon). \end{array} \right\} \varepsilon \in (a_1, a_2 \rangle \qquad \dots (6.20)$$

In part C all the fibers form both components are broken and therefore the bundle force as well as the bundle specific stress is equal to zero. This is shown below

$$F_b(\varepsilon) = \sigma_b(\varepsilon) = 0, \quad \varepsilon > a_2.$$ ... (6.21)

The behaviors of $\sigma_b(\varepsilon)$ in accordance with Eqs. (6.19) to (6.21) are illustrated in Fig. 6.3a–c.

Note: There exist always two local maxima (black points) of the function $\sigma_b(\varepsilon)$, one of them can be higher than the other – Fig. 6.3a or 6.3b – or both of them can be the same – Fig. 6.3c.

Breaking force and specific strength in bundle. In part A, the bundle shows the maximum force at $\varepsilon = a_1$ – see Fig. 6.3. This force and the corresponding maximum specific stress of the bundle can be expressed as follows

$$\left. \begin{array}{l} F_b(a_1) = T\left[g_1 \dfrac{F_1(a_1)}{t_1} + g_2 \dfrac{F_2(a_1)}{t_2} \right] = T\left[g_1 \dfrac{F_1^*}{t_1} + g_2 \dfrac{F_2(a_1)}{t_2} \right], \\[3mm] \sigma_b(a_1) = g_1\sigma_1(a_1) + g_2\sigma_2(a_1) = g_1\sigma_1^* + g_2\sigma_2(a_1). \end{array} \right\}$$ ... (6.22)

This expression is obtained from Eq. (6.19) by using Eqs. (6.10) and (6.11).

Note: The specific stress $\sigma_2(a_1)$ is given by the ratio $F_2(a_1)/t_2$; the force $F_2(a_1)$ is shown in Fig. 6.2.

In part B, the maximum force in the bundle is originated at $\varepsilon = a_2$. This force and the corresponding maximum specific stress can be expressed from Eq. (6.20) using Eqs. (6.10) and (6.11) as follows

$$\left. \begin{array}{l} F_b(a_2) = Tg_2 \dfrac{F_2(a_2)}{t_2} = Tg_2 \dfrac{F_2^*}{t_2}, \\[3mm] \sigma_b(a_2) = g_2\sigma_2(a_2) = g_2\sigma_2^*. \end{array} \right\}$$ ... (6.23)

The bundle breaking force F_b^* and the corresponding bundle specific strength σ_b^* are equal to the total maximum of the bundle force and the bundle specific stress. Using Eqs. (6.22) and (6.23) the following expression must be valid to write

$$\begin{array}{l} F_b^* = \max\left\{ F_b(a_1), F_b(a_2) \right\} = \\[3mm] \qquad = \max\left\{ T\left[g_1 \dfrac{F_1^*}{t_1} + g_2 \dfrac{F_2(a_1)}{t_2} \right], Tg_2 \dfrac{F_2^*}{t_2} \right\}. \end{array}$$ ... (6.24)

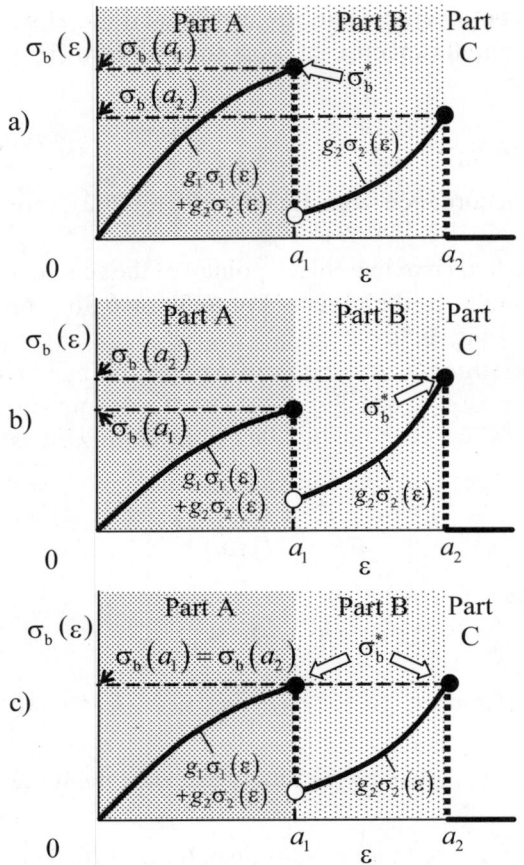

6.3 Scheme of specific stress of bundle according to Eqs. from (6.19) to (6.21). Total maximum: (a) at a_1, (b) at a_2, (c) both same.

$$\sigma_b^* = \max\left\{\sigma_b(a_1), \sigma_b(a_2)\right\} = \max\left\{g_1\sigma_1^* + g_2\sigma_2(a_1), g_2\sigma_2^*\right\}. \qquad \ldots (6.25)$$

In accordance with Fig. 6.3, the bundle breaking strain a_b is given by the following equations

$$\left.\begin{array}{l} a_b = a_1 \cdots\cdots\cdots \text{if } \sigma_b^* = \sigma_b(a_1) > \sigma_b(a_2), \\ a_b = a_2 \cdots\cdots\cdots \text{if } \sigma_b^* = \sigma_b(a_2) > \sigma_b(a_1), \\ a_b \text{ is undefined if } \sigma_b^* = \sigma_b(a_1) = \sigma_b(a_2). \end{array}\right\} \qquad \ldots (6.26)$$

Note: If both of the local maxima possess the same value in accordance with Fig. 6.3c then – purely mathematically – there should exist two values a_1, a_2 of the bundle braking strain a_b. However, this result cannot be obtained in reality. Practically, such a bundle shall have the breaking strain lying "somewhere" in the interval from a_1 to a_2 in relation to very small difference from that of the real bundle.

Influence of blending. The function of the bundle specific strength and the corresponding values of the bundle braking strain are shown in Fig. 6.4 in relation to the mass fraction of fibers in the bundle, according to Eqs. (6.25), (6.26) and (6.15). The mass fraction of the second fiber component g_2 increases from left to right and the mass fraction of the first component g_1 increases from right to left on the abscissa (X-axis) of the each graph.

Two dashed lines show the two parts of the summation $g_1\sigma_1^* + g_2\sigma_2(a_1)$ separately and one full line represents the summation of the two parts. The second full line represents $g_2\sigma_2^*$. The maximum of the mentioned two full lines expresses the bundle specific strength σ_b^* as the function of mass fraction g_2 (or g_1) according to Eq. (6.25). It is graphically illustrated by the triple-lines as shown in the four graphs in Fig. 6.4.

The point C refers to the point of intersection of the two full lines mentioned earlier. In this point $g_1 = g_{1,C}$, $g_2 = g_{2,C}$, and evidently the following expressions are valid

$$g_{1,C}\sigma_1^* + g_{2,C}\sigma_2(a_1) = g_{2,C}\sigma_2^*, \text{ where } g_{1,C} + g_{2,C} = 1. \qquad \ldots (6.27)$$

After rearrangement of Eq. (6.27) we obtain the relations as follows

$$\left(1 - g_{2,C}\right)\sigma_1^* + g_{2,C}\sigma_2(a_1) = g_{2,C}\sigma_2^*, \quad -g_{2,C}\sigma_1^* + g_{2,C}\sigma_2(a_1) - g_{2,C}\sigma_2^* = -\sigma_1^*,$$

$$g_{2,C} = \frac{\sigma_1^*}{\sigma_1^* + \sigma_2^* - \sigma_2(a_1)}, \quad g_{1,C} = 1 - g_{2,C} = \frac{\sigma_2^* - \sigma_2(a_1)}{\sigma_1^* + \sigma_2^* - \sigma_2(a_1)}.$$

$$\ldots (6.28)$$

Note: The point $g_{1,C}$ or $g_{2,C}$ is marked by the gray triangle on the abscissa (X-axis).

The value of bundle specific strength $\sigma_{b,C}^*$ shown by point C results from Eqs. (6.25), (6.27) and (6.28) as follows

$$\sigma_{b,C}^* = g_{1,C}\sigma_1^* + g_{2,C}\sigma_2(a_1) = g_{2,C}\sigma_2^* = \frac{\sigma_1^*\sigma_2^*}{\sigma_1^* + \sigma_2^* - \sigma_2(a_1)}. \qquad \ldots (6.29)$$

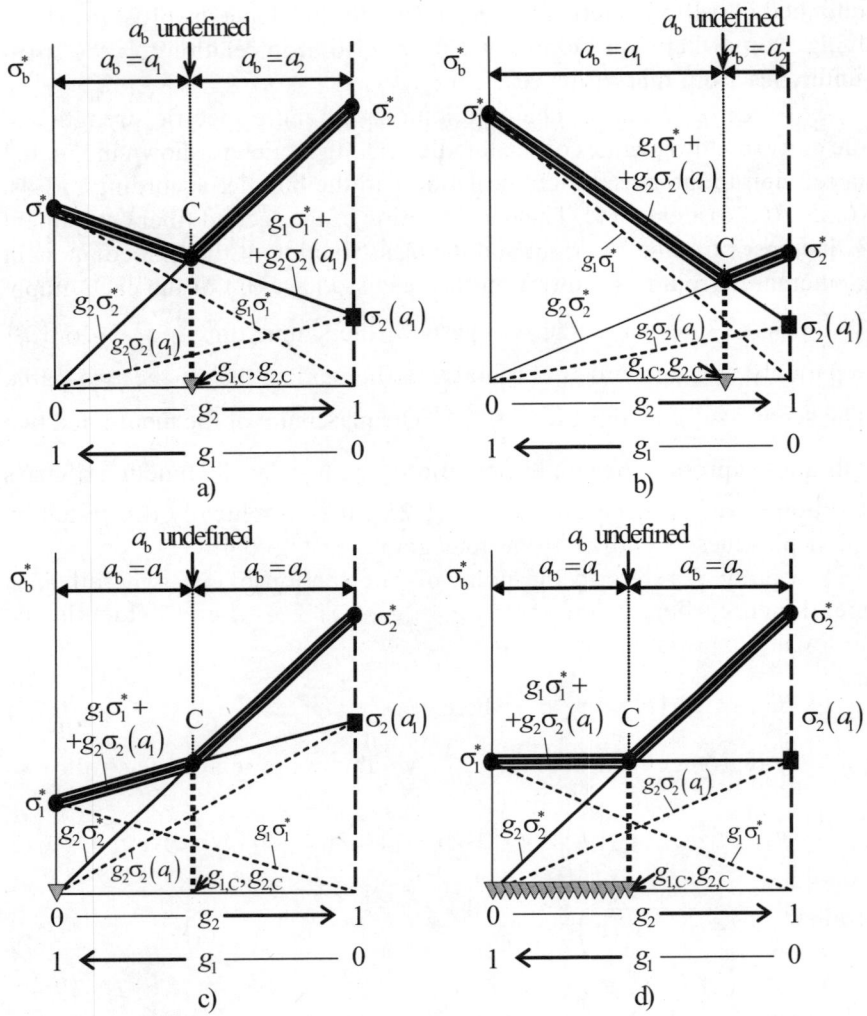

6.4 Behavior of specific strength and breaking strain of bundle in relation to mass fraction of fibers in bundle; (a) $\sigma_1^* < \sigma_2^*$ and $\sigma_1^* > \sigma_2(a_1)$, (b) $\sigma_1^* > \sigma_2^*$ and $\sigma_1^* > \sigma_2(a_1)$, (c) $\sigma_1^* < \sigma_2(a_1)$, (d) $\sigma_1^* = \sigma_2(a_1)$.

Minimum specific strength. An enough high value of bundle tenacity is often considered to be an important attribute of quality in practice. From this point of view it is useful to know the worse blending ratio that would bring the smallest tenacity of the bundle.

Case 1: It is shown in Figs. 1.4a and 1.4b that $\sigma_1^* > \sigma_2(a_1)$. The minimum bundle specific strength $\sigma_{b\,min}^*$ (i.e. the minimum σ_b^*) refers to the point C, $\sigma_{b\,min}^* = \sigma_{b,C}^*$, the corresponding mass fractions related to the minimum specific strength of the bundle (gray triangle) are $g_{1min} = g_{1,C}$, $g_{2min} = g_{2,C}$.

Case 2: It is shown in Fig. 6.4c that $\sigma_1^* < \sigma_2(a_1)$. The minimum value $\sigma_{b\min}^* = \sigma_1^*$ corresponds to the point $g_{1\min} = 1$, $g_{2\min} = 0$ (mono-component bundle, gray triangle).

Case 3: If $\sigma_1^* = \sigma_2(a_1)$ then the graph shown in Fig. 6.4d is valid and according to Eq. (6.29) $\sigma_{b,C}^* = g_{1,C}\sigma_1^* + g_{2,C}\sigma_1^* = (g_{1,C} + g_{2,C})\sigma_1^* = \sigma_1^*$. Then $\sigma_{b\min}^* = \sigma_{b,C}^* = \sigma_1^*$, the line $g_1\sigma_1^* + g_2\sigma_2(a_1)$ is horizontal, and the corresponding mass fractions (gray triangles) can be found from the interval $g_{1\min} \in \langle g_{1,C}, 1 \rangle$ or $g_{2\min} \in \langle 0, g_{2,C} \rangle$.

Altogether the minimum specific strength of the bundle and the corresponding mass fractions are shown below

$$
\left.
\begin{array}{l}
\text{If } \sigma_1^* > \sigma_2(a_1), \text{ then:} \quad g_{1\min} = g_{1,C}, \quad g_{2\min} = g_{2,C}, \quad \sigma_{b\min}^* = \sigma_{b,C}^*. \\
\text{If } \sigma_1^* < \sigma_2(a_1), \text{ then:} \quad g_{1\min} = 1, \quad g_{2\min} = 0, \quad \sigma_{b\min}^* = \sigma_1^*. \\
\text{If } \sigma_1^* = \sigma_2(a_1), \text{ then:} \quad g_{1\min} \in \langle g_{1,C}, 1 \rangle, \quad g_{2\min} \in \langle 0, g_{2,C} \rangle, \quad \sigma_{b\min}^* = \sigma_{b,C}^* = \sigma_1^*.
\end{array}
\right\}
$$

$$\dots (6.30)$$

For the previous equation we calculate the required values $g_{1,C}$, $g_{2,C}$ and $\sigma_{b,C}^*$ from Eqs. (6.28) and (6.29).

Example 6.1: Let us think about a cotton–polyester blended fiber bundle. The cotton fibers possess specific strength (tenacity) $\sigma_1^* = 0.36$ N tex^{-1} and breaking strain (extension) $a_1 = 0.11$ (11%). The polyester fibers possess specific strength $\sigma_2^* = 0.41$ N tex^{-1}, breaking strain $a_2 = 0.46$ (46%), and specific stress $\sigma_2(a_1) = 0.12$ Ntex^{-1} $\sigma_2(a_1) = 0.12$ N tex^{-1} corresponding to strain $\varepsilon = a_1 = 0.11$. Because $a_1 < a_2$, the choice of subscripts is valid and the scheme shown in Fig. 6.4a is also valid in this case. The mass fraction of the second material $g_{2,C} = 0.554$ according to Eq. (6.28) and the corresponding mass fraction of the first component (cotton) is $g_{1,C} = 1 - g_{2,C} = 0.446$. The value of specific stress of the bundle is $\sigma_{b,C}^* = 0.227$ N tex^{-1} and this corresponds to the point C according to Eq. (6.29). Because $\sigma_1^* > \sigma_2(a_1)$, the minimum bundle specific strength (bundle tenacity) is $\sigma_{b\min}^* = \sigma_{b,C}^* = 0.227$ N tex^{-1} according to Eq. (6.30). It is shown that the specific strength of the blended fiber bundle (44.6% cotton and 55.4% polyester) is even smaller than that of the less tenacious single-component, i.e., cotton fiber bundle.

Let us be conscious of a "paradox" which is observed while blending of two components. If we blend fibers having higher value of tenacity with fibers having smaller value of tenacity then – by a choice of "bad" blending ratio – we can obtain a bundle having smaller tenacity than that of the single components. This phenomenon is significant especially if components are having high difference in their breaking strains, as we see in the earlier example. In such cases, it is necessary to "carefully" choose a suitable blending ratio.

Stress, strength and minimum strength of bundle. In practice, we mostly talk about specific stresses and specific strengths, expressed in N tex^{-1}. But, this does not need to be a suitable strategy for solving some problems, especially for technical purposes. In such cases, we need to use stresses and strengths expressed in Pascal (Pa) or MegaPascal (MPa) as in physics. Then we need to rearrange the previous equations.

The total cross-sectional area S of all the fibers in the bundle is contributed by n_1 fibers each of cross-sectional area s_1 and n_2 fibers each of cross-sectional area s_2. Then, in accordance with Eqs. (6.7) and (6.18), the following equation can be written

$$S = n_1 s_1 + n_2 s_2 = \left(g_1 T/t_1\right)\left(t_1/\rho_1\right) + \left(g_2 T/t_2\right)\left(t_2/\rho_2\right) =$$
$$= T\left[g_1/\rho_1 + g_2/\rho_2\right].$$
$$\ldots (6.31)$$

The mechanical stress of the bundle is $\sigma_b'(\varepsilon) = F_b(\varepsilon)/S$, which is immediately followed from the definition. Using Eqs. (6.7), (6.9), (6.19) and (6.31), the following relation is valid for the strain interval $\varepsilon \in \langle 0, a_1 \rangle$

$$\sigma_b'(\varepsilon) = \frac{F_b(\varepsilon)}{S} = \frac{T\left[g_1 \dfrac{F_1(\varepsilon)}{t_1} + g_2 \dfrac{F_2(\varepsilon)}{t_2}\right]}{T\left[g_1/\rho_1 + g_2/\rho_2\right]} = \frac{g_1 \dfrac{F_1(\varepsilon)}{s_1 \rho_1} + g_2 \dfrac{F_2(\varepsilon)}{s_2 \rho_2}}{g_1/\rho_1 + g_2/\rho_2}$$

$$= \frac{\dfrac{g_1}{\rho_1}\sigma_1'(\varepsilon) + \dfrac{g_2}{\rho_2}\sigma_2'(\varepsilon)}{\dfrac{g_1}{\rho_1} + \dfrac{g_2}{\rho_2}}, \quad \varepsilon \in \langle 0, a_1 \rangle. \qquad \ldots (6.32)$$

But, according to Eq. (1.42), the following expressions are valid

$$g_1/\rho_1 = v_1/\rho, \quad g_2/\rho_2 = v_2/\rho, \quad v_1 + v_2 = 1. \qquad \ldots (6.33)$$

The quantities v_1, v_2 are known as the volume fractions of the components and ρ is known as the mean fiber density, expressed by Eq. (1.41). Using these expressions in Eq. (6.32) we obtain

$$\sigma_b'(\varepsilon) = \frac{\dfrac{v_1}{\rho}\sigma_1'(\varepsilon) + \dfrac{v_2}{\rho}\sigma_2'(\varepsilon)}{\dfrac{v_1}{\rho} + \dfrac{v_2}{\rho}} = v_1\sigma_1'(\varepsilon) + v_2\sigma_2'(\varepsilon), \quad \varepsilon \in \langle 0, a_1 \rangle. \qquad \ldots (6.34)$$

Similarly, by using Eqs. (6.20) and (6.31), the following equation is obtained for the strain interval $\varepsilon \in \left(a_1, a_2\right\rangle$.

$$\sigma_b'(\varepsilon) = \frac{F_b(\varepsilon)}{S} = \frac{Tg_2 \dfrac{F_2(\varepsilon)}{t_2}}{T\left[g_1/\rho_1 + g_2/\rho_2\right]} = \frac{g_2 \dfrac{F_2(\varepsilon)}{S_2\rho_2}}{g_1/\rho_1 + g_2/\rho_2} = \frac{\dfrac{g_2}{\rho_2}\sigma_2'(\varepsilon)}{\dfrac{g_1}{\rho_1} + \dfrac{g_2}{\rho_2}} = \frac{\dfrac{v_2}{\rho}\sigma_2'(\varepsilon)}{\dfrac{v_1}{\rho} + \dfrac{v_2}{\rho}},$$

$$\sigma_b'(\varepsilon) = v_2\sigma_2'(\varepsilon), \quad \varepsilon \in \left(a_1, a_2\right\rangle.$$

$$\ldots (6.35)$$

At last, from Eq. (6.2), it is valid

$$\sigma_b'(\varepsilon) = F_b(\varepsilon)/S = 0/S = 0, \quad \varepsilon > a_2. \tag{6.36}$$

Let us now compare Eqs. (6.19), (6.20), (6.21), which are valid for the specific stress $\sigma_b(\varepsilon)$, with Eqs. (6.34), (6.35), (6.36), which are valid for the stress $\sigma_b'(\varepsilon)$. The mathematical structure of the corresponding expressions is the same, but in the place of specific stresses $\sigma_b(\varepsilon)$, $\sigma_1(\varepsilon)$, $\sigma_2(\varepsilon)$ the stresses $\sigma_b'(\varepsilon), \sigma_1'(\varepsilon), \sigma_2'(\varepsilon)$ are used and in the place of mass fractions g_1, g_2 the volume fractions v_1, v_2 are used.

It is possible to derive all other expressions in the same way as before. Then, in place of Eq. (6.22) we obtain

$$\sigma_b'(a_1) = v_1\sigma_1'(a_1) + v_2\sigma_2'(a_1) = v_1\sigma_1'^* + v_2\sigma_2'(a_1). \qquad \ldots (6.37)$$

Also, in place of Eq. (6.23) we obtain

$$\sigma_b'(a_2) = v_2\sigma_2'(a_2) = v_2\sigma_2'^*. \qquad \ldots (6.38)$$

Further in place of Eq. (6.25) we obtain

$$\sigma_b'^* = \max\left\{\sigma_b'(a_1), \sigma_b'(a_2)\right\} = \max\left\{v_1\sigma_1'^* + v_2\sigma_2'(a_1), v_2\sigma_2'^*\right\} \qquad \ldots (6.39)$$

Furthermore, in place of Eq. (6.26) we obtain

$$\left.\begin{array}{l} a_b = a_1 \cdots\cdots\cdots \text{if } \sigma_b'^* = \sigma_b'(a_1) > \sigma_b'(a_2) \\ a_b = a_2 \cdots\cdots\cdots \text{if } \sigma_b'^* = \sigma_b'(a_2) > \sigma_b'(a_1) \\ a_b \text{ is undefined if } \sigma_b'^* = \sigma_b'(a_1) = \sigma_b'(a_2). \end{array}\right\} \qquad \ldots (6.40)$$

In place of Eq. (6.27) we obtain

$$v_{1,C}\sigma_1'^* + v_{2,C}\sigma_2'(a_1) = v_{2,C}\sigma_2'^*, \text{ where } v_{1,C} + v_{2,C} = 1. \qquad \ldots (6.41)$$

In place of Eq. (6.28) we obtain

$$v_{2,C} = \frac{\sigma_1'^*}{\sigma_1'^* + \sigma_2'^* - \sigma_2'(a_1)}, \quad v_{1,C} = 1 - v_{2,C} = \frac{\sigma_2'^* - \sigma_2'(a_1)}{\sigma_1'^* + \sigma_2'^* - \sigma_2'(a_1)}. \quad \dots (6.42)$$

In place of Eq. (6.29) we obtain

$$\sigma_{b,C}'^* = v_{1,C}\sigma_1'^* + v_{2,C}\sigma_2'(a_1) = v_{2,C}'\sigma_2'^* = \frac{\sigma_1'^*\sigma_2'^*}{\sigma_1'^* + \sigma_2'^* - \sigma_2'(a_1)} \quad \dots (6.43)$$

At last, in place of Eq. (6.30) we obtain

$$\left.\begin{array}{l}
\text{If } \sigma_1'^* > \sigma_2'(a_1) \text{ then } v_{1\min} = v_{1,C}, \quad v_{2\min} = v_{2,C}, \quad \sigma_{b\min}'^* = \sigma_{b,C}'^*. \\[4pt]
\text{If } \sigma_1'^* < \sigma_2'(a_1) \text{ then } v_{1\min} = 1, \quad v_{2\min} = 0, \quad \sigma_{b\min}'^* = \sigma_1'^*. \\[4pt]
\text{If } \sigma_1'^* = \sigma_2'(a_1) \text{ then } v_{1\min} \in \langle v_{1,C}, 1\rangle, \quad v_{2\min} \in \langle 0, v_{2,C}\rangle, \quad \sigma_{b\min}'^* = \sigma_{b,C}'^* = \sigma_1'^*.
\end{array}\right\}$$

$$\dots (6.44)$$

After changing of the symbols, the graphical interpretation looks analogically to Figs. 6.3 and 6.4.

Table 6.2 Replacement of fiber characteristics by yarn characteristics.

Symbols	Original sense	Modified sense for yarn
σ_1^*, σ_2^*	Specific strengths of fibers	Specific strengths of single-component yarns
$\sigma_1'^*$, $\sigma_2'^*$	Strengths of fibers	Strengths of single-component yarns
$a_1 \leq a_2$	Breaking strains of fibers	Breaking strains of single-component yarns
$\sigma_2'(a_1)$	Specific stress in the fiber of the second component at the breaking strain of fiber of the first component	Specific stress in the single-component yarn from the second material at the breaking strain of the single-component yarn from the first material
$\sigma_2'(a_1)$	Stress in the fiber of the second component at the breaking strain of the first component	Stress in the single-component yarn from second material at the breaking strain of the single-component yarn from the first material
g_1, g_2	Mass fraction in fiber bundle	Mass fraction in blended yarn
v_1, v_2	Volume fraction in fiber bundle	Volume fraction in blended yarn

Notes to application for yarns. The blended staple yarn is a type of blended fiber bundle, but the assumptions 1 and 2 in Section 6.1 (ideal fiber bundle) and the assumption 3* in this chapter are not satisfied enough – mainly the fibers are not mutually independent because of the friction among fibers, the fibers are not quite parallel because of the influence of twist, and the fibers do not possess same mechanical properties. Therefore, the immediate application of the previous results cannot be recommended.

The idea, based on the replacement of earlier fiber characteristics to analogical yarn characteristics, offers better results. This substitution is shown in Table 6.2.

6.3   Mechanics of multi-component parallel fiber bundle[3]

Let us think of an ideal fiber bundle in accordance with Section 6.2. Let us then modify the assumption 3* mentioned in Section 6.2 as follows.

3** In an ideal fiber bundle,

(I)   there are K components, $K \geq 2$.
(II) Each fiber of the same component exhibits
    (a)   same fiber density ρ,
    (b)   same fineness t,
    (c)   same continuously increasing force–strain relation $F = F(\varepsilon)$,
    (d)   same breaking force F^* and
    (e)   same breaking strain a.
(III) The properties of fibers between components are generally different.

Table 6.3 introduces the symbols used for such a fiber bundle.

We use the convention, by which the quantities related to a component of smaller breaking strain are displayed with the smaller subscript i. Strictly speaking,

$$a_{i-1} \leq a_i, \quad i = 1, 2, \ldots, K, \qquad \qquad \ldots (6.45)$$

where we formally introduce

$$a_0 = 0. \qquad \qquad \ldots (6.46)$$

It is observed that the introduction of the quantity a_0 results in better mathematical formulation. So, each set $\{a_i\}_{i=0}^{K}$ creates a non-decreasing progression.

Initial quantities. The following equations are valid for each general i-th component $i = 1, 2, \ldots, K$, in an analogy[4] to earlier Eqs. from (6.7) to (6.16).

The cross-sections of the fibers are expressed as follows

$$s_i = t_i / \rho_i . \qquad \qquad \ldots (6.47)$$

---

3. It is recommended to study the previous chapter before studying this chapter.
4. The logic of derivation is quite the same as earlier.

Table 6.3 Symbols used for components.

Quantity	i-th component
Sequential number (subscript) of component	$i = 1, 2, ..., K$
Fiber density	ρ_i
Fiber fineness	t_i
Force–strain function of fiber	$F_i(\varepsilon)$
Specific stress of fiber	$\sigma_i(\varepsilon)$
Stress of fiber	$\sigma_i'(\varepsilon)$
Breaking strain of fiber	a_i
Breaking force of fiber[+]	$F_i^* \equiv F_i(a_i)$
Specific strength of fiber[+]	$\sigma_i^* \equiv \sigma_i(a_i)$
Strength of fiber[+]	$\sigma_i'^* \equiv \sigma_i'(a_i)$
Number of fibers in bundle	n_i
Mass fraction in bundle	g_i
Mass[++] of component in bundle	m_i

(+) The second expressions are preferred.
(++) This corresponds to the fibers present in between the jaws A and B separated by (gauge) length h in Fig. 6.1b.

The fiber specific stresses and the stresses are stated below

$$\sigma_i(\varepsilon) = F_i(\varepsilon)/t_i, \quad \sigma_i'(\varepsilon) = F_i(\varepsilon)/s_i . \qquad \text{... (6.48)}$$

The fiber breaking forces, the specific strengths and the strengths are expressed as follows

$$F_i^* = F_i(a_i), \qquad \text{... (6.49)}$$

$$\sigma_i^* = \sigma_i(a_i) = F_i^*/t_i , \qquad \text{... (6.50)}$$

$$\sigma_i'^* = \sigma_i'(a_i) = F_i^*/s_i . \qquad \text{... (6.51)}$$

The total number of fibers in the bundle is evidently

$$n = \sum_{i=1}^{K} n_i . \qquad \text{... (6.52)}$$

The total mass of bundle is

$$m = \sum_{i=1}^{K} m_i \qquad \text{... (6.53)}$$

Evidently, Eq. (1.17), i.e., $T = m/h$, where m denotes the mass of the bundle and h indicates the (gauge) length according to Fig. 6.1, now holds true for the bundle fineness also. Therefore, the following equations are valid, analogous to Eq. (6.18), for the fiber fineness and for the numbers of fibers in bundle,

$$t_i = \frac{m_i}{n_i h}, \quad n_i = \frac{m_i}{t_i h} = \frac{g_i m}{t_i h} = g_i \frac{T}{t_i}. \qquad \ldots (6.54)$$

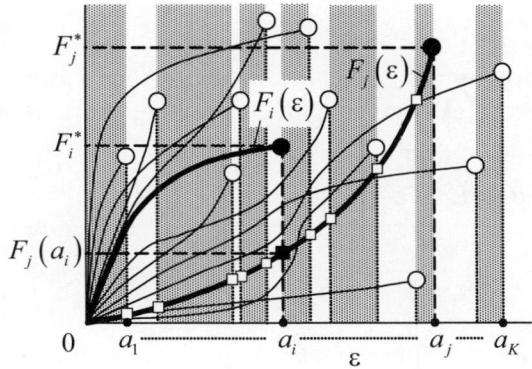

6.5 Scheme of force–strain functions of fibers from individual components.

Forces in fibers. The force–strain function of the fibers from the individual components is schematically illustrated in Fig. 6.5. The end (ring) point of function $F_i(\varepsilon)$ characterizes the breaking strain a_i and the breaking force F_i^* of the fiber from a general i-th component. Similarly, the function $F_j(\varepsilon)$, the breaking strain a_j and the breaking force F_j^* characterize the fiber from j-th component. Another force $F_j(a_i)$ (which exists because $a_j > a_i$) expresses the force in the fiber from j-th component at the strain value $\varepsilon = a_i$, i.e., at breaking strain of the fiber from i-th component – see the black square mark in Fig. 6.5. (The increasing progression $\left\{ F_j(a_i) \right\}_{i=1}^{j}$ is existing for each j-th fiber – see the square marks in Fig. 6.5).

Force and specific stress in bundle. Let us elongate the fiber bundle to strain ε. This strain lies in one of the intervals $(a_0, a_1\rangle, (a_1, a_2\rangle, (a_2, a_3\rangle, \cdots,$ $(a_{K-1}, a_K\rangle, (a_K, \infty)$. If $\varepsilon \in (a_0, a_1\rangle \equiv (0, a_1\rangle$ then no one fiber will break because no one component will have its braking strain smaller than ε. If $\varepsilon \in (a_1, a_2\rangle$ then the fibers from the first component will be broken ($a_1 < \varepsilon$), but all the other components will not break. That is, their breaking strains are not smaller than ε. If $\varepsilon \in (a_2, a_3\rangle$ then the fibers from the first and second components will be broken ($a_1 < \varepsilon$ and $a_2 < \varepsilon$) and the fibers from other components will evidently not break, etc. If $\varepsilon \in (a_{K-1}, a_K)$ then, except the last K-th component, all the other fibers will be broken ($a_1, a_2, \ldots, a_{K-1}$ are smaller than ε, but $a_K \geq \varepsilon$). At last, if $\varepsilon > a_K$ then all the fibers in the bundle will be completely broken. Consequently, the following equations must be valid for the bundle force $F_b(\varepsilon)$ in this case, by using of Eq. (6.54)

$$\text{If } \varepsilon \in (a_{i-1}, a_i), \quad i = 1, 2, \ldots K, \text{ then } F_b(\varepsilon) = \sum_{j=i}^{K} n_j F_j(\varepsilon) = T \sum_{j=i}^{K} g_j \frac{F_j(\varepsilon)}{t_j}.$$

$$\text{If } \varepsilon > a_K \text{ then } F_b(\varepsilon) = 0.$$

$$\ldots (6.55)$$

Applying the first expression of Eq. (6.48) in the previous expressions, the bundle specific stress $\sigma_b(\varepsilon)$ is given by the following expressions

$$\sigma_b(\varepsilon) = \frac{F_b(\varepsilon)}{T} = \sum_{j=i}^{K} g_j \sigma_j(\varepsilon), \quad \text{if } \varepsilon \in (a_{i-1}, a_i), \quad i = 1, 2, \ldots K,$$

$$\sigma_b(\varepsilon) = \frac{F_b(\varepsilon)}{T} = 0, \quad \text{if } \varepsilon > a_K.$$

$$\ldots (6.56)$$

Note: If $K = 2$ then Eqs. (6.55) and (6.56) are identical to Eqs. (6.19), (6.20) and (6.21).

Breaking force and specific strength in bundle. The local maxima of breaking force and/or specific stress of the bundle lie in the upper limits of the strain intervals $(a_0, a_1), (a_1, a_2), (a_2, a_3), \cdots, (a_{K-1}, a_K)$. The values of these local maxima of breaking force and/or specific stress of the bundle accord to Eqs. (6.55) and (6.56)

$$F_b(a_i) = T \sum_{j=i}^{K} g_j \frac{F_j(a_i)}{t_j}, \quad \sigma_b(a_i) = \sum_{j=i}^{K} g_j \sigma_j(a_i) \ldots i = 1, 2, \ldots K, \quad \ldots (6.57)$$

where the values $F_i(a_i) = F_i^*$ and $\sigma_i(a_i) = \sigma_i^*$ represent the breaking forces and the specific strengths of fibers.

Note: If $K = 2$ then Eq. (6.57) is identical to Eq. (6.22) and Eq. (6.23).

The bundle breaking force F_b^* and the corresponding bundle specific strength σ_b^* are the total maximum of all the corresponding local maxima. Using Eq. (6.57) the following equations must be valid

$$F_b^* = \max \left\{ F_b(a_i) \right\}_{i=1}^{K} = \max \left\{ T \sum_{j=i}^{K} g_j \frac{F_j(a_i)}{t_j} \right\}_{i=1}^{K}, \quad \ldots (6.58)$$

$$\sigma_b^* = \max \left\{ \sigma_b \left(a_i \right) \right\}_{i=1}^{K} = \max \left\{ \sum_{j=i}^{K} g_j \sigma_j \left(a_i \right) \right\}_{i=1}^{K} . \qquad \ldots (6.59)$$

Note: If $K = 2$ then Eqs. (6.58) and (6.59) change to Eqs. (6.24) and (6.25). (The symbols according to Eqs. (6.49) and (6.50) are still valid). The bundle breaking strain a_b is given by the following expression

$$\left. \begin{array}{l} a_b = a_{i=k} \text{ if } \sigma_b^* = \max \left\{ \sigma_b \left(a_i \right) \right\}_{i=1}^{K} = \sigma_b \left(a_k \right) \text{ is valid} \\ \qquad \text{for only one subscript } k \in \left\{ 1, 2, \cdots K \right\}, \\ a_b \text{ is undefined if } \sigma_b^* = \max \left\{ \sigma_b \left(a_i \right) \right\}_{i=1}^{K} = \sigma_b \left(a_k \right) \text{ is valid} \\ \qquad \text{for minimum two subscripts } k \in \left\{ 1, 2, \cdots K \right\}. \end{array} \right\} \qquad \ldots (6.60)$$

Note: 1. Usually, there is only one value $\sigma_b(a_k)$ from the set $\left\{ \sigma_b \left(a_i \right) \right\}_{i=1}^{K}$ which is the highest. Then the bundle breaking strain exists and it corresponds to the value a_k. However, if there are two or more values from the set $\left\{ \sigma_b \left(a_i \right) \right\}_{i=1}^{K}$ that have same value and they are all the maximum value, then the bundle "has" two or more breaking strains. Of course, it is physically not real (see the similar note preceding Eq. (6.26)). If $K = 2$ then Eq. (6.60) is changed to Eq. (6.26).

Mathematical rearrangement of $\sigma_b(a_i)$. At some set of mass fractions $\left\{ g_i \right\}_{i=1}^{K}$ the bundle specific strength (tenacity) is the smallest in the case of bi-component fiber bundle (see Fig. 6.4 and subsequent discussions). Nevertheless, finding such a "worst" blending ratio is more difficult in the general case of K components. To solve such a problem, the following mathematical rearrangement is useful.

Let us define the quantities

$$G_i = \sum_{j=i}^{K} g_j, \quad i = 1, 2, \cdots, K. \qquad \ldots (6.61)$$

The quantity G_i represents a cumulative mass fraction of the partial group of components, say from i-th component to the last K-th component. This is written as follows

$$G_1 = \sum_{j=1}^{K} g_j = 1, \, G_K = \sum_{j=K}^{K} g_j = g_K, \, G_{i+1} = \sum_{j=i+1}^{K} g_j = \sum_{j=i}^{K} g_j - g_i = G_i - g_i.$$

$$\ldots (6.62)$$

Further let us define the quantities

$$g_i^* = \frac{g_i}{G_i}, \quad i = 1, 2, \cdots, K.$$ ... (6.63)

The value g_i^* represents a "relative" mass fraction of only i-th component in the earlier mentioned partial group of components. It follows from the last equation and Eq. (6.62)

$$g_1^* = g_1/G_1 = g_1/1 = g_1, \quad g_K^* = g_K/G_K = g_K/g_K = 1.$$ ... (6.64)

We also define the following quantities

$$r_i^* = 1 - g_i^* \quad (g_i^* + r_i^* = 1), \quad i = 1, 2, \cdots, K.$$ ... (6.65)

The value r_i^* represents a "relative" mass fraction of the other "remaining" fibers in the mentioned partial group of components. Using Eqs. (6.62) and (6.63) in the last expression, the following equation is obtained

$$r_i^* = 1 - \frac{g_i}{G_i} = \frac{G_i - g_i}{G_i} = \frac{G_{i+1}}{G_i}, \quad i < K.$$ ... (6.66)

Especially, for $i = 1$ and $i = K$ the following expression is valid to write in accordance with Eqs. (6.64) and (6.65)

$$r_1^* = 1 - g_1^* = 1 - g_1, \quad r_K^* = 1 - g_K^* = 1 - 1 = 0.$$ ... (6.67)

At last, let us define the following functions

$$\left. \begin{aligned} Z_j(a_i) &= \frac{g_j}{G_j}\sigma_j(a_i) + \frac{G_{j+1}}{G_j}Z_{j+1}(a_i) = \\ &= g_j^*\sigma_j(a_i) + r_j^* Z_{j+1}(a_i), \quad j = 1, 2, \cdots K-1, \quad i \le j. \\ Z_K(a_i) &= \sigma_K(a_i) \quad \text{(i.e. by } j = K, \quad i \le j). \end{aligned} \right\}$$ ... (6.68)

The sense of the function $Z_j(a_i)$ is shown by the result of the following rearrangement, based on a repeated use of Eq. (6.68) and then a final use of Eq. (6.62).

$$Z_j(a_i) = \frac{g_j}{G_j}\sigma_j(a_i) + \frac{G_{j+1}}{G_j}Z_{j+1}(a_i)$$

$$= \frac{g_j}{G_j}\sigma_j(a_i) + \frac{G_{j+1}}{G_j}\left[\frac{g_{j+1}}{G_{j+1}}\sigma_{j+1}(a_i) + \frac{G_{j+2}}{G_{j+1}}Z_{j+2}(a_i)\right]$$

$$= \frac{g_j}{G_j}\sigma_j(a_i) + \frac{g_{j+1}}{G_j}\sigma_{j+1}(a_i) + \frac{G_{j+2}}{G_j}Z_{j+2}(a_i)$$

$$= \frac{g_j}{G_j}\sigma_j(a_i) + \frac{g_{j+1}}{G_j}\sigma_{j+1}(a_i) + \frac{G_{j+2}}{G_j}\left[\frac{g_{j+2}}{G_{j+2}}\sigma_{j+2}(a_i) + \frac{G_{j+3}}{G_{j+2}}Z_{j+3}(a_i)\right]$$

$$= \frac{g_j}{G_j}\sigma_j(a_i) + \frac{g_{j+1}}{G_j}\sigma_{j+1}(a_i) + \frac{g_{j+2}}{G_j}\sigma_{j+2}(a_i) + \frac{G_{j+3}}{G_j}Z_{j+3}(a_i)$$

$$\vdots$$

$$= \frac{g_j}{G_j}\sigma_j(a_i) + \frac{g_{j+1}}{G_j}\sigma_{j+1}(a_i) + \frac{g_{j+2}}{G_j}\sigma_{j+2}(a_i) + \cdots + \frac{g_{K-1}}{G_j}\sigma_{K-1}(a_i) + \frac{G_K}{G_j}Z_K(a_i)$$

$$= \frac{1}{G_j}\left\{g_j\sigma_j(a_i) + g_{j+1}\sigma_{j+1}(a_i) + g_{j+2}\sigma_{j+2}(a_i) + \cdots + g_{K-1}\sigma_{K-1}(a_i) + g_K\sigma_K(a_i)\right\}.$$

$$\ldots (6.69)$$

It is valid $\sigma_j(a_{i-1}) \leq \sigma_j(a_i)$ for each $i \leq j$. (That is to say, each of $\sigma_j(\varepsilon)$ is an increasing function according to the assumption 3**II)c) mentioned in the introductory part of this chapter). So, the following inequality arising from Eq. (6.69) is valid

$$Z_j(a_{i-1}) \leq Z_j(a_i) \qquad\qquad \ldots (6.70)$$

Now, we can express the values $\sigma_b(a_i)$ of the local maxima of bundle specific stress according to Eqs. (6.57) and (6.69) by the following form

$$\sigma_b(a_i) = G_i Z_i(a_i) \quad \ldots i = 1, 2, \ldots K . \qquad\qquad \ldots (6.71)$$

The set of local maxima of bundle specific stress, determined according to Eq. (6.71) in the basic form, is possible to rearrange to two alternative expressions by using Eq. (6.66) – form A – or by using Eq. (6.68) – form B. The derived expressions are shown in Table 6.4.

Higher value from $\sigma_b(a_{i-1})$ *and* $\sigma_b(a_i)$. In order to solve a more general case for the future, let us study the partial problem of higher value from the two adjacent local maxima $\sigma_b(a_{i-1})$ and $\sigma_b(a_i)$. We will use the value $\sigma_b(a_{i-1})$ in the form B and the value $\sigma_b(a_i)$ in the form A according to Table 6.4 (underlined expressions). So, we must know the following couple of equations

$$\left.\begin{array}{l}\sigma_b(a_{i-1}) = G_{i-1}\left[g_{i-1}^*\sigma_{i-1}(a_{i-1}) + r_{i-1}^* Z_i(a_{i-1})\right], \\[2mm] \sigma_b(a_i) = G_{i-1}r_{i-1}^* Z_i(a_i).\end{array}\right\} \qquad \ldots (6.72)$$

Table 6.4 Local maxima of bundle specific stress.

Local maximum	BASIC FORM according to Eq. (6.71)	FORM A Basic form after using Eq. (6.66)	FORM B Basic form after using Eq. (6.68)
$\sigma_b(a_1)=$	$G_1 Z_1(a_1)=$		$G_1\left[g_1^* \sigma_1(a_1)+r_1^* Z_2(a_1)\right]$
$\sigma_b(a_2)=$	$G_2 Z_2(a_2)=$	$G_1 r_1^* Z_2(a_2)=$	$G_2\left[g_2^* \sigma_2(a_2)+r_2^* Z_3(a_2)\right]$
$\vdots$	$\vdots$	$\vdots$	$\vdots$
$\sigma_b(a_{i-1})=$	$G_{i-1} Z_{i-1}(a_{i-1})=$	$G_{i-2} r_{i-2}^* Z_{i-1}(a_{i-1})=$	$\underline{G_{i-1}\left[g_{i-1}^* \sigma_{i-1}(a_{i-1})+r_{i-1}^* Z_i(a_{i-1})\right]}$
$\sigma_b(a_i)=$	$G_i Z_i(a_i)=$	$\underline{G_{i-1} r_{i-1}^* Z_i(a_i)=}$	$G_i\left[g_i^* \sigma_i(a_i)+r_i^* Z_{i+1}(a_i)\right]$
$\vdots$	$\vdots$	$\vdots$	$\vdots$
$\sigma_b(a_{K-3})=$	$G_{K-3} Z_{K-3}(a_{K-3})=$	$G_{K-4} r_{K-4}^* Z_{K-3}(a_{K-3})=$	$G_{K-3}\left[g_{K-3}^* \sigma_{K-3}(a_{K-3})+r_{K-3}^* Z_{K-2}(a_{K-3})\right]$
$\sigma_b(a_{K-2})=$	$G_{K-2} Z_{K-2}(a_{K-2})=$	$G_{K-3} r_{K-3}^* Z_{K-2}(a_{K-2})=$	$G_{K-2}\left[g_{K-2}^* \sigma_{K-2}(a_{K-2})+r_{K-2}^* Z_{K-1}(a_{K-2})\right]$
$\sigma_b(a_{K-1})=$	$G_{K-1} Z_{K-1}(a_{K-1})=$	$G_{K-2} r_{K-2}^* Z_{K-1}(a_{K-1})=$	$G_{K-1}\left[g_{K-1}^* \sigma_{K-1}(a_{K-1})+r_{K-1}^* Z_K(a_{K-1})\right]$
$\sigma_b(a_K)=$	$G_K Z_K(a_K)=$	$G_{K-1} r_{K-1}^* Z_K(a_K)$	

Let us assume that we know three values in the last couple of equations: $\sigma_{i-1}(a_{i-1})$, $Z_i(a_{i-1})$ and $Z_i(a_i)$. However, the values of next triplet of parameters – $G_{i-1}, g_{i-1}^*, r_{i-1}^*$ – are not known at this moment.

We introduce the symbol X_{i-1} for the higher value from $\sigma_b(a_{i-1})$ and $\sigma_b(a_i)$. Using Eq. (6.72) we can write

$$X_{i-1} = \max\left\{\sigma_b(a_{i-1}), \sigma_b(a_i)\right\}, \qquad \ldots (6.73)$$

$$X_{i-1} = G_{i-1} Y_{i-1}, \quad Y_{i-1} = \max\left\{g_{i-1}^* \sigma_{i-1}(a_{i-1})+r_{i-1}^* Z_i(a_{i-1}), \; r_{i-1}^* Z_i(a_i)\right\} \ldots (6.74)$$

Note: It is sufficient to determine the maximum of the quantity Y_{i-1}, introduced by the last equation, because the both values $\sigma_b(a_{i-1})$ and $\sigma_b(a_i)$ are multiplied by the same parameter G_{i-1} in Eq. (6.72).

The two unknown quantities – g_{i-1}^* and r_{i-1}^* – are expressed in the second expression of Eq. (6.74), but it is valid to write Eq. (6.65), i.e., $r_i^* = 1 - g_i^*$.

The second expression in Eq. (6.74) is similar to Eq. (6.25) in the previous chapter, but there are differences in the symbols, shown on the next page.

Because of the similarity exists, it is possible to apply the considerations from the previous Section 6.2. The graphical interpretation of the second expression of Eq. (6.74) is similar to Fig. 6.4. The graphs in Fig. 6.6 illustrate the possible behavior which is valid now. The behavior of Y_{i-1} is shown by the triple lines in the graphs. (The construction of such graphs is already discussed in more detail in the previous chapter).

In the place of earlier quantity according to Eq. (6.25)		This is used in the second expression of Eq. (6.74).
σ_b^*	$\rightarrow$	Y_{i-1}
a_1	$\rightarrow$	a_{i-1}
$a_2 \quad (a_1 \le a_2)$	$\rightarrow$	$a_i \quad (a_{i-1} \le a_i)$
a_b	$\rightarrow$	$a_{Y,i-1}$
$\sigma_1(a_1) = \sigma_1^*$ (+)	$\rightarrow$	$\sigma_{i-1}(a_{i-1}) = \sigma_{i-1}^*$ (++)
$\sigma_2(a_1)$	$\rightarrow$	$Z_i(a_{i-1})$
$\sigma_2^* \quad (\sigma_2(a_1) \le \sigma_2^*)$	$\rightarrow$	$Z_i(a_i) \quad (Z_i(a_{i-1}) \le Z_i(a_i))$ (+++)
g_1	$\rightarrow$	g_{i-1}^*
$g_2 \quad (g_1 + g_2 = 1)$	$\rightarrow$	$r_{i-1}^* \quad (g_{i-1}^* + r_{i-1}^* = 1)$

(+) Equation (6.11). (++) Equation (6.50). (+++) Equation (6.70).

The point C of intersection has the values $r_{i-1}^* = r_{i-1,C}^*$ (and/or $g_{i-1}^* = g_{i-1,C}^* = 1 - r_{i-1,C}^*$) and $Y_{i-1} = Y_{i-1,C}$; the equality $g_{i-1,C}^*\sigma_{i-1}(a_{i-1}) + r_{i-1,C}^* Z_i(a_{i-1}) = r_{i-1,C}^* Z_i(a_i)$ is valid at this point (similar to Eq. (6.27) in the previous chapter). Rearranging this equation together with $g_{i-1}^* = 1 - r_{i-1,C}^*$ we obtain the following expressions as follows:

$$r_{i-1,C}^* = \frac{\sigma_{i-1}(a_{i-1})}{\sigma_{i-1}(a_{i-1}) + Z_i(a_i) - Z_i(a_{i-1})}, \qquad \dots (6.75)$$

$$g_{i-1,C}^* = 1 - r_{i-1,C}^* = \frac{Z_i(a_i) - Z_i(a_{i-1})}{\sigma_{i-1}(a_{i-1}) + Z_i(a_i) - Z_i(a_{i-1})}$$

$$Y_{i-1,C} = g_{i-1,C}^*\sigma_{i-1}(a_{i-1}) + r_{i-1,C}^* Z_i(a_{i-1}) = r_{i-1,C}^* Z_i(a_i) =$$
$$= \frac{\sigma_{i-1}(a_{i-1})Z_i(a_i)}{\sigma_{i-1}(a_{i-1}) + Z_i(a_i) - Z_i(a_{i-1})}. \qquad \dots (6.76)$$

The last two expressions are analogical to the expressions mentioned in Eqs. (6.28) and (6.29) in the previous chapter.

It is evident from the graphs shown in Fig. 6.6 that

1. If $r_{i-1}^* < r_{i-1,C}^*$ (left part of each graph) then $Y_{i-1} = g_{i-1}^*\sigma_{i-1}(a_{i-1}) + r_{i-1}^* Z_i(a_{i-1})$ – see the thick line in the graphs – and the corresponding value of strain, denoted by $a_{Y,i-1}$, is $a_{Y,i-1} = a_{i-1}$.

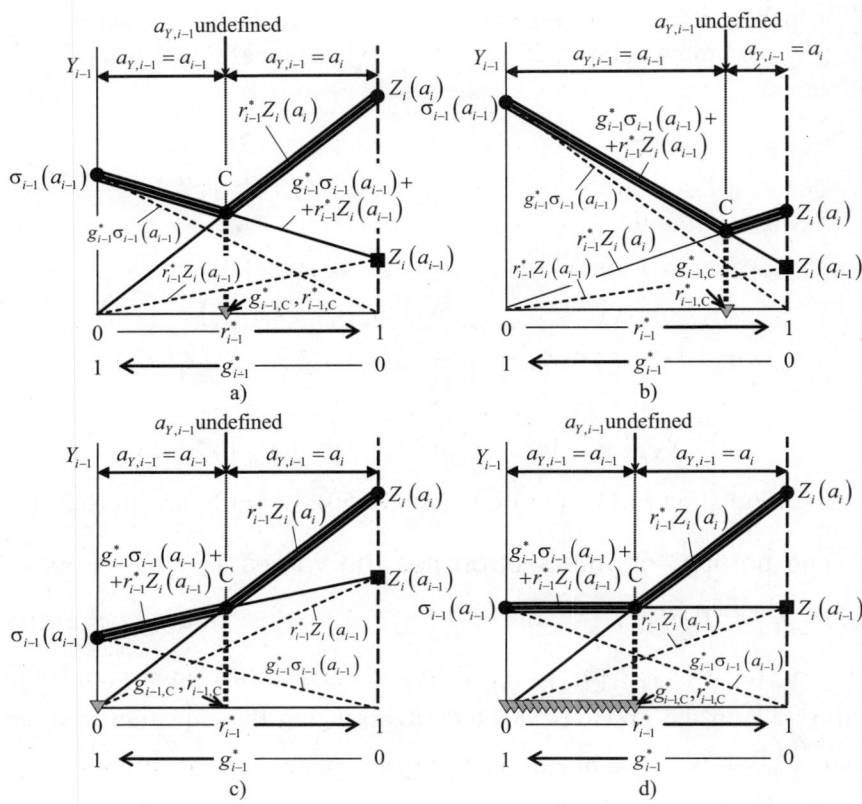

6.6 Behavior of Y_{i-1} and corresponding $a_{Y,i-1}$ in relation to r^*_{i-1} and/or g^*_{i-1};

(a) $\sigma_{i-1}(a_{i-1}) < Z_i(a_i)$ and $\sigma_{i-1}(a_{i-1}) > Z_i(a_{i-1})$,

(b) $\sigma_{i-1}(a_{i-1}) > Z_i(a_i)$ and $\sigma_{i-1}(a_{i-1}) > Z_i(a_{i-1})$,

(c) $\sigma_{i-1}(a_{i-1}) < Z_i(a_{i-1})$,

(d) $\sigma_{i-1}(a_{i-1}) = Z_i(a_{i-1})$.

Point C of intersection: $r^*_{i-1} = r^*_{i-1,C}$ and/or $g^*_{i-1} = g^*_{i-1,C}$.

2. If $r^*_{i-1} > r^*_{i-1,C}$ (right part of each graph) then $Y_{i-1} = r^*_{i-1}Z_i(a_i)$ – see the second thick line in the graphs – and the corresponding value of strain is $a_{Y,\,i-1} = a_i$.

3. If $r^*_{i-1} = r^*_{i-1,C}$ (the intersection of both thick lines) then Eq. (6.76) is valid, i.e., $Y_{i-1} = Y_{i-1,C} = \left[\sigma_{i-1}(a_{i-1})Z_i(a_i)\right]/\left[\sigma_{i-1}(a_{i-1}) + Z_i(a_i) - Z_i(a_{i-1})\right]$. The corresponding value of strain $a_{Y,i-1}$ is undefined. (Formally, $a_{Y,i-1}$ is equal to a_{i-1} and a_i at the same time, but two values are not physically real).

Minimum value of Y_{i-1} and X_{i-1}. Let us continue our consideration to the couple of adjacent local maxima $\sigma_b(a_{i-1})$, $\sigma_b(a_i)$, and the values X_{i-1}, Y_{i-1} according to Eqs. (6.73) and (6.74). The variable Y_{i-1} obtains its minimum value $Y_{i-1,min}$ at some value of the parameter $r_{i-1}^* = r_{i-1,min}^*$ (and/or $g_{i-1}^* = g_{i-1,min}^* = 1 - r_{i-1,min}^*$); see the gray triangles in the graphs in Fig. 6.6. We denote a value $a_{Y,i-1}$ corresponding to $Y_{i-1} = Y_{i-1,min}$ as $a_{Y,i-1,min}$.

In consideration of the graphs shown in Fig. 6.6 and the considerations similar to Section 6.2, we obtain the value $Y_{i-1,min}$, and the values $g_{i-1,min}^*$, $r_{i-1,min}^*$ corresponding to it, according to the following expressions similar to Eq. (6.30).

If $\sigma_{i-1}(a_{i-1}) > Z_i(a_{i-1})$ – Figure 6.6 a) and b), then

$\qquad g_{i-1,min}^* = g_{i-1,C}^*$, $r_{i-1,min}^* = r_{i-1,C}^*$, $Y_{i-1,min} = Y_{i-1,C}$, $a_{Y,i-1,min}$ is undefined.

If $\sigma_{i-1}(a_{i-1}) < Z_i(a_{i-1})$ – Figure 6.6 c), then

$\qquad g_{i-1,min}^* = 1$, $r_{i-1,min}^* = 0$, $Y_{i-1,min} = \sigma_{i-1}(a_{i-1})$, $a_{Y,i-1,min} = a_{i-1}$.

If $\sigma_{i-1}(a_{i-1}) = Z_i(a_{i-1})$ – Figure 6.6 d), then

$\qquad g_{i-1,min}^* \in \langle g_{i-1,C}^*, 1 \rangle$, $r_{i-1,min}^* \in \langle 0, r_{i-1,C}^* \rangle$, $Y_{i-1,min} = Y_{i-1,C} = \sigma_{i-1}(a_{i-1})$,

$\qquad a_{Y,i-1,min} = a_{i-1}$ if $r_{i-1,min}^* \in \langle 0, r_{i-1,C}^* \rangle$ or $a_{Y,i-1,min}$ is undefined when $r_{i-1,min}^* = r_{i-1,C}^*$.

$$\dots (6.77)$$

Let us remember that it is necessary to use Eqs. (6.75) and (6.76) for practical evaluation of the quantities $g_{i-1,C}^*, r_{i-1,C}^*$ and $Y_{i-1,C}$. The last expression defines the practical way for calculation of $Y_{i-1,min}$ and the corresponding values $g_{i-1,min}^*$, $r_{i-1,min}^*$.

The minimum of X_{i-1}, called $X_{i-1,min}$, can be formulated according to Eq. (6.74) as follows

$$X_{i-1,min} = G_{i-1,min} Y_{i-1,min} \qquad \dots (6.78)$$

Note: We will discuss about the "suitable" value of $G_{i-1} = G_{i-1,min}$ later on.

Minimum specific strength – evaluation. Equation (6.77) determines the quantity $r_{i-1,min}^*$ (and also the quantity $g_{i-1,min}^* = 1 - r_{i-1,min}^*$) by only one value in the cases according to the graphs (a), (b) and (c) shown in Fig. 6.6. However, this quantity can be an arbitrary value taken from the whole interval $\langle 0, r_{i-1,C}^* \rangle$ in graph (d). It infers that there are a lot of blending ratios that can bring the same minimum value of (partial) specific stress. Nevertheless, on the one hand, this case of absolutely precise equality $\sigma_{i-1}(a_{i-1}) = Z_i(a_{i-1})$ is practically very unique, and on the other hand, the mathematical solving of this special case brings lot of difficulty[5]. Therefore, let us assume that the mentioned equality is valid for no one subscript i. (Only the graphs (a), (b) and (c) shown in Fig. 6.6 can be actual).

The bundle specific strength σ_b^*, determined by Eq. (6.59), obtains its minimum value $\sigma_{b\,min}^*$ by one[6] set of mass fractions $\{g_i\}_{i=1}^{K} \equiv \{g_{i\,min}\}_{i=1}^{K}$ of individual components. It is suitable to determine this progression in two parts. We determine the "relative" mass fractions r_i^*, g_i^* $(g_i^* + r_i^* = 1,\ i = 1,2,\cdots,K)$ in the first part and then the mass fractions g_i $(i = 1,2,\ldots, K)$ in the second part.

For the first part of calculation we need to know the set of input values $\sigma_j(a_i),\ i \leq j,\ j = 1, 2, \ldots,K$.

Note: Let us remember that $\sigma_j(a_j) = \sigma_j^*$ is the specific strength of the fiber from j-th component, and the values $\sigma_j(a_i)$ for $i < j$ express the specific stresses in the mentioned fiber at $\varepsilon = a_1, a_2, \ldots a_{j-1},$, i.e., by breaking strains of the fibers from all previous components.

The scheme of the respective calculation is shown in Table 6.5. All the values $Z_K(a_i)$ in column 1 are known from the last expression mentioned in Eq. (6.68) – they are directly the input values $\sigma_K(a_i)$, because $j = K$ in this equation. Using the first (bold printed) couple of values, i.e. $Z_K(a_K) = \sigma_K(a_K)$, and $Z_K(a_{K-1}) = \sigma_K(a_{K-1})$, and Eq. (6.75) at $i = K$, we can evaluate the quantities $r_{K-1,min}^*$, $g_{K-1,min}^*$ from Eq. (6.77)[7] at $i = K$.

Further, using the values $r_{K-1}^* = r_{K-1,min}^*$, $g_{K-1}^* = g_{K-1,min}^*$, known now, and the values $Z_K(a_i)$, all from the first column, we can calculate all values $Z_{K-1}(a_i)$ in the second column according to Eq. (6.68) by $j = K - 1$, as shown. Using the first (bold printed) couple of values, i.e., $Z_{K-1}(a_{K-1})$ and $Z_{K-1}(a_{K-2})$, and $i = K - 1$ in Eqs. (6.75) and (6.77), we can – analogically as formerly – evaluate the quantities $r_{K-2,min}^*$, $g_{K-2,min}^*$. But the known values $r_{K-2,min}^*$, $g_{K-2,min}^*$ and the values $Z_{K-1}(a_i)$ from the second column allow us to calculate all values $Z_{K-2}(a_i)$ in the third column according to Eq. (6.68) by $j = K - 2$, as shown, etc., to the last column $K - 1$. In this manner, we get – beside others – all the values $g_{i,min}^*$ and $r_{i,min}^*$ for $i = 1,2,\ldots,K-1$ and the last values,

---

5. Generally, such a bundle shows the same minimum specific strength for the whole area of blending ratios.

6. See the previous assumption.

7. Only the first two alternatives can be actual, based on our previous assumption.

Table 6.5 Calculated values – first part.

	Calculated values of $Z_j(a_i)$ according to Eq. (6.68)			
Input values, $Z_K(a_i) = \sigma_K(a_i)$	Using $g^*_{K-1,\min}$, $r^*_{K-1,\min}$ and $Z_K(a_i)$ from the previous column	Using $g^*_{K-2,\min}$, $r^*_{K-2,\min}$ and $Z_{K-1}(a_i)$ from the previous column	$\cdots$	Using $g^*_{2,\min}$, $r^*_{2,\min}$ and $Z_3(a_i)$ from the previous column
1	2	3	$\cdots$	K-1
$Z_K(a_K)$	–	–	$\cdots$	–
$Z_K(a_{K-1})$	$Z_{K-1}(a_{K-1})$	–	$\cdots$	–
$Z_K(a_{K-2})$	$Z_{K-1}(a_{K-2})$	$Z_{K-2}(a_{K-2})$	$\cdots$	–
$Z_K(a_{K-3})$	$Z_{K-1}(a_{K-3})$	$Z_{K-2}(a_{K-3})$	$\cdots$	–
$\vdots$	$\vdots$	$\vdots$	$\vdots$	$\vdots$
$Z_K(a_2)$	$Z_{K-1}(a_2)$	$Z_{K-2}(a_2)$	$\cdots$	$Z_2(a_2)$
$Z_K(a_1)$	$Z_{K-1}(a_1)$	$Z_{K-2}(a_1)$	$\cdots$	$Z_2(a_1)$
Evaluated quantities according to Eq. (6.77)				
Using $Z_K(a_K)$ and $Z_K(a_{K-1})$	Using $Z_{K-1}(a_{K-1})$ and $Z_{K-1}(a_{K-2})$	Using $Z_{K-2}(a_{K-2})$ and $Z_{K-2}(a_{K-3})$	$\cdots$	Using $Z_2(a_2)$ and $Z_2(a_1)$
$r^*_{K-1,\min}$	$r^*_{K-2,\min}$	$r^*_{K-3,\min}$	$\cdots$	$r^*_{1,\min}$
$g^*_{K-1,\min}$	$g^*_{K-2,\min}$	$g^*_{K-3,\min}$	$\cdots$	$g^*_{1,\min}$

i.e., $g^*_{K,\min} = g^*_K = 1$ and $r^*_{K,\min} = r^*_K = 0$, are determined according to Eqs. (6.64) and (6.65)[8]. So, it is valid to write the complete progression $\{g^*_{i,\min}\}_{i=1}^K$ and/or $\{r^*_{i,\min}\}_{i=1}^K$.

The second part of evaluation utilizes Eqs. (6.62) and (6.63) for determination of the set $\{g_{i,\min}\}_{i=1}^K$ of mass fractions related to the minimum strength of the bundle. The mentioned equations have the following form now.

$$G_{i+1,\min} = G_{i,\min} - g_{i,\min}, \quad G_{1,\min} = 1, \ G_{K,\min} = g_{K,\min}. \quad \dots (6.79)$$

$$g^*_{i,\min} = g_{i,\min}/G_{i,\min}. \quad \dots (6.80)$$

---

8. $g^*_{K,\min}$ and $r^*_{K,\min}$ take some values of g^*_K and r^*_K, so that these equations must be valid too.

The equality

$$g_{1,min}^* = g_{1,min} \qquad \qquad \text{... (6.81)}$$

is also valid, according to Eq. (6.64). We also keep the set of values $\left\{ g_{i,min}^* \right\}_{i=1}^{K}$ from the first part of evaluation.

The value $g_{1,min}$ is given from Eq. (6.81) immediately. According to Eq. (6.79) we can calculate $G_{2,min} = G_{1,min} - g_{1,min}$ and then it is valid $g_{2,min} = g_{2,min}^* G_{2,min}$ according to Eq. (6.80). Then, it is possible to calculate $G_{3,min} = G_{2,min} - g_{2,min}$ and $g_{3,min} = g_{3,min}^* G_{3,min}$, etc., and $G_{K-1,min} = G_{K-2,min} - g_{K-2,min}$, $g_{K-1,min} = g_{K-1,min}^* G_{K-1,min}$, and finally $G_{K,min} = G_{K-1,min} - g_{K-1,min}$ and according to Eq. (6.79) $g_{K,min} = G_{K,min}$. In this way, we obtain the required progression $\left\{ g_{i,min} \right\}_{i=1}^{K}$.

At last, we can determine the total minimum of the breaking strength $\sigma_{b,min}^*$ of the bundle using the mentioned progression in Eq. (6.59) as follows

$$\sigma_{b,min}^* = \max \left\{ \sum_{j=i}^{K} g_{j,min} \sigma_j \left(a_i \right) \right\}_{i=1}^{K}. \qquad \qquad \text{... (6.82)}$$

Easiest case – equations for three-component bundle. The previous expressions make it possible to calculate all necessary quantities for the arbitrarily high number K of components. Nevertheless, three-component bundles are practically most frequent blends, except mono-component and bi-component bundles. Therefore, we introduce the previous expressions in special forms for the three components now.

Let us imagine a three-component parallel fiber bundle ($K = 3$) created from three types of fibers with breaking strains $a_1 \le a_2 \le a_3$ – see the relation expressed by (6.45). Then we need to know the following input values: (1) the specific breaking strengths (tenacities) $\sigma_1 \left(a_1 \right), \sigma_2 \left(a_2 \right), \sigma_3 \left(a_3 \right)$ and the specific stresses $\sigma_2 \left(a_1 \right), \sigma_3 \left(a_1 \right), \sigma_3 \left(a_2 \right)$ of the fibers – e.g. see Fig. 6.7 preliminarily, (2) the values of mass fractions g_1, g_2, g_3 of the components. Then, the following expressions can be written for the local maxima $\sigma_b(a_1), \sigma_b(a_2), \sigma_b(a_3)$ and for the bundle specific strength σ_b^* according to Eqs. (6.57) and (6.59)

$$\left.\begin{array}{ll}\sigma_b\left(a_1\right)=g_1\sigma_1\left(a_1\right)+g_2\sigma_2\left(a_1\right)+g_3\sigma_3\left(a_1\right),\\[4pt]\sigma_b\left(a_2\right)=\qquad\qquad g_2\sigma_2\left(a_2\right)+g_3\sigma_3\left(a_2\right),\\[4pt]\sigma_b\left(a_3\right)=\qquad\qquad\qquad\qquad g_3\sigma_3\left(a_3\right).\end{array}\right\}\qquad\dots(6.83)$$

$$\sigma_b^* = \max\left\{\sigma_b\left(a_1\right),\sigma_b\left(a_2\right),\sigma_b\left(a_2\right)\right\}.\qquad\dots(6.84)$$

We need to know the following six values only $\sigma_1\left(a_1\right),\sigma_2\left(a_1\right),\sigma_2\left(a_2\right),\sigma_3\left(a_1\right),\sigma_3\left(a_2\right),\sigma_3\left(a_3\right)$ for determination of minimum specific strength $\sigma_{b,\min}^*$ of the bundle and for corresponding progression of the mass fractions $\left\{g_{1,\min},g_{2,\min},g_{3,\min}\right\}$. The following expressions are then valid according to Eq. (6.68) for $j = K = 3$

$$Z_3\left(a_3\right)=\sigma_3\left(a_3\right),\quad Z_3\left(a_2\right)=\sigma_3\left(a_2\right),\quad Z_3\left(a_1\right)=\sigma_3\left(a_1\right).\qquad\dots(6.85)$$

Further we can use Eq. (6.75) for $i = 3$.

$$r_{2,C}^* = \frac{\sigma_2\left(a_2\right)}{\sigma_2\left(a_2\right)+Z_3\left(a_3\right)-Z_3\left(a_2\right)},\quad g_{2,C}^* = 1 - r_{2,C}^*.\qquad\dots(6.86)$$

Now, we shall use Eq. (6.77) for $i = 3$ to determine the values $g_{2,\min}^*$ and $r_{2,\min}^*$ as follows

$$\left.\begin{array}{l}\text{If } \sigma_2\left(a_2\right)>Z_3\left(a_2\right) \text{ then } g_{2,\min}^* = g_{2,C}^*,\ r_{2,\min}^* = r_{2,C}^*,\\[4pt]\text{if } \sigma_2\left(a_2\right)<Z_3\left(a_2\right) \text{ then } g_{2,\min}^* = 1,\ r_{2,\min}^* = 0.\end{array}\right\}\qquad\dots(6.87)[9]$$

Let us continue to calculate according to Eq. (6.68) for $j = 2$ and the values $g_2^* = g_{2,\min}^*$ and $r_2^* = r_{2,\min}^*$ as follows

$$\left.\begin{array}{l}Z_2\left(a_2\right)=g_{2,\min}^*\sigma_2\left(a_2\right)+r_{2,\min}^*Z_3\left(a_2\right),\\[4pt]Z_2\left(a_1\right)=g_{2,\min}^*\sigma_2\left(a_1\right)+r_{2,\min}^*Z_3\left(a_1\right).\end{array}\right\}\qquad\dots(6.88)$$

Further we use Equation (6.75) for $i = 2$. So we obtain

$$r_{1,C}^* = \frac{\sigma_1\left(a_1\right)}{\sigma_1\left(a_1\right)+Z_2\left(a_2\right)-Z_2\left(a_1\right)},\quad g_{1,C}^* = 1 - r_{1,C}^*.\qquad\dots(6.89)$$

---

9. Do not forget that the case of equality was neglected according to our assumption.

Now, we shall use Eq. (6.77) for $i = 2$ to determine the values $g_{1,\min}^*$ and $r_{1,\min}^*$ as follows

$$\left.\begin{array}{l} \text{If } \sigma_1(a_1) > Z_2(a_1) \text{ then } g_{1,\min}^* = g_{1,C}^*, \ r_{1,\min}^* = r_{1,C}^*, \\ \text{if } \sigma_1(a_1) < Z_2(a_1) \text{ then } g_{1,\min}^* = 1, \ r_{1,\min}^* = 0. \end{array}\right\} \quad \ldots (6.90)$$

We can also write the following expressions from Eqs. (6.64) and (6.65) for $K = 3$.

$$g_{3,\min}^* = 1, \ r_{3,\min}^* = 0. \qquad \ldots (6.91)^{10}$$

In this way, we find the complete triplet of values $g_{1,\min}^*, g_{2,\min}^*, g_{3,\min}^*$. Equation (6.81) determines the quantity

$$g_{1,\min} = g_{1,\min}^*.$$

We get the values $G_{1,\min}, G_{2,\min}$ from Eq. (6.79) for $i = 1$

$$G_{1,\min} = 1, \quad G_{2,\min} = G_{1,\min} - g_{1,\min}. \qquad \ldots (6.92)$$

Using $i = 2$ in Eq. (6.80), we obtain

$$g_{2,\min} = g_{2,\min}^* G_{2,\min}. \qquad \ldots (6.93)$$

Further, we use Eq. (6.79) once more but for $i = 2$

$$G_{3,\min} = G_{2,\min} - g_{2,\min}. \qquad \ldots (6.94)$$

Finally, we use Eq. (6.80) once more for $i = 3$ and also $g_{3,\min}^* = 1$ according to Eq. (6.91)

$$g_{3,\min} = g_{3,\min}^* G_{3,\min} = G_{3,\min}. \qquad \ldots (6.95)$$

So, we find the triplet of mass fractions $g_{1,\min}, g_{2,\min}, g_{3,\min}$ pertaining to the minimum bundle specific strength $\sigma_{b,\min}^*$. Applying Eqs. (6.83) and (6.84) we determine this value as follows

$$\left.\begin{array}{l} \sigma_{b,\min}(a_1) = g_{1,\min}\sigma_1(a_1) + g_{2,\min}\sigma_2(a_1) + g_{3,\min}\sigma_3(a_1), \\ \sigma_{b,\min}(a_2) = \qquad\qquad g_{2,\min}\sigma_2(a_2) + g_{3,\min}\sigma_3(a_2), \\ \sigma_{b,\min}(a_3) = \qquad\qquad\qquad\qquad\qquad g_{3,\min}\sigma_3(a_3). \end{array}\right\} \quad \ldots (6.96)$$

---

10. $g_{3,\min}^*$ and $r_{3,\min}^*$ take some values of g_3^* and r_3^*, so that these equations must be valid too.

$$\sigma_{b,\min}^* = \max\left\{\sigma_{b,\min}\left(a_1\right), \sigma_{b,\min}\left(a_2\right), \sigma_{b,\min}\left(a_2\right)\right\}. \qquad \ldots (6.97)$$

Example 6.2: Hypothetical input data. Let us think about the triplet of (hypothetical) fibers according to Fig. 6.7. The fiber number 1 possesses the breaking strain a_1, the fiber number 2 shows its breaking strain $a_2 > a_1$, and the fiber number 3 displays the highest breaking strain $a_3 > a_2$. The necessary values of tenacities and specific stresses are determined immediately from Fig. 6.7.

We find the values as follows:

$$\left.\begin{array}{l} \sigma_1\left(a_1\right) = 10, \\[4pt] \sigma_2\left(a_1\right) = 8, \quad \sigma_2\left(a_2\right) = 15, \\[4pt] \sigma_3\left(a_1\right) = 7, \quad \sigma_3\left(a_2\right) = 12, \quad \sigma_3\left(a_3\right) = 20. \end{array}\right\} \qquad \ldots (6.98)$$

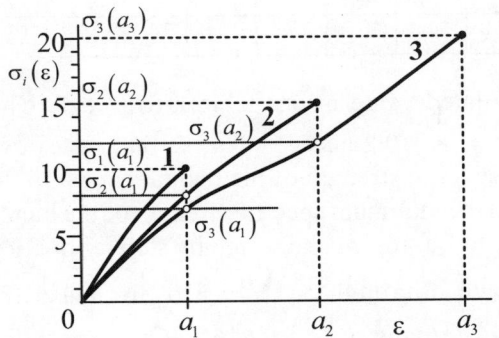

6.7 Specific stress–strain curves of hypothetical fibers 1, 2 and 3.

It is possible to calculate the specific strength σ_b^* of the bundle according to Eqs. (6.83) and (6.84) for each triplet of mass fractions g_1, g_2, g_3, now.

The values $g_1 = 0, 0.1,\ldots 0.9, 1$ and $g_2 = 0, 0.1,\ldots,0.9, 1$ are used in Table 6.6.

Note: It can be written that the value $g_3 = 1 - g_1 - g_2$. The values of the specific strength of the bundle for a constant value of g_3 create a diagonal set in Table 6.6; e.g., the diagonal values from 10 to 15 correspond to the value $g_3 = 0$, etc.

It can be seen from the table that

(1) The values often show a decreasing trend followed by an increasing trend by a constant value of one mass fraction; e.g., for $g_1 = 0$ (case of two components – second and third) the values decrease from 20 to 13.2 and then increase to 15, etc. Such trend is known from Hamburger's theory presented in Section 6.2.

Table 6.6 Example 1 – Calculated values of specific strength σ_b^* of bundle.

		g_2										
		0	0.1	0.2	0.3	0.4	0.5	0.6	0.7	0.8	0.9	1
	1	10										
	0.9	9.7	9.8									
	0.8	9.4	9.5	9.6								
	0.7	9.1	9.2	9.3	9.4							
	0.6	8.8	8.9	9.0	9.1	9.2						
g_1	0.5	10.0	8.6	8.7	8.8	8.9	9.0					
	0.4	12.0	10.0	**8.4**	8.5	8.6	8.7	9.0				
	0.3	14.0	12.0	10.0	9.3	9.6	9.9	10.2	10.5			
	0.2	16.0	14.0	12.0	10.5	10.8	11.1	11.4	11.7	12.0		
	0.1	18.0	16.0	14.0	12.0	12.0	12.3	12.6	12.9	13.2	13.5	
	0	20.0	18.0	16.0	14.0	13.2	13.5	13.8	14.1	14.4	14.7	15.0

(2)   The smallest calculated value in our table is $\sigma_b^* = 8.4$, which was obtained by $g_1 = 0.4$, $g_2 = 0.2$ and $g_3 = 0.4$, so that we can wait, the total minimum of specific strength of the bundle is near to this case.

Further, we calculated the minimum specific strength of the bundle using the input data according to Eq. (6.98) and – step by step – Equations from (6.85) to (6.97), and we obtained $\sigma_{b,min}^* = 8.310$ for mass fractions $g_{1,min} = 0.3629$, $g_{2,min} = 0.2216$ and $g_{3,min} = 0.4155$. (Our expectation from the table was right).

Example 6.3: Cotton/viscose/polyester. Let us think about three type of real fibers: (1) cotton fibers[11] (breaking strain $a_1 = 0.08$), (2) viscose fibers (breaking strain $a_2 = 0.17$), and (3) polyester fibers (breaking strain $a_3 = 0.27$). Beside the breaking strain values we found the necessary values for the tenacities and the specific stresses from (mean) stress–strain curves, available for these fibers

$$\text{Cotton: } \sigma_1(a_1) = 40\,\text{cN tex}^{-1},$$
$$\text{Viscose: } \sigma_2(a_1) = 16\,\text{cN tex}^{-1}, \quad \sigma_2(a_2) = 26\,\text{cN tex}^{-1},$$
$$\text{Polyester: } \sigma_3(a_1) = 30\,\text{cN tex}^{-1}, \quad \sigma_3(a_2) = 50\,\text{cN tex}^{-1}, \quad \sigma_3(a_3) = 53\,\text{cN tex}^{-1}.$$

$$\ldots (6.99)$$

---

11. We assume that each cotton fiber is gripped by both jaws of the tensile tester in this case.

The specific strengths σ_b^* of the bundle were calculated according to Eqs. (6.83) and (6.84), similarly as in the previous example, and the results are displayed in Table 6.7; the values from Eq. (6.99) were used.

Table 6.7 Example 2 – Calculated values of specific strength σ_b^* [cN tex^{-1}] of the bundle.

		g_2										
		0	0.1	0.2	0.3	0.4	0.5	0.6	0.7	0.8	0.9	1
	1	40.0										
	0.9	39.0	37.6									
	0.8	38.0	36.6	35.2								
	0.7	37.0	35.6	34.2	32.8							
	0.6	36.0	34.6	33.2	31.8	30.4						
g_1	0.5	35.0	33.6	32.2	30.8	29.4	28.0					
	0.4	34.0	32.6	31.2	29.8	28.4	27.0	25.6				
	0.3	37.1	32.6	30.2	28.8	27.4	26.0	24.6	23.2			
	0.2	42.4	37.6	35.2	32.8	30.4	28.0	25.6	23.2	**20.8**		
	0.1	47.7	42.6	40.2	37.8	35.4	33.0	30.6	28.2	25.8	23.4	
	0	53.0	47.7	45.2	42.8	40.4	38.0	35.6	33.2	30.8	28.4	26.0

The "broken" trends are shown only for the constant value of g_3 on diagonal directions in this case; e.g., for $g_3 = 0$ (diagonal from 40 to 26) the minimum value is 20.8 cN tex^{-1} and this is also the smallest value in the whole table. So, we can wait, the total minimum is near to $g_1 = 0.2$, $g_2 = 0.8$ and $g_3 = 0$.

The minimum specific strength of the bundle was calculated using the input data according to Eq. (6.99) and – step by step – Equations from (6.85) to (6.97). We obtained $\sigma_{b,min}^* = 20.8000$ cN tex^{-1} for mass fractions $g_{1,min} = 0.2000$ (cotton), $g_{2,min} = 0.8000$ (viscose) and $g_{3,min} = 0$ (polyester) – the blend without polyester fibers. (Coincidentally, the result is quite the same as our expectation from the table, thanks to values from Eq. (6.99). Usually, it is not so).

6.4   Mechanics of a complex parallel fiber bundle with variable fiber properties

A real fiber bundle consists of many single fibers that have different physical and mechanical characteristics. When such a fiber bundle is tested for its mechanical behavior, we observe its (specific) stress–strain curve, breaking force, strength and/or specific strength, and breaking elongation and/or breaking strain, differ from those average results of single fibers. This is known due to the effect of distribution of breaking points of single fibers and the effect of fiber crimp and its variability. Many earlier works [2–17] dealt with different aspects of this phenomenon under various assumptions. In this work, we made attempts to derive these effects of a bundle from a common basis given by stress–strain curves, distribution of breaking points, and crimp and its distribution of single fibers [18].

Straining of single fiber. Let us think of one slack fiber of initial length l_0, which is clamped between two jaws where the line of joining of two clamped points is parallel to the jaw axis.

Initially, the actual distance d between the jaws is equal to the gauge length $h \le l_0$. This is shown in Fig. 6.8 (Case 1). The initial value of acting force is $F = 0$.

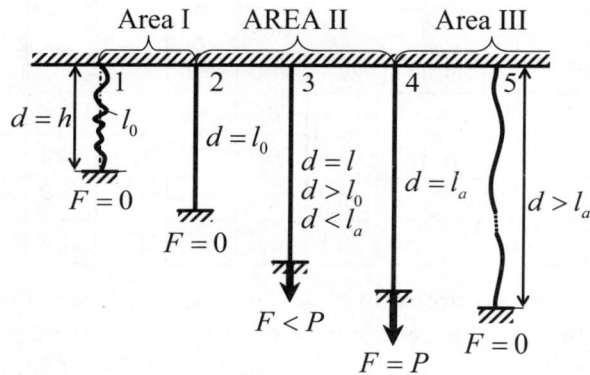

6.8 Straining of fiber between jaws.

Let us now increase the distance d. The slack fiber is straightened and obtained a quite straight position, where $d = l_0$ (Figure 6.8, Case 2). In Area I, the general fiber length is $l = l_0$ and the acting force is $F = 0$.

Further increase of the distance d causes elongation of the fiber so that $l = d > l_0$ (Case 3). In Area II, the distance increases from $d = l_0$ (Case 2) to fiber breaking length $d = l = l_a$ (Case 4). And the force increases from $F = 0$ (Case 2) to fiber breaking force (strength) $F = P$ (Case 4).

If the distance d is higher than the fiber breaking length l_a (Area III) then the fiber breaks (Case 5), the fiber length l cannot be defined, and the force becomes $F = 0$ again.

Table 6.8 summarizes the obtained relations. It can be noted that a positive value of force F relates only to the fiber in Area II.

Table 6.8 Relations among d, l, and F.

Situation	Fiber length l	Distance d	Acting force F
Area I	$l = l_0$	$d \in \langle h, l_0 \rangle$	$F = 0$
Area II	$l = d \in \langle l_0, l_a \rangle$	$d \in \langle l_0, l_a \rangle$	$F \in \langle 0, P \rangle$
Area III	Broken fiber	$d > l_a$	$F = 0$

Let us now define the following relative length quantities: jaw displacement ε, fiber strain ε_f, fiber breaking strain a_f, and fiber crimp (waviness) λ

$$\varepsilon = (d - h)/h = d/h - 1, \ \varepsilon \geq 0, \qquad \ldots (6.100)$$

$$\varepsilon_f = (l - l_0)/l_0 = l/l_0 - 1, \ \varepsilon_f \geq 0, \qquad \ldots (6.101)$$

$$a_f = (l_a - l_0)/l_0 = l_a/l_0 - 1, \ a_f \geq 0, \qquad \ldots (6.102)$$

$$\lambda = (l_0 - h)/h = l_0/h - 1, \ \lambda \geq 0. \qquad \ldots (6.103)$$

Let us rewrite Eqs. (6.100) and (6.103) below

$$d = h(1 + \varepsilon), \qquad \ldots (6.104)$$

$$l_0 = h(1 + \lambda). \qquad \ldots (6.105)$$

The one (lower) limit of Area II, when force $F = 0$, is $d = l = l_0$ (Table 6.8). Then, using the last two equations, we obtain the following expression

$$d = l_0, \ h(1 + \varepsilon) = h(1 + \lambda), \ \varepsilon = \lambda. \qquad \ldots (6.106)$$

The other (upper) limit of Area II, when $F = P$, is $d = l = l_a$ (Table 6.8). Then, we obtain the following expression by using Eqs. (6.100), (6.102), and (6.103)

$$\varepsilon = \frac{d}{h} - 1 = \frac{l_a}{h} - 1 = \frac{l_a}{l_0} \frac{l_0}{h} - 1 = (1 + a_f)(1 + \lambda) - 1 = a_f \lambda + a_f + \lambda. \ \ldots (6.107)$$

From the last equation we also obtain the following expressions for the upper limit of the Area II

$$\varepsilon = \lambda\left(1+a_f\right)+a_f, \quad \lambda = \left(\varepsilon-a_f\right)\big/\left(1+a_f\right), \qquad \dots (6.108)$$

$$\varepsilon = a_f\left(1+\lambda\right)+\lambda, \quad a_f = \left(\varepsilon-\lambda\right)\big/\left(1+\lambda\right). \qquad \dots (6.109)$$

Note: The upper limit of Area II is given by relation among the triplet of variables ε, a_f, λ. Therefore, all three Eqs. (6.107), (6.108), and (6.109) say the same information.

The limit lines are shown in Fig. 6.9.

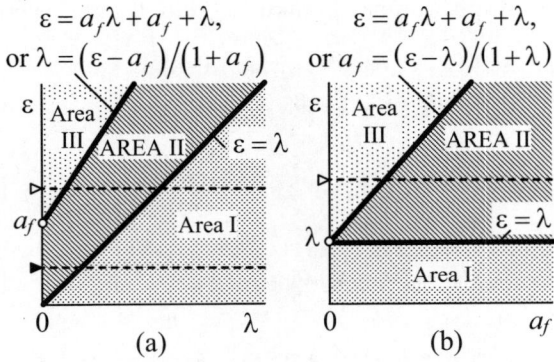

6.9 Graphical representation of the borders among Areas I, II, and III.

Let us now consider that we know the values of ε and a_f and we want to define the fiber in Area II by averages of the quantity λ. This can be done by following expressions, obtained from Fig. 6.9a by using Eq. (6.108)

If $\varepsilon \leq a_f$ then $\lambda \in \langle 0,\varepsilon \rangle$, (See ▶).

If $\varepsilon > a_f$ then $\lambda \in \left\langle \left(\varepsilon-a_f\right)\big/\left(1+a_f\right),\varepsilon \right\rangle$, (See ▷). $\dots (6.110)$

In another case, let us consider that we know the values of ε and λ and we want to define the fiber in Area II by the quantity a_f. Then, it is valid to write the following expressions, obtained from Fig. 6.9b, by using Eq. (6.109).

If $\varepsilon \geq \lambda$ then $a_f \in \left\langle \left(\varepsilon-\lambda\right)/\left(1+\lambda\right),\infty \right\rangle$, (See ▷).

If $\varepsilon < \lambda$ then a_f do not exist for the Area II. $\dots (6.111)$

Note: The fiber in Area I is given by the relation $\varepsilon < \lambda$ and the fiber in Area III corresponds to the expression $\varepsilon > a_f\lambda + a_f + \lambda$, and/or $\lambda < \left(\varepsilon-a_f\right)\big/\left(1+a_f\right)$, and/or $a_f < \left(\varepsilon-\lambda\right)/\left(1+\lambda\right)$.

For the whole Area II, it is valid to write that $l = d$ – see Fig. 6.8 and/or Table 6.8. Then the strain ε, described generally according to Eq. (6.100), can have the form $\varepsilon = l/h - 1$ for Area II, and we can rearrange it using Eqs. (6.101) and (6.103) as follows

$$\varepsilon = \frac{d}{h} - 1 = \frac{l}{h} - 1 = \frac{l}{l_0}\frac{l_0}{h} - 1 = (1+\varepsilon_f)(1+\lambda) - 1 = \varepsilon_f \lambda + \varepsilon_f + \lambda,$$

$$\varepsilon_f = \frac{\varepsilon - \lambda}{1+\lambda}. \qquad \text{... (6.112)}$$

Furthermore, let us now consider an increasing force–strain function between fiber force F and fiber strain ε_f or jaw displacement ε, as shown below

$$F = S(\varepsilon_f) = S\left(\frac{\varepsilon - \lambda}{1+\lambda}\right), \quad \varepsilon_f \in \langle 0, a_f\rangle, (\, 0 = S(0), P = S(a_f)). \quad \text{... (6.113)}$$

Each fiber in a bundle has its own force–strain curve $S(\varepsilon_f)$, strength P, breaking strain a_f, and crimp λ. The quantities a_f, P, and λ are random variables having average values $\bar{a}_f$, $\bar{P}$, and $\bar{\lambda}$.

We often assume that there exists an average force–strain function $\bar{S}(\varepsilon_f)$ that is common for all fibers (Figure 6.10). For this, it is valid to write the followings:

(a) The function $\bar{S}(\varepsilon_f)$ is an increasing function, defined for all needed values of ε_f and a_f.

(b) The curve of this function starts from the point $(\varepsilon_f = 0, \bar{S}(0) = 0)$ and comes (conventionally) through the middle point $(\bar{a}_f, \bar{P})$ so that $\bar{P} = \bar{S}(\bar{a}_f)$.

(c) The so-called "theorem of similarity" says that the force–strain function of each fiber (before breaking point) is proportional to the average force–strain function. Then $F = S(\varepsilon_f) = K\bar{S}(\varepsilon_f)$, where K is a suitable constant of proportionality. If $F = P$ then $\varepsilon_f = a_f$, and the expressions $P = K\bar{S}(a_f)$, $K = P/\bar{S}(a_f)$ are valid. Applying the last expression in the first equation we obtain the relation as follows

$$F = \frac{P}{\bar{S}(a_f)}\bar{S}(\varepsilon_f) = \frac{P}{\bar{S}(a_f)}\bar{S}\left(\frac{\varepsilon - \lambda}{1+\lambda}\right). \qquad \text{... (6.114)}$$

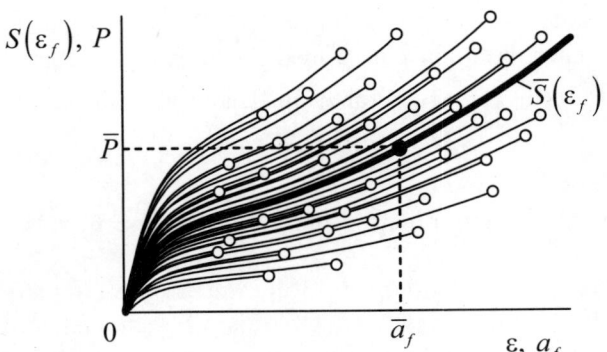

6.10 Force–strain curves of fibers:

—... curves of single fibers; O...breaking points of single
fibers; ▬...average function; ●...middle point of break.

(Equation (6.112) was used for the second expression). The breaking
force P and the breaking strain a_f are only two scalar characteristics of
individual fiber; $\overline{S}(\varepsilon_f)$ is a common function for all fibers. Assuming, for
example, a linear force–strain function of fibers, it is possible to write the
following expressions based on assumption (b) and Eqs. (6.113) and (6.114)

$$\overline{S}(\varepsilon_f) = \frac{\overline{P}}{\overline{a}_f}\varepsilon_f = \frac{\overline{P}}{\overline{a}_f}\frac{\varepsilon - \lambda}{1 + \lambda}, \qquad \qquad \ldots (6.115)$$

$$F = S(\varepsilon_f) = S\left(\frac{\varepsilon - \lambda}{1 + \lambda}\right) = \frac{P}{a_f}\varepsilon_f = \frac{P}{a_f}\frac{\varepsilon - \lambda}{1 + \lambda}. \qquad \ldots (6.116)$$

Furthermore, let us consider an "average fiber" having average strength
$\overline{P}$, average braking strain $\overline{a}_f$, and average crimp $\overline{\lambda}$. Such a hypothetical
fiber reaches to its strength when the jaw displacement is ε^*, then, according
to Eq. (6.107), we obtain

$$\varepsilon^* = \overline{a}_f\overline{\lambda} + \overline{a}_f + \overline{\lambda}. \qquad \qquad \ldots (6.117)$$

We will compare the tensile properties of such an "average" fiber with
that of a fiber bundle in subsequent sections.

Straining of a big fiber bundle. Let us imagine a big fiber bundle composed
of many slack fibers that are mutually independent to each other and the
fiber parameters a_f, P, and λ are random quantities. The distribution of such
random triplets can be described by a joint probability density function[12]
(PDF) $w(a_f, P, \lambda)$ where, in general, $a_f \in \langle 0, \infty)$, $P \in \langle 0, \infty)$, and

---

12. This is similar to the distribution of random vectors (triplets).

$\lambda \in \langle 0, \infty \rangle$. The average force $\bar{F}$ per fiber of the bundle is given by

$$\bar{F} = \iiint_{\substack{a_f \in \langle 0,\infty \rangle \\ P \in \langle 0,\infty \rangle \\ \lambda \in \langle 0,\infty \rangle}} F\, w(a_f, P, \lambda)\, \mathrm{d}a_f\, \mathrm{d}P\, \mathrm{d}\lambda \qquad \dots (6.118)$$

(The force F is different for individual fibers, in relation to their individual values a_f, P, λ).

As we do not have enough information to solve this function, we introduce two assumptions to simplify this problem.

(a) Fiber breaking points and fiber crimps are mutually independent. Then, we can write

$$w(a_f, P, \lambda) = v(\lambda)\, u(a_f, P), \qquad \dots (6.119)$$

where $v(\lambda)$ is a PDF of λ and $u(a_f, P)$ is a joint PDF of a_f and P. According to the theory of probability, we know

$$g(a_f) = \int_0^\infty u(a_f, P)\, \mathrm{d}P, \qquad \dots (6.120)$$

$$\overline{P(a_f)} = \int_0^\infty P u(a_f, P)\, \mathrm{d}P \bigg/ g(a_f), \qquad \dots (6.121)$$

where $g(a_f)$ denotes the marginal PDF[13] of a_f and $\overline{P(a_f)}$ indicates the conditional mean value[14] of P.

(b) Force–strain curves of single fibers satisfy the "theorem of similarity" in accordance with Eq. (6.114) and Fig. 6.10.

In fact, only the fibers from Area II contribute to the integral expressed by Eq. (6.118), so that the general integral borders can be reduced. The fiber breaking force P does not influence on the determination of Area II so that we need to think about the full interval $P \in (0, \infty)$. Nevertheless, not all possible couples of λ and a_f correspond to the Area II. It is shown from Eq. (6.111) that it must be valid to write $\lambda \le \varepsilon$ and $a_f \ge (\varepsilon - \lambda)/(1 + \lambda)$ so as to be in the Area II. Therefore, we can write the following expression

$$\bar{F} = \iiint_{\substack{a_f \in \langle 0,\infty \rangle \\ P \in \langle 0,\infty \rangle \\ \lambda \in \langle 0,\infty \rangle}} F\, w(a_f, P, \lambda)\, \mathrm{d}a_f\, \mathrm{d}P\, \mathrm{d}\lambda = \int_0^\varepsilon \left\{ \int_{\frac{\varepsilon-\lambda}{1+\lambda}}^\infty \left[\int_0^\infty F\, w(a_f, P, \lambda)\, \mathrm{d}P \right] \mathrm{d}a_f \right\} \mathrm{d}\lambda .$$

$$\dots (6.122)$$

---

13. It tells about the distribution of a_f only.
14. This is the average value of fiber strength P that can be obtained from a subset of fibers having same value of breaking strain a_f. See Fig. 6.13 preliminarily.

Let us rearrange Eq. (6.122) by using Eqs. (6.114), (6.119), and (6.121)

$$\bar{F} = \int\limits_0^\varepsilon \left\{ \int\limits_{\frac{\varepsilon-\lambda}{1+\lambda}}^\infty \left[\int\limits_0^\infty F\, w\left(a_f, P, \lambda\right) dP \right] da_f \right\} d\lambda$$

$$= \int\limits_0^\varepsilon \left\{ \int\limits_{\frac{\varepsilon-\lambda}{1+\lambda}}^\infty \left[\int\limits_0^\infty \frac{P}{\bar{S}(a_f)}\, \bar{S}\left(\frac{\varepsilon-\lambda}{1+\lambda}\right)\, v(\lambda)u\left(a_f, P\right) dP \right] da_f \right\} d\lambda$$

$$= \int\limits_0^\varepsilon \left\{ \int\limits_{\frac{\varepsilon-\lambda}{1+\lambda}}^\infty \left[\int\limits_0^\infty P u\left(a_f, P\right) dP \right] \frac{1}{\bar{S}(a_f)}\, da_f \right\} \bar{S}\left(\frac{\varepsilon-\lambda}{1+\lambda}\right) v(\lambda)\, d\lambda, \qquad \ldots (6.123)$$

$$\bar{F} = \int\limits_0^\varepsilon \left\{ \int\limits_{\frac{\varepsilon-\lambda}{1+\lambda}}^\infty \frac{\overline{P(a_f)}}{\bar{S}(a_f)}\, g\left(a_f\right) da_f \right\} \bar{S}\left(\frac{\varepsilon-\lambda}{1+\lambda}\right) v(\lambda)\, d\lambda.$$

The maximum of average force per fiber in the bundle $\bar{F} = \bar{F}_{\max}$ characterizes the bundle breaking force. (This can be obtained by multiplying $\bar{F}_{\max}$ by the number of fibers present in the bundle). The value $\bar{F} = \bar{F}_{\max}$ corresponds to the breaking strain $\varepsilon = a$ of the bundle. Comparing the breaking behavior of the "average fiber", expressed in Eq. (6.117) with that of the bundle, we define the strength utilization coefficient η_P and the breaking force utilization coefficient η_a as follows

$$\eta_P = \bar{F}_{\max}/\bar{P}, \qquad \ldots (6.124)$$

$$\eta_a = a/\varepsilon^* = a/\left(\bar{a}_f\bar{\lambda} + \bar{a}_f + \bar{\lambda}\right). \qquad \ldots (6.125)$$

Fibers of same strength and same breaking elongation. Let us suppose that $S(\varepsilon_f) = \bar{S}(\varepsilon_f)$, $a_f = \bar{a}_f = $ constant, $P = \bar{P} = \bar{S}(a_f) = $ constant and the general PDF $w(a_f, P, \lambda)$ reduces to the PDF of fiber crimp $v(\lambda)$ only. Then, Eq. (6.114) can be written as $F = S(\varepsilon_f) = S\left(\frac{\varepsilon-\lambda}{1+\lambda}\right)$, Eq. (6.118) simplifies to $\bar{F} = \int_0^\infty F v(\lambda)\, d\lambda$, and using Eq. (6.110) we derive the following expression

$$\text{If } \varepsilon \leq a_f \text{ then } \bar{F} = \int\limits_0^\varepsilon S\left(\frac{\varepsilon-\lambda}{1+\lambda}\right) v(\lambda)\, d\lambda.$$

$$\text{If } \varepsilon > a_f \text{ then } \bar{F} = \int\limits_{\frac{\varepsilon-a_f}{1+a_f}}^\varepsilon S\left(\frac{\varepsilon-\lambda}{1+\lambda}\right) v(\lambda)\, d\lambda. \qquad \ldots (6.126)$$

As an example, let us consider the linear force–strain function of fibers according to Eq. (6.116) and a lognormal distribution of fiber crimp, shown below

$$v(\lambda) = \frac{1}{\sqrt{2\pi}\,\sigma\lambda} e^{-\frac{(\ln\lambda-\mu)^2}{2\sigma^2}}, \quad \mu = \ln\frac{\overline{\lambda}}{\sqrt{CV_\lambda^2+1}}, \quad \sigma = \sqrt{\ln(CV_\lambda^2+1)} \quad .... \text{(6.127)}$$

The quantity $\overline{\lambda}$ indicates the average value of λ and CV_λ denotes the coefficient of variation[15] of λ.

We calculated $\overline{F}$ from Eq. (6.126) using Eqs. (6.116) and (6.127) applying a numerical method of integration. Some results are shown in Fig. 6.11. Each thick curve represents the relation between the jaw displacement ε and the ratio $\overline{F}/P$. (If average force per fiber in the bundle reaches to the strength of single fiber then we obtain $\overline{F}/P = 1$).

In Fig. 6.11, the breaking points of the bundles (○) are shown to lie on the thin line. Their coordinates express the strength utilization coefficients $\overline{F}_{max}/P = \eta_P$ – Equation (6.124) – and the breaking strain of bundle is $\varepsilon = a$. Also, using Eq. (6.125), we can evaluate the breaking strain utilization coefficient as $\eta_a = a/(a_f\overline{\lambda} + a_f + \overline{\lambda})$.

Note: Do not forget that still each $P = \overline{P}$ and each $a_f = \overline{a}_f$ in this case.

The strength utilization coefficient is equal to the maximum of the ratio $\overline{F}/P$ so that $d\overline{F}/d\varepsilon = 0$ at $\varepsilon = a$. This idea allows us to determine the breaking strain of bundle a and the bundle breaking force per one fiber $\overline{F}_{max}$.

Let us rewrite the second expression of Eq. (6.126) as follows

$$\overline{F} = \int_{\varphi_1(\varepsilon)}^{\varphi_2(\varepsilon)} f(\lambda,\varepsilon)\, d\lambda, \text{ where } f(\lambda,\varepsilon) = S\left(\frac{\varepsilon-\lambda}{1+\lambda}\right)v(\lambda), \quad \varphi_1(\varepsilon) = \frac{\varepsilon-a_f}{1+a_f}, \quad \varphi_2(\varepsilon) = \varepsilon.$$

$$... \text{(6.128)}$$

Then, it is valid to write that

$$\frac{\partial f(\lambda,\varepsilon)}{\partial\varepsilon} = \frac{\partial S\left(\frac{\varepsilon-\lambda}{1+\lambda}\right)}{\partial\varepsilon} v(\lambda), \quad \frac{d\varphi_1(\varepsilon)}{d\varepsilon} = \frac{1}{1+a_f}, \quad \frac{d\varphi_2(\varepsilon)}{d\varepsilon} = 1 .... \text{(6.129)}$$

---

15. We understand CV as a simple ratio of the standard deviation to the average value, not as percentage.

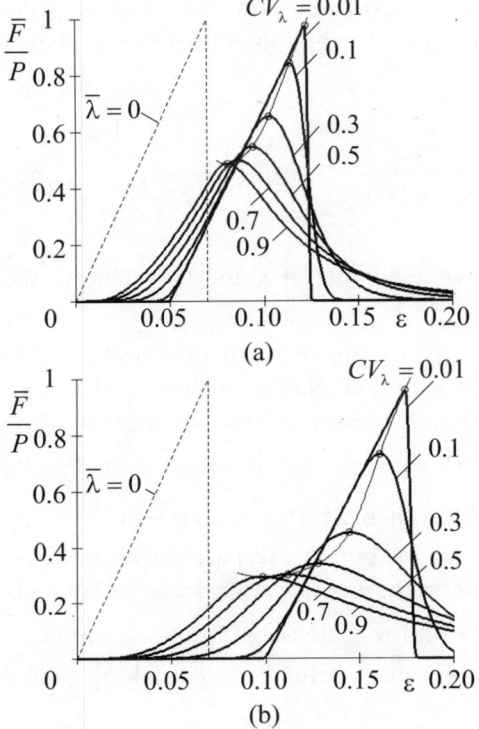

6.11 Graphical representation of the relation between ε and $\overline{F}/P$ for different values of a_f and $\overline{\lambda}$ (━): (a) $a_f = 0.07$ (7%), $\overline{\lambda} = 0.05$, (b) $a_f = 0.07$ (7%), $\overline{\lambda} = 0.1$ ∘...breaking points, ---... bundle of quite straight fibers.

Using the last two equations we obtain

$$\frac{d\overline{F}}{d\varepsilon} = \frac{d}{d\varepsilon}\left[\int_{\varphi_1(\varepsilon)}^{\varphi_2(\varepsilon)} f(\lambda,\varepsilon)\,d\lambda\right] = \int_{\varphi_1(\varepsilon)}^{\varphi_2(\varepsilon)} \frac{\partial f(\lambda,\varepsilon)}{\partial\varepsilon}\,d\lambda + \frac{d\varphi_2(\varepsilon)}{d\varepsilon} f\big(\varphi_2(\varepsilon),\varepsilon\big) - \frac{d\varphi_1(\varepsilon)}{d\varepsilon} f\big(\varphi_1(\varepsilon),\varepsilon\big)$$

$$= \int_{\frac{\varepsilon-a_f}{1+a_f}}^{\varepsilon} \frac{\partial S\left(\frac{\varepsilon-\lambda}{1+\lambda}\right)}{\partial\varepsilon} v(\lambda)\,d\lambda + 1\cdot S\left(\frac{\varepsilon-\varepsilon}{1+\varepsilon}\right) v(\varepsilon) - \frac{1}{1+a_f}\cdot S\left(\frac{\varepsilon-\frac{\varepsilon-a_f}{1+a_f}}{1+\frac{\varepsilon-a_f}{1+a_f}}\right) v\left(\frac{\varepsilon-a_f}{1+a_f}\right)$$

$$= \int_{\frac{\varepsilon-a_f}{1+a_f}}^{\varepsilon} \frac{\partial S\left(\frac{\varepsilon-\lambda}{1+\lambda}\right)}{\partial\varepsilon} v(\lambda)\,d\lambda - \frac{1}{1+a_f}\cdot S(a_f) v\left(\frac{\varepsilon-a_f}{1+a_f}\right).$$

$$\ldots (6.130)$$

Note: It was used $S(0) = 0$ according to Eq. (6.113), and

$$\left(\varepsilon - \frac{\varepsilon-a_f}{1+a_f}\right)\bigg/\left(1 + \frac{\varepsilon-a_f}{1+a_f}\right) = \frac{\varepsilon + \varepsilon a_f - \varepsilon + a_f}{1+a_f+\varepsilon-a_f} = \frac{a_f(1+\varepsilon)}{1+\varepsilon} = a_f.$$

The quantity $d\bar{F}/d\varepsilon = 0$ when $\bar{F}$ is maximum, i.e. $\bar{F} = \bar{F}_{max}$, and just there it is valid $\varepsilon = a$. So, we can write

$$0 = \int_{\frac{a-a_f}{1+a_f}}^{a} \frac{\partial S\left(\frac{a-\lambda}{1+\lambda}\right)}{\partial a} v(\lambda)\, d\lambda - \frac{1}{1+a_f} \cdot S(a_f) v\left(\frac{a-a_f}{1+a_f}\right),$$

$$1 = \frac{\displaystyle\int_{\frac{a-a_f}{1+a_f}}^{a} \frac{\partial S\left(\frac{a-\lambda}{1+\lambda}\right)}{\partial a} v(\lambda)\, d\lambda}{\dfrac{1}{1+a_f} \cdot S(a_f) v\left(\dfrac{a-a_f}{1+a_f}\right)}. \qquad \ldots (6.131)$$

The root a of the last equation determines the breaking strain of the bundle.

Applying especially Eq. (6.116) we can derive the following expressions

$$\frac{\partial S\left(\frac{a-\lambda}{1+\lambda}\right)}{\partial a} = \frac{\partial}{\partial a}\left[\frac{P}{a_f}\frac{a-\lambda}{1+\lambda}\right] = \frac{P}{a_f}\frac{1}{1+\lambda}, \qquad \ldots (6.132)$$

$$S(a_f) = \frac{P}{a_f} a_f = P. \qquad \ldots (6.133)$$

Accepting the idea of lognormal distribution according to Eq. (6.127) and then by $\lambda = (a - a_f)/(1 + a_f)$ we obtain

$$v\left(\frac{a-a_f}{1+a_f}\right) = \frac{1}{\sqrt{2\pi}\,\sigma\,\dfrac{a-a_f}{1+a_f}} e^{-\frac{\left(\ln\frac{a-a_f}{1+a_f} - \mu\right)^2}{2\sigma^2}}. \qquad \ldots (6.134)$$

Now, using Eq. (6.127) and Eqs. (6.132), (6.133), (6.134) in Eq. (6.131), we can write

$$
1 = \frac{\displaystyle\int_{\frac{a-a_f}{1+a_f}}^{a} \frac{\partial S\!\left(\frac{a-\lambda}{1+\lambda}\right)}{\partial a} v(\lambda)\,\mathrm{d}\lambda}{\dfrac{1}{1+a_f}\cdot S(a_f) v\!\left(\dfrac{a-a_f}{1+a_f}\right)} = \frac{\displaystyle\int_{\frac{a-a_f}{1+a_f}}^{a} \frac{P}{a_f}\frac{1}{1+\lambda}\frac{1}{\sqrt{2\pi}\,\sigma\lambda}e^{-\frac{(\ln\lambda-\mu)^2}{2\sigma^2}}\,\mathrm{d}\lambda}{\dfrac{1}{1+a_f}\cdot P \dfrac{1}{\sqrt{2\pi}\,\sigma\dfrac{a-a_f}{1+a_f}}e^{-\frac{\left(\ln\frac{a-a_f}{1+a_f}-\mu\right)^2}{2\sigma^2}}}, \quad \dots (6.135)
$$

$$
1 = \frac{\displaystyle\int_{\frac{a-a_f}{1+a_f}}^{a} \frac{1}{(1+\lambda)\lambda}e^{-\frac{(\ln\lambda-\mu)^2}{2\sigma^2}}\,\mathrm{d}\lambda}{\dfrac{a_f}{a-a_f}e^{-\frac{\left(\ln\frac{a-a_f}{1+a_f}-\mu\right)^2}{2\sigma^2}}},
$$

where $\mu = \ln\!\left(\bar{\lambda}\big/\sqrt{CV_\lambda^2+1}\right)$ and $\sigma = \sqrt{\ln\left(CV_\lambda^2+1\right)}$ according to Eq. (6.26).

The root a of the last equation, evaluated by a numerical method, represents the breaking strain of the bundle in this special case. We calculated also $\bar{F}_{max}$ from Eq. (6.126) using Eqs. (6.116), (6.127) and $\varepsilon = a$, applying again a numerical method of integration.

The graphical illustration of both of the utilization coefficients η_P and η_a is shown in Figs. 6.12a and 6.12b. These quantities are decreasing with the increase in the average value of fiber crimp $\bar{\lambda}$ as well as with the increase in the coefficient of variation CV_λ, but they are increasing with the increase in the fiber breaking strain a_f.

Note: Remember the definition of breaking strain utilization coefficient η_a of a bundle consisting of "average fibers" whose crimp is $\bar{\lambda}$, so that $\varepsilon^* = \left(a_f\bar{\lambda}+a_f+\bar{\lambda}\right) > a_f$ – Equations (6.117) and (6.125). For such a coefficient, it is always valid that $\eta_a \leq 1$ (see Fig. 6.12). Nevertheless, the breaking strain of a bundle is naturally higher than the breaking strain of a straight fiber a_f (see the peaks in Fig. 6.11).

Completely straight fibers. Let us imagine that all values of fiber crimp, having a probability density function $v(\lambda)$, are lying in the interval $\lambda \in \langle 0, \lambda_{max}\rangle$, where λ_{max} is a very small value. Then it is valid $\int_0^\infty v(\lambda)\,\mathrm{d}\lambda = \int_0^{\lambda_{max}} v(\lambda)\,\mathrm{d}\lambda = 1$ for each values $\varepsilon \geq \lambda_{max}$. Now, let us think that

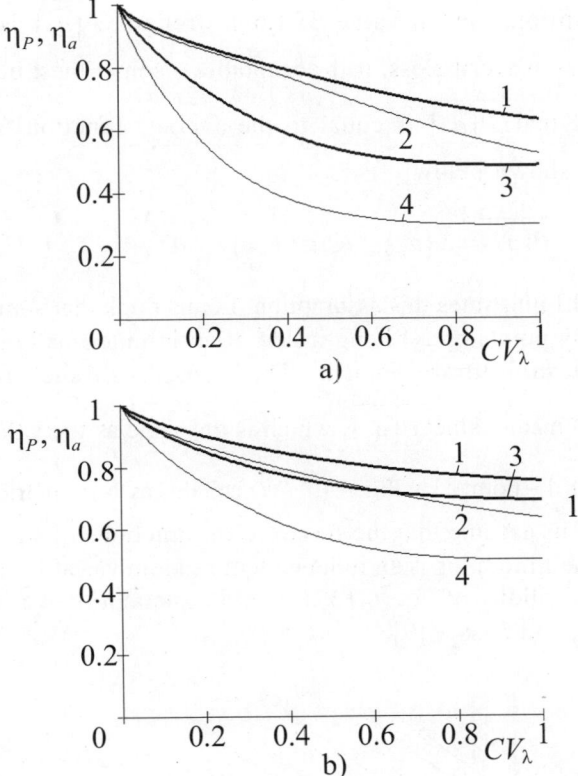

6.12 Behaviors of utilization coefficients:

(a) $a_f = 0.07$ and (b) $a_f = 0.15$,

curve 1...η_a for $\bar{\lambda} = 0.05$,

curve 2...η_a for $\bar{\lambda} = 0.1$,

curve 3...η_p for $\bar{\lambda} = 0.05$, and

curve 4...η_p for $\bar{\lambda} = 0.1$.

λ_{max} is limited to zero. Then (1) all fibers came to be straight (2) also all values of λ are limited to zero, and (3) the equation $\int_0^\varepsilon v(\lambda)\,d\lambda = 1$ is valid for all values $\varepsilon \geq 0$. Applying this type of limitation in Eq. (6.123) we obtain the expression as follows

$$\bar{F} = \int_0^\varepsilon \left\{ \int_\varepsilon^\infty \frac{\overline{P(a_f)}}{\overline{S(a_f)}} g(a_f)\,da_f \right\} \bar{S}(\varepsilon) v(\lambda)\,d\lambda = \bar{S}(\varepsilon) \left\{ \int_\varepsilon^\infty \frac{\overline{P(a_f)}}{\overline{S(a_f)}} g(a_f)\,da_f \right\} \int_0^\varepsilon v(\lambda)\,d\lambda,$$

$$\bar{F} = \bar{S}(\varepsilon) \int_\varepsilon^\infty \frac{\overline{P(a_f)}}{\overline{S(a_f)}} g(a_f)\,da_f.$$

$$\ldots (6.136)$$

The conditional mean value of fiber strength $\overline{P(a_f)}$ is generally a function of a_f. Nevertheless, it is acceptable – sometimes, but not always – to assume that $\overline{P(a_f)}$ is equal to the average function $\overline{S}(a_f)$ for all values of a_f, shown below

$$\overline{P(a_f)} = \overline{S}(a_f), \quad a_f \in \langle 0, \infty). \qquad \qquad \text{... (6.137)}$$

Figure 6.13 illustrates this assumption. Let us think that some fibers have their breaking points (gray) lying inside of an infinitesimally small strip of width da_f at an arbitrary point a_f. The strengths of such fibers have a (conditional) mean value $\overline{P(a_f)}$, which is the same as the value of average function $\overline{S}(a_f)$ – point $\square$ in Fig. 6.13. (We call this as "symmetrical strength").

Note: Let us assume that the force–strain functions of single fibers are linear and their modulus is an independent random variable. Then, we can establish the validity of Eq. (6.137). Similar assumption was made earlier by Cui, Suh, and Sasser [9].

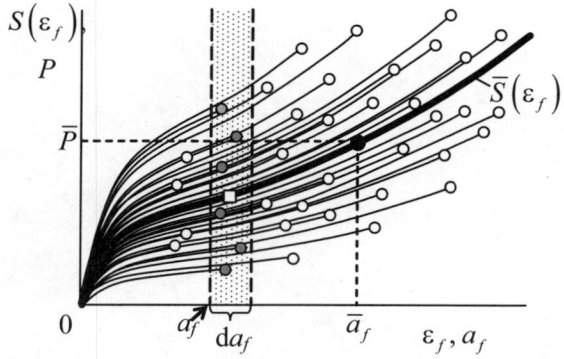

6.13 Force–strain curves of fibers: —...curves of individual fibers; O...breaking points of fibers; ▬...average function; □...the value of average function at $\varepsilon_f = a_f$.

Substituting Eq. (6.137) into Eq. (6.136), we obtain the following expression

$$\overline{F} = \overline{S}(\varepsilon)[1 - G(\varepsilon)], \quad G(\varepsilon) = \int_0^\varepsilon g(a_f) \, da_f . \qquad \text{... (6.138)}$$

Here $G(a_f)$ denotes the distribution function of fiber breaking strain.

Specially, when the fibers have linear force–strain functions then the following expression is valid to write in accordance with Eq. (6.115)

$$\bar{S}(\varepsilon) = \frac{\bar{P}}{a_f}\varepsilon, \quad \frac{\mathrm{d}\bar{S}(\varepsilon)}{\mathrm{d}\varepsilon} = \frac{\bar{P}}{a_f}. \qquad \ldots (6.139)$$

Notes: 1. Because of straight fibers, the fiber strain ε_f is equal to the jaw displacement ε in this case.
2. Equations (6.138) and (6.139) were derived by Peirce [1] under the assumption of independency of a_f and P in lieu of the assumption stated in Eq. (6.137) and by using the concept of linearity stated in Eq. (6.139). So, he obtained

$$\bar{F} = \left(\bar{P}/\bar{a}_f\right)\varepsilon \int_\varepsilon^\infty \left[g(a_f)\right]\mathrm{d}a_f.$$

Let us consider that the fiber breaking strain a_f follows e.g. lognormal distribution as shown below

$$g(a_f) = \frac{1}{\sqrt{2\pi}\,\sigma' a_f}e^{-\frac{\left(\ln a_f - \mu'\right)^2}{2\sigma'^2}},$$

$$\mu' = \ln\frac{\bar{a}_f}{\sqrt{CV_{a_f}^2 + 1}}, \qquad \ldots (6.140)$$

$$\sigma' = \sqrt{\ln\left(CV_{a_f}^2 + 1\right)}$$

Here $\bar{a}_f$ represents the average value of a_f and CV_{af} indicates the coefficient of variation of a_f.

Using Eqs. (6.139) and (6.140) in Eq. (6.138) we calculated $\bar{F}$ and $\bar{F}/\bar{P}$ by a numerical method. Figure 6.14 illustrates some of the results.

The maximum of each curve (breaking point O) determines the strength utilization coefficient ($\eta_P = \bar{F}_{max}/\bar{P}$) and the breaking strain $\varepsilon = a$ of the bundle. Now the breaking strain unitization coefficient, according to Eq. (6.125), is $\eta_a = a/\bar{a}_f$ (because $\bar{\lambda} = 0$).

The strength utilization coefficient is equal to the maximum of the ratio $\bar{F}/\bar{P}$ so that $\mathrm{d}\bar{F}/\mathrm{d}\varepsilon = 0$ at $\varepsilon = a$. Using Eq. (6.136) we find

$$\frac{\mathrm{d}\bar{F}}{\mathrm{d}\varepsilon} = \frac{\mathrm{d}}{\mathrm{d}\varepsilon}\left[\bar{S}(\varepsilon)\int_\varepsilon^\infty \frac{\overline{P(a_f)}}{\bar{S}(a_f)}g(a_f)\mathrm{d}a_f\right]$$

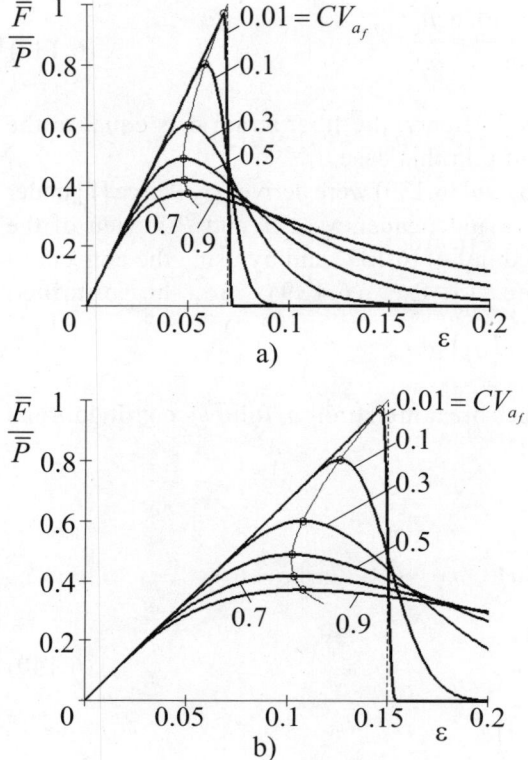

a)

b)

6.14 Graphical representation of the relation between ε and $\overline{F}/\overline{P}$ for different values of CV_{a_f}: (a) $\overline{a}_f = 0.07\,(7\%)$, (b) $\overline{a}_f = 0.15\,(15\%)$, O...breaking points, ---... bundle consisting of identical fibers ($CV_{a_f} = 0$).

$$= \frac{d\overline{S}(\varepsilon)}{d\varepsilon} \int\limits_{\varepsilon}^{\infty} \frac{\overline{P(a_f)}}{\overline{S}(a_f)} g(a_f)\,da_f + \overline{S}(\varepsilon)\frac{d}{d\varepsilon}\left[\int\limits_{\varepsilon}^{\infty} \frac{\overline{P(a_f)}}{\overline{S}(a_f)} g(a_f)\,da_f\right]$$

$$= \frac{d\overline{S}(\varepsilon)}{d\varepsilon} \int\limits_{\varepsilon}^{\infty} \frac{\overline{P(a_f)}}{\overline{S}(a_f)} g(a_f)\,da_f + \overline{S}(\varepsilon)\left[-\frac{\overline{P(\varepsilon)}}{\overline{S}(\varepsilon)} g(\varepsilon)\right],$$

$$\frac{d\overline{F}}{d\varepsilon} = \frac{d\overline{S}(\varepsilon)}{d\varepsilon} \int\limits_{\varepsilon}^{\infty} \frac{\overline{P(a_f)}}{\overline{S}(a_f)} g(a_f)\,da_f - \overline{P(\varepsilon)}g(\varepsilon). \qquad \ldots (6.141)$$

We know $d\bar{F}/d\varepsilon = 0$ at $\varepsilon = a$. Then,

$$0 = \frac{d\bar{S}(a)}{da} \int_a^\infty \frac{\overline{P(a_f)}}{S(a_f)} g(a_f) da_f - \overline{P(a)} g(a),$$

$$1 = \frac{\dfrac{d\bar{S}(a)}{da} \displaystyle\int_a^\infty \frac{\overline{P(a_f)}}{S(a_f)} g(a_f) da_f}{\overline{P(a)} g(a)}.$$

$$\qquad\qquad\qquad\qquad\qquad \ldots (6.142)$$

Further, using the special value a on the place of a_f in Eq. (6.140) and introducing the quantities

$$u = \frac{\ln a_f - \mu'}{\sigma'}, \quad u_a = \frac{\ln a - \mu'}{\sigma'}, \qquad \ldots (6.143)$$

we can rewrite the mentioned expression in Eq. (6.140) as follows

$$a\, g(a) = \frac{1}{\sigma'} \frac{1}{\sqrt{2\pi}} e^{-\frac{(\ln a - \mu')^2}{2\sigma'^2}} = \frac{1}{\sigma'} \frac{1}{\sqrt{2\pi}} e^{-\frac{u_a^2}{2}} = \frac{\varphi(u_a)}{\sigma'} = \frac{\varphi(u_a)}{\sqrt{\ln\left(CV_{a_f}^2 + 1\right)}},$$

$$\qquad\qquad\qquad\qquad\qquad \ldots (6.144)$$

where $\varphi(u_a)$ is the PDF of standard normal distribution. According to the second expression stated in Eq. (6.138) and Eq. (6.140), it is also valid to write that

$$G(a) = \int_0^a g(a_f) da_f = \int_0^a \frac{1}{\sqrt{2\pi}\,\sigma' a_f} e^{-\frac{(\ln a_f - \mu')^2}{2\sigma'^2}} da_f = \int_{-\infty}^{\frac{\ln a - \mu'}{\sigma'} = u_a} \frac{1}{\sqrt{2\pi}} e^{-\frac{u^2}{2}} du = \Phi(u_a)$$

$$\qquad\qquad\qquad\qquad\qquad \ldots (6.145)$$

Note: The substitution $u = \left(\ln a_f - \mu'\right)/\sigma'$, i.e. $du = da_f / \left(\sigma' a_f\right)$, was used while solving the previous integral.

Evidently, $\Phi(u_a)$ is the distribution function for the standard normal distribution.

Finally, let us rearrange Eq. (6.142) using Eqs. (6.137), (6.139), 1.6.143), and (6.145)

$$1 = \frac{\dfrac{\mathrm{d}\bar{S}(a)}{\mathrm{d}a} \displaystyle\int_a^\infty \overline{\dfrac{P(a_f)}{S(a_f)}} g(a_f)\,\mathrm{d}a_f}{P(a)g(a)} = \frac{\dfrac{\bar{P}}{\bar{a}_f} \displaystyle\int_a^\infty g(a_f)\,\mathrm{d}a_f}{\bar{S}(a)g(a)}$$

$$= \frac{\dfrac{\bar{P}}{\bar{a}_f} \displaystyle\int_a^\infty g(a_f)\,\mathrm{d}a_f}{\dfrac{\bar{P}}{\bar{a}_f}a\,g(a)} = \frac{1-\Phi(u_a)}{\dfrac{\varphi(u_a)}{\sqrt{\ln\left(CV_{a_f}^2+1\right)}}}, \qquad \ldots (6.146)$$

$$1 = \sqrt{\ln\left(CV_{a_f}^2+1\right)}\,\frac{1-\Phi(u_a)}{\varphi(u_a)}.$$

The root u_a of the last equation, evaluated by a numerical method, depends on CV_{af} only[16].

Because each $\lambda = 0$ in this case, the breaking force utilization coefficient is $\eta_a = a/\bar{a}_f$ according to Eq. (6.125). Using this relation, let us rearrange Eq. (6.143) by using Eq. (6.140) as follows

$$u_a = \frac{\ln a - \mu'}{\sigma'}, \quad u_a\sigma' = \ln a - \mu', \quad u_a\sqrt{\ln\left(CV_{a_f}^2+1\right)} = \ln a - \ln\frac{\bar{a}_f}{\sqrt{CV_{a_f}^2+1}},$$

$$u_a\sqrt{\ln\left(CV_{a_f}^2+1\right)} = \ln a - \ln\bar{a}_f + \ln\sqrt{CV_{a_f}^2+1} = \ln\frac{a}{\bar{a}_f} + \ln\sqrt{CV_{a_f}^2+1}$$

$$= \ln\eta_a + \ln\sqrt{CV_{a_f}^2+1},$$

$$\eta_a = \exp\left[u_a\sqrt{\ln\left(CV_{a_f}^2+1\right)} - \ln\sqrt{CV_{a_f}^2+1}\right].$$

$$\ldots (6.147)$$

Applying the relation $\eta_a = a/\bar{a}_f$, Eq. (6.139) for $\varepsilon = a$ (that is, $\bar{S}(a) = \left(\bar{P}/\bar{a}_f\right)a$), and Eq. (6.145), we can rearrange Eq. (6.138), for $\varepsilon = a$ (where $\bar{F} = \bar{F}_{\max}$), as follows

$$\bar{F}_{\max} = \bar{S}(a)[1-G(a)] = \frac{\bar{P}}{\bar{a}_f}a[1-\Phi(u_a)], \quad \frac{\bar{F}_{\max}}{\bar{P}} = \frac{a}{\bar{a}_f}[1-\Phi(u_a)],$$

$$\ldots (6.148)$$

$$\eta_P = \eta_a[1-\Phi(u_a)].$$

---

16. The probability density function $\varphi(u_a)$ and the distribution function $\Phi(u_a)$ of standardized normal (Gaussian) distribution are generally known and still remaining as the same functions.

(The definition of the strength utilization coefficient η_P is given by Eq. (6.124)). The strength utilization coefficient η_P also depends on CV_{a_f} only. The curves in Fig. 6.15 display the behaviors of both of these utilization coefficients.

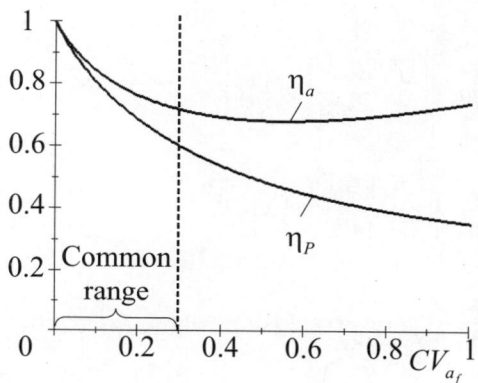

6.15 Behaviors of strength utilization coefficient η_P and breaking strain utilization coefficient η_a.

Note: Let us remark that the utilization coefficients η_P and η_a are only functions of CV_{a_f} in the studied case (linear force–strain curves, lognormal distribution, etc.), but also in a lot of other cases; e.g., for force strain curves type $\overline{S}(\varepsilon) = \left(\overline{P}/\overline{a}_f^c\right)\varepsilon^c$, where c is a parameter, for normal distribution of a_f. May be, CV_{a_f} is a crucial quantity that determinates both of the utilization coefficients for a major part of real fiber bundles made up of "straight" fibers. (The step-by-step derivation of Eqs. from (6.142) to (6.148) are mentioned in Ref. [8]).

Fibers having variable crimp, strength, and breaking strain. Because the universal expression for the average force per fiber in bundle stated in Eq. (6.123) is concretized, which is also valid in this case, let us accept the following assumptions that are already mentioned and explained in previous sections:

- "theorem of similarity", stated in Eq. (6.114),
- mutual independency of crimp, strength, and breaking strain distributions, stated in Eq. (6.119),
- linear force–strain function of each fiber, stated in Eq. (6.116),
- lognormal distribution of fiber crimp, stated in Eq. (6.127),
- "symmetrical strengths" of fibers, stated in Eq. (6.137),
- lognormal distribution of fiber breaking strain, stated in Eq. (6.140).

Let us rearrange Eq. (6.123) using Eqs. (6.137), (6.115) and the second expression stated in Eq. (6.138)[17] as follows

$$\bar{F} = \int_0^\varepsilon \left[\int_{\frac{\varepsilon-\lambda}{1+\lambda}}^\infty \frac{\overline{P(a_f)}}{\overline{S(a_f)}} g(a_f) \mathrm{d}a_f \right] \overline{S}\left(\frac{\varepsilon-\lambda}{1+\lambda}\right) v(\lambda) \mathrm{d}\lambda =$$

$$= \int_0^\varepsilon \left[\int_{\frac{\varepsilon-\lambda}{1+\lambda}}^\infty g(a_f) \mathrm{d}a_f \right] \left(\frac{\overline{P}}{\overline{a}_f} \frac{\varepsilon-\lambda}{1+\lambda} \right) v(\lambda) \mathrm{d}\lambda$$

$$= \int_0^\varepsilon \left[1 - G\left(\frac{\varepsilon-\lambda}{1+\lambda}\right) \right] \left(\frac{\overline{P}}{\overline{a}_f} \frac{\varepsilon-\lambda}{1+\lambda} \right) v(\lambda) \mathrm{d}\lambda,$$

$$\frac{\overline{F}}{\overline{P}} = \frac{1}{\overline{a}_f} \int_0^\varepsilon \left[1 - G\left(\frac{\varepsilon-\lambda}{1+\lambda}\right) \right] \frac{\varepsilon-\lambda}{1+\lambda} v(\lambda) \mathrm{d}\lambda, \text{ where } G\left(\frac{\varepsilon-\lambda}{1+\lambda}\right) = \int_0^{\frac{\varepsilon-\lambda}{1+\lambda}} g(a_f) \mathrm{d}a_f.$$

$$\ldots (6.149)$$

The last equation can be numerically solved by substituting $v(\lambda)$ and $g(a_f)$ from Eqs. (6.127) and (6.140) to Eq. (6.149).

Figure 6.16 displays some of the results. The thick curve No. 1 represents the combined effect of fiber crimp and fiber breaking strain variability together. The thin curve No. 2 corresponds to a near-zero value of CV_{a_f}, so the influence of breaking strain variability is not significant here; this curve is (practically) identical to those shown in Fig. 6.11. Another thin curve No. 3 corresponds to a near-zero value of $\overline{\lambda}$, so the effect of fiber crimp is not significant here; this is (practically) the same as those shown in Fig. 6.14. It is shown here that the bundle strength (strength utilization coefficient η_P) decreases by the average of a common effect of fiber crimp variability and fiber breaking strain variability. Furthermore, fiber crimp increases mainly the breaking strain of the bundle whereas the variability of fiber breaking strain decreases it, but not so markedly.

Note: Based on our initial experimental results, curve No. 1 in Fig. 9a represents – very roughly – a bundle of cotton fibers tested at gauge length $h = 10\text{mm}$.

Note: Cui, Suh, and Sasser [10] derived a similar expression as mentioned in Eq. (6.149). They assumed: (1) force–strain function of single fibers is linear, $F = k\varepsilon_f$, $k = P/a_f$; (2) modulus k is an independent random variable having PDF $u(k)$; (3) fiber crimp is small only, so that $1+\lambda = 1$. Using first two assumptions, it is possible to establish the validity of

---

17. Now, we use the variable $(\varepsilon - \lambda)/(1 + \lambda)$ in place of the variable ε used in Eq. (6.138).

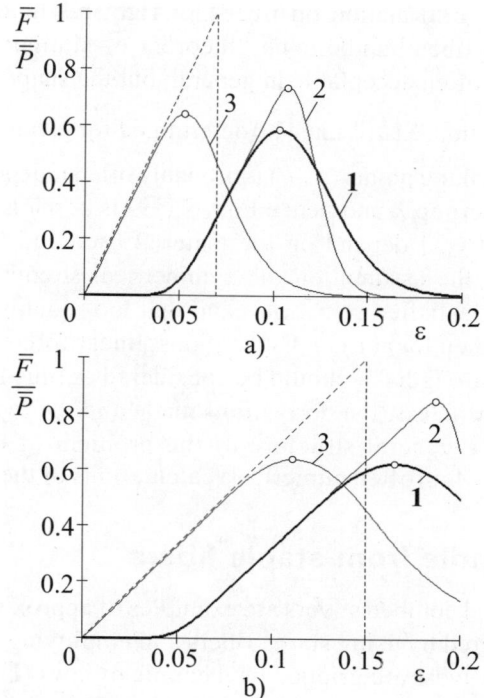

Figure 6.16 Relation between $\bar{F}/\bar{P}$ and ε:

(a) $\bar{a}_f = 0.07$, $CV_\lambda = 0.2$,

(b) $\bar{a}_f = 0.15$, $CV_\lambda = 0.2$,

O...breaking points, --- bundle consisting of identical straight fibers,

Curve 1 ... $CV_{a_f} = 0.25$, $\bar{\lambda} = 0.05$,

Curve 2... $CV_{a_f} = 0.01(\to 0)$, $\bar{\lambda} = 0.05$,

Curve 3... $CV_{a_f} = 0.25$, $\bar{\lambda} = 0.001(\to 0)$.

Eq. (6.137) so that Eq. (6.149) is valid too. Applying the third assumption and using $\bar{k} = \bar{P}/\bar{a}_f$ we obtain $\bar{F} \quad \bar{k} \int_0^\varepsilon \left[1 - \int_0^{\varepsilon-\lambda} g(a_f) da_f \right](\varepsilon - \lambda) v(\lambda) d\lambda$.

After rearrangement of this expression we obtain $\bar{F} \quad \bar{k} \left\{ \varepsilon \int_0^\varepsilon v(\lambda) d\lambda - \varepsilon \int_0^\varepsilon \zeta(\lambda) d\lambda + \int_0^\varepsilon \lambda \zeta(\lambda) d\lambda \right\}$, where the function $\zeta(\lambda) = v(\lambda) \int_0^{\varepsilon-\lambda} g(a_f) da_f$ represents the PDF of broken fiber at a given value of ε. In accordance with the theory of probability, we write $\bar{\lambda} = \int_0^\varepsilon \lambda \zeta(\lambda) d\lambda / \int_0^\varepsilon \zeta(\lambda) d\lambda$, then we obtain $\bar{F} \quad \bar{k} \left\{ \varepsilon \int_0^\varepsilon v(\lambda) d\lambda - \int_0^\varepsilon \lambda v(\lambda) d\lambda - \varepsilon \int_0^\varepsilon \zeta(\lambda) d\lambda + \bar{\lambda} \int_0^\varepsilon \zeta(\lambda) d\lambda \right\}$. This is identical to what was derived by Cui, Suh, and Sasser [10].

We need to know much information on fibers for right calculation of mechanical behavior of a fiber bundle. The "theorem of similarity" as expressed in Eq. (6.114) is often acceptable in general, but the shape of the "average" force–strain function $\overline{S}\left(\varepsilon_f\right)$ must be determined for given fibers. The distribution of fiber breaking points (a_f, P) is probably often independent of the distribution of fiber crimp λ and hence Eq. (6.119) is perhaps valid, but the PDFs $u(a_f, P)$ and $v(\lambda)$ depend on the material used and bundle preparation method. Also, the assumption of "symmetrical strengths" as expressed in Eq. (6.137) is satisfied sometimes and that too roughly.

The illustrations – based on lognormal distributions, linear force–strain curves, and "symmetrical strengths" – should be considered as illustrations of basic trends only. Nevertheless, the derivations made and the resulting equations obtained show a general structure of the problem of bundle mechanics and also the way for (often numerical) calculations of the same.

6.5   Notes to bundle from staple fibers

Introduction. The drawn and combed slivers are examples of approximately parallel fiber bundle prepared by using staple fibers and employing textile spinning process. If such slivers are gripped by a couple of jaws (I and II) of a tensile tester, then some of the fibers are clamped by only one jaw and some of the fibers are just lying "free" in the region of gauge length as shown in Fig. 6.17a. Such fibers contribute a little, by means of cohesive force only, to the tensile force applied to the bundle.

Note: Similarly, the broken fibers also result in cohesive force during tensile loading of a real fiber bundle.

Nevertheless, the cohesive force is probably much smaller as compared to the force required to extend the fibers. We therefore neglect the cohesive force in our model. We can then simply take that the fibers, which are gripped by both the jaws simultaneously, contribute significantly to the tensile force applied to the bundle.

Consider that the total number of fibers present in the cross-section of the bundle is n. Nevertheless, there are only $n_e \in \langle 0, n \rangle$ fibers, which are gripped by both the jaws simultaneously, contribute to the tensile force significantly.

On the basis of two quantities n and n_e introduced earlier let us define the fiber length utilization coefficient λ as follows

$$\lambda = \frac{n_e}{n}, \quad \lambda \in \langle 0, 1 \rangle. \qquad \dots (6.150)$$

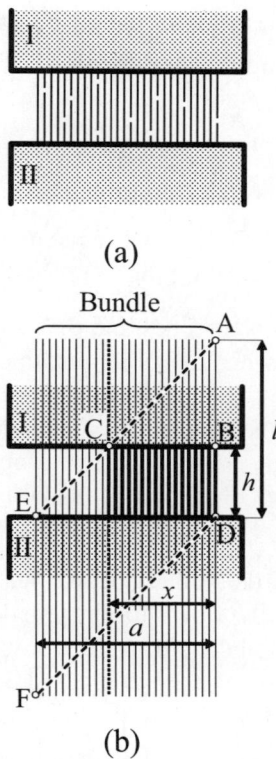

(a)

(b)

6.17 Bundle (sliver) of staple fibers gripped in jaws.

Simplest ideal fiber bundle with constant fiber length. The model of simplest ideal fiber bundle is introduced in Section 6.1. This model is considered here, but with a little modification as stated below:

A. The fiber bundle consists of a large number n of fibers.
B. The fibers are straight and parallel to the axis of the jaws, but they need not be gripped by both the jaws simultaneously.
C. All of the fibers have the same length l (constant).
D. The positions of the individual fibers are random in the bundle.

According to these assumptions, it is possible to imagine a model of fiber bundle where the fibers are distributed regularly across the bundle and thus create a parallelogram as shown in Fig. 6.17b. Consider that the length of one side of the parallelogram ADFE is l. While clamping such a bundle in-between two jaws I and II separated by gauge length $h \leq l$, it may so happen that some of the fibers are gripped by both the jaws simultaneously (thick lines in Fig. 6.17b) but the others are not. Further consider that all n fibers are lying in the width of a of the fiber bundle, however, a part of them n_e are lying in the width x. Because the cross-section of fibers is assumed to be regular it can be stated that n is proportional to a, n_e is proportional to x, and using Eq. (6.150) we can write the following equation

$$\eta = \frac{n_e}{n} = \frac{x}{a}.$$ ... (6.151)

The similarity of the triangles ABC and ADE as shown in Fig. 6.17b and Eq. (6.151) allow us to write the following expressions

$$\frac{l-h}{l} = \frac{x}{a},$$

$$\left.\begin{array}{l} \eta = 1 - \dfrac{h}{l}, \quad h \leq l, \\[2mm] \eta = 0, \quad h > l. \end{array}\right\}.$$ ... (6.152)[18]

One may remember that the model of simplest ideal fiber bundle introduced in Section 6.1 accounts all n fibers for the tensile force applied to the bundle. But, here, only a partial strip of n_e fibers, width BC $= x$, is functional while applying tensile force to the bundle and the rest of $n - n_e$ fibers are totally non-functional. It means that all forces and stresses are required to be reduced by the ratio $n_e/n = \eta$. This modification results in mechanical quantities of the bundle as displayed in Table 6.9.

Table 6.9 Original and modified equations of mechanical quantities[+] of bundle.

Quantity	Section 6.1		Modified equation
	Equation	No.	
Bundle force	$F_b(\varepsilon) = nF(\varepsilon)$	(6.2)	$F_b(\varepsilon) = nF(\varepsilon)\eta$
Bundle breaking force	$F_b^* = nF^* = nF(a)$		$F_b^* = nF^* = nF(a)\eta$
Bundle force per one fiber	$F_f = F(\varepsilon)$	(6.3)	$F_f = F(\varepsilon)\eta$
Bundle breaking force per one fiber	$F_f^* = F^* = F(a)$		$F_f^* = F^* = F(a)\eta$
Bundle specific stress	$\sigma_b(\varepsilon) = \sigma(\varepsilon)$	(6.4)	$\sigma_b(\varepsilon) = \sigma(\varepsilon)\eta$
Bundle specific strength	$\sigma_b^* = \sigma^*$		$\sigma_b^* = \sigma^*\eta$
Bundle stress	$\sigma_b'(\varepsilon) = \sigma'(\varepsilon)$	(6.6)	$\sigma_b'(\varepsilon) = \sigma'(\varepsilon)\eta$
Bundle strength	$\sigma_b'^* = \sigma'^*$		$\sigma_b'^* = \sigma'^*\eta$

(+) The symbols are already defined in Section 6.1.

---

18. If $h > l$ (i.e. if the upper jaw is lying over the point A shown in Fig. 6.17b) then no one fiber can be gripped by both jaws simultaneously.

Note: It is shown in Table 6.9 that the modified equations always contain two factors namely, length utilization coefficient η and force or stress of fiber (force–strain relation of fiber $F(\varepsilon)$, breaking force of fiber $F^* \equiv F(a)$, specific stress–strain relation of fiber $\sigma(\varepsilon)$, specific strength of fiber σ^*, stress–strain relation of fiber $\sigma'(\varepsilon)$, and strength of fiber σ'^*). The value of η is $\eta < 1$ because all n fibers are not contributing to the bundle extension in reality. In another way, it can be imagined that all n fibers are fully functional, but all the mentioned functions and values of fiber mechanics are smaller, reduced by the length utilization coefficient η. Such imagination will be found useful later on.

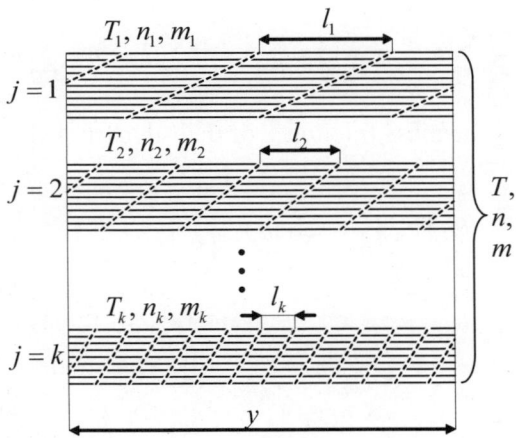

6.18 Doubling of partial slivers.

Simplest ideal fiber bundle with finite number of fiber lengths. Let us consider the simplest ideal fiber bundle (sliver) which is created by blending of fibers of different lengths $l_1, l_2,...,l_j,...,l_k$. Except the length, all other fiber properties are considered to remain the same. It can be understood that such a sliver is the result of doubling of k virtual partial slivers, $j = 1, 2,..., k$, where each of them is created by fibers of same length. This is illustrated in Fig. 6.18. The fibers in the partial slivers are arranged to resemble a parallelograms as shown in Fig. 6.18. Consider that all partial slivers share a common length y.

Each j-th partial sliver has fineness T_j, mass $m_j = T_j y$ [19], and the number of fibers in the cross-section of the sliver, in accordance with Eq. (6.1) is $n_j = T_j / t$, where t is fiber fineness. Further, in accordance with Eq. (6.152),

---

19. This accords to the general standard definition of the quantity "fineness" stated in Eq. (1.3).

the fiber length utilization coefficient η_j of each partial sliver is expressed as follows

$$\left.\begin{array}{l} \eta_j = 1 - \dfrac{h}{l_j}, \quad h \le l_j, \\[3mm] \eta_j = 0, \quad h > l_j, \end{array}\right\}, \qquad \text{... (6.153)}$$

where h denotes the (common) gauge length. The resulting sliver has fineness T, mass $m = Ty$, and contains $n = T/t$ number of fibers in its cross-section. Then the following expressions are valid to write

$$m = \sum_{j=1}^{k} m_j, \quad T = \frac{m}{y} = \sum_{j=1}^{k} \frac{m_j}{y} = \sum_{j=1}^{k} T_j, \quad n = \sum_{j=1}^{k} n_j . \quad \text{... (6.154)}$$

Let us express the mass fraction γ_j of the j-th partial sliver, having fiber length l_j as follows

$$\gamma_j = \frac{m_j}{m}, \quad \sum_{j=1}^{k} \gamma_j = \sum_{j=1}^{k} \frac{m_j}{m} = 1 . \qquad \text{... (6.155)}$$

It is then evident that

$$T_j = \frac{m_j}{y} = \frac{m\gamma_j}{y} = T\gamma_j, \qquad \text{... (6.156)}$$

$$n_j = \frac{T_j}{t} = \frac{T\gamma_j}{t} = n\gamma_j . \qquad \text{... (6.157)}$$

The number of fibers in j-th partial sliver that are gripped by both the jaws simultaneously is expressed in accordance with Eqs. (6.150) and (6.157) as follows

$$n_{e,j} = n_j \eta_j = n\gamma_j \eta_j . \qquad \text{... (6.158)}$$

The total number of fibers gripped by both jaws simultaneously is $n_e = \sum_{j=1}^{k} n_{e,j}$. Applying the last equation and the definition of fiber length utilization coefficient as expressed by Eq. (6.150) the following expressions are obtained

$$n_e = \sum_{j=1}^{k} n_{e,j} = n \sum_{j=1}^{k} \left(\gamma_j \eta_j \right), \qquad \text{... (6.159)}$$

$$\eta = \frac{n_e}{n} = \sum_{j=1}^{k} \left(\gamma_j \, \eta_j \right), \qquad \qquad \ldots (6.160)$$

where η is the fiber length utilization coefficient corresponding to the complete (doubled) sliver.

It is necessary to know the fiber lengths l_j, mass fractions γ_j, values η_j calculated according to Eq. (6.153), and determine the value of η according to Eq. (6.160). Then all modified equations stated in Table 6.9 can be solved.

Simplest ideal fiber bundle with continuous distribution of fiber length. Let us generalize the previous idea of finite number of fiber lengths illustrated in Fig. 6.18. Let us imagine now that the number of partial slivers is limited to infinity and the mass of each sliver (containing fibers of same lengths l only) is differentially small at the same time. We are dealing with elemental slivers. Obviously, it is not possible to identify such an elemental sliver by a subscript j now, but can be identified as an elemental sliver containing fibers of length l. The mass fraction of such a sliver (earlier γ_j) is elementally small. Let this mass fraction be $\gamma(l)dl$. The summation of all mass fractions must be equal to one, according to

Eq. (6.155), so that the following integral must be valid $\int_0^{l_{max}} \gamma(l)\, dl = 1$.

The introduced function $\gamma(l)$ is a suitable probability density function of mass weighted distribution of fiber lengths. (It is often determined experimentally under the term "weighted staple length distribution" of fiber material).

Fiber length utilization coefficient η, expressed formerly by Eq. (6.160), must be rearranged for this case as follows

- γ_j is substituted by $\gamma(l)dl$,
- η_j – according to Eq. (6.153) – is replaced by the general expression for the fiber length utilization coefficient expressed in Eq. (6.152), and
- The discrete summation is replaced by the continuous definite integral ranging from $l = 0$ to $l = l_{max}$.

In this way, the following expression is obtained from Eq. (6.160)

$$\eta = \int_0^{l_{max}} \eta \gamma(l)\, dl,$$

$$\left. \begin{array}{l} \eta = \displaystyle\int_0^{l_{max}} \left(1 - \frac{h}{l} \right) \gamma(l)\, dl, \quad h \le l_{max}, \\[4mm] \eta = 0, \quad h > l_{max}. \end{array} \right\} \qquad \ldots (6.161)$$

Using the determined value of η we can calculate all mechanical quantities of the bundle by means of the modified equations listed in Table 6.9.

Bi-component and multi-component parallel fiber bundle. The note stated below Table 6.9 reminds us of the possibility to assume (formerly) that all fibers are fully functional but all functions and values of fiber mechanics are smaller, that is, reduced by the length utilization coefficient η.

The bi-component fiber bundle is created from two components of fibers, one is designed by number 1 (smaller fiber breaking strain) and the other, by number 2 (higher fiber breaking strain). The corresponding mechanical quantities of the fiber components are shown in Table 6.1 in Section 6.2. Such a blended bundle of staple fibers can be imagined as a result of doubling of two mono-component slivers. The first sliver is created from the fibers designated by number 1 only and it has fiber length utilization coefficient $\eta = \eta_1$ determined according to Eq. (6.160) when the fibers have only a finite number of different lengths or according to Eq. (6.161) when the fibers have a continuous mass weighted distribution of fiber lengths. Similarly, the fiber length utilization coefficient of the second sliver prepared by fibers designated by number 2 only is $\eta = \eta_2$. Then the original mechanical quantities and the related functions of fiber mechanics must be modified by multiplying with the values of η_1 and η_2 as shown in Table 6.10.

Analogically, the modified functions and quantities for the fibers in multi-component bundle can be expressed. It is necessary to determine all values λ_i, $i = 1, 2, ..., K$, by means of Eq. (6.160) or Eq. (6.161), for each i-th component. Then the original fiber functions or quantities of fiber mechanics, related to the fibers of i-th component, must be modified by multiplying with the values of η_i.

Table 6.10 Modified functions and quantities for staple fibers in bi-component bundle.

Functions and quantities	Original from Table 6.1		Modified	
	First component	Second component	First component	Second component
Force–strain function of fiber	$F_1(\varepsilon)$	$F_2(\varepsilon)$	$F_1(\varepsilon)\lambda_1$	$F_2(\varepsilon)\lambda_2$
Specific stress of fiber	$\sigma_1(\varepsilon)$	$\sigma_2(\varepsilon)$	$\sigma_1(\varepsilon)\lambda_1$	$\sigma_2(\varepsilon)\lambda_2$
Stress of fiber	$\sigma_1'(\varepsilon)$	$\sigma_2'(\varepsilon)$	$\sigma_1'(\varepsilon)\lambda_1$	$\sigma_2'(\varepsilon)\lambda_2$
Breaking force of fiber	F_1^*	F_2^*	$F_1^*\lambda_1$	$F_2^*\lambda_2$
Specific strength of fiber	σ_1^*	σ_2^*	$\sigma_1^*\lambda_1$	$\sigma_2^*\lambda_2$
Strength of fiber	$\sigma_1'^*$	$\sigma_2'^*$	$\sigma_1'^*\lambda_1$	$\sigma_2'^*\lambda_2$

Note: A reader can apply an analogous way of thinking also for parallel fiber bundles with variable properties of staple fibers, i.e. to extend the problem described in Section 6.4. Nevertheless, the process of solving such a complex problem is generally complicated. In a general sense, we need to work with conjugated probability density function of fiber breaking strain, fiber specific stress, fiber crimp and fiber length. It is usually difficult to find the required input values and functions in order to solve such a problem. Even a suitable simplification for a specific fiber material is hardly possible. (Let us point out an example of the problem of fiber crimp, where it is necessary to use the crimped fiber lengths for the derivation of length utilization coefficients).

Note: The cohesive force among fibers was neglected in this chapter for simplification and because they are usually too small. However, they can sometimes play a significant role. Remember, the cohesive force exists among the fibers which are not gripped by both jaws simultaneously and also among the fibers which are broken during the application of tensile force to the fiber bundle. Based on our models, the determination of number of such fibers is relatively easy. Nevertheless, a suitable expression for fiber-to-fiber cohesion is required to be utilized in the aforesaid model.

6.6   References

1. Hamburger, W. J. (1949). The industrial application of the stress-strain relationship, *Journal of Textile Institute*, **40**, P700–P718.
2. Kemp, A., and Owen, J. D. (1955). The strength and behavior of nylon/cotton blended yarns undergoing strain, *Journal of Textile Institute*, **46**, T468–T698.
3. Noshi, H., Ishida, T., and Yamada, Y. (1959). Study on blended yarns, Part I: The tensile strength of twisted yarns consisting of two kinds of continuous filaments, *Journal of Textile Machinery Society of Japan*, **12**(2), 1–6.
4. Ratnam, T. V., Shankaranarayana, K. S., Underwood, C., and Govindarajulu, K. (1968). Prediction of the quality of blended yarns from that of the individual components, *Textile Research Journal*, **38**, 360–365.
5. Monego, C. J., and Backer, S. (1968). Tensile rupture of blended yarns, *Textile Research Journal*, **38**, 762–766.
6. Peirce, F. T. (1926). Theorems on the strength of long and of composite specimens, *Journal of Textile Institute*, **17**, 335–368.
7. Coleman, B. D. (1958). On the strength of classical fibers and fiber bundles, *Journal of Mechanics and Physics of Solids*, **7**, 60–70.
8. Phoenix, S. L., and Taylor, H. M. (1973). The asymptotic strength distribution of a generalized fiber bundle, *Advanced Applied Probability*, **5**, 200–216.
9. Phoenix, S. L. (1974). Probabilistic strength analysis of fiber bundle structures, *Fiber Science and Technology*, **7**, 15–31.
10. Phoenix, S. L. (1975). Probabilistic inter-fiber dependence and the asymptotic strength distribution of a classical fiber bundle, *International Journal of Engineering Science*, **13**, 287–303.

11. Nachane, R. P., and Iyer, K. R. K. (1980). Prediction of bundle strength from single-fiber test data, *Textile Research Journal*, **50**, 639–641.
12. Daniels, H. E. (1989). The maximum of a Gaussian process whose average path has a maximum, with application to the strength of fiber bundles, *Advanced Applied Probability*, **21**, 315–333.
13. Neckář, B. (1998). "Morphology and Structural Mechanics of General Fiber Assemblies", *Technical University of Liberec*, Czech Republic.
14. Cui, X., Suh, M. W., and Sasser, P. E. (1999). Tensile behavior of slack fiber bundles – Theory and application to HVI testing, *Textile Research Journal*, **69**, 497–502.
15. Cui, X., Suh, M. W, and Sasser, P. E. (2003). Estimating single cotton fiber tensile properties from the load-elongation curves of slack bundle, *Textile Research Journal*, **73**, 1066–1070.
16. Yu, W., Yan, H., and Postle, R. (2003). Evaluating single fiber and fiber bundle tensile curves, *Textile Research Journal*, **73**, 875–882.
17. Pan, N. (1996). Development of a constitutive theory for short-fiber yarns, Part IV: The mechanics of blended fibrous structures, *Journal of Textile Institute*, **87**, 467–483.
18. Neckář, B., and Das, D. (2006). Mechanics of parallel fiber bundles, *Fibers and Textiles in Eastern Europe*, **14**, 3(57), 23–28.

Mechanics of non-parallel fiber bundles

7.1   Multi-axial textiles

Introduction. In industrial practice, the bundles consisting of non-parallel fibers, yarns, and other linear textiles are very frequently produced. They are often known as "flat" bundles, they are produced by means of textile manufacturing processes, and they are used as reinforcements of fiber composites or for other special technical applications [1–19]. The structural units – fibers, yarns, and other linear textiles – can be oriented to a finite number of directions, or they can display a continuous distribution of directions. The current chapter is directed to study the mechanical behavior of a bundle where the structural units are oriented to a finite number of directions.

The multi-axial textiles are formed from several systems of parallel objects, which can be fibers but are mostly yarns, including monofilament, multifilament, and staple fiber yarns. The basic idea, concepts, and results of mechanics of multi-axial textiles are reported in Ref. [20].

Note: In spite of different linear objects we speak conventionally about "yarns" in this chapter.

The scheme of a multi-axial textile consisting of four yarn systems is displayed inside a visible circle in Fig. 7.1a.

Simple multi-axial textile. Let us think of a simple multi-axial textile that satisfies the following assumptions.

1. All yarns are infinitely long and straight.
2. A single yarn system consists of parallel and equidistant yarns of identical properties.
3. Yarns do not mutually influence.
4. The multi-axial textile consists of $K \geq 2$ number of yarn systems and each i-th system ($i = 1, 2, ..., K$) possesses different directions.

The direction of i-th yarn system is characterized by a unit vector $\mathbf{j}_i$ which is defined by the angle $\psi_i \in (-\pi/2, \pi/2)$ taken from the y axis in a given Cartesian coordinate (x, y) system. This is shown in Fig. 7.1b.

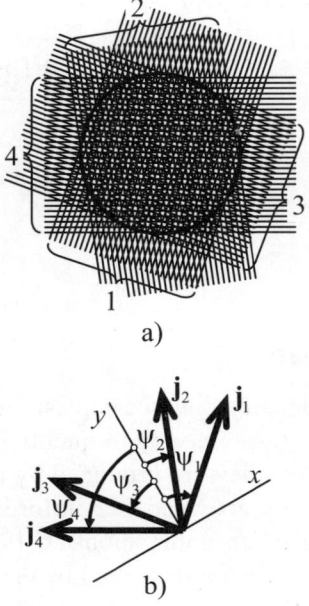

7.1 Scheme of multi-axial textile.

(a) Principle of textile; (b) Directions of systems.

Geometry of one strained and oblique yarn in-between jaws. We would like to study the mechanical behavior of a multi-axial textile in three steps. At first the mechanical behavior of one single yarn would be studied, then the mechanical behavior of one yarn system would be studied, and finally the mechanical behavior of one complete multi-axial textile would be studied. The mechanical behavior of one single yarn is illustrated in a scheme shown in Fig. 7.2. An oblique yarn of length l is gripped by two jaws A and B of a tensile tester at gauge length h. The direction of the y-axis represents the direction of (dash-and-dot) the jaw axis. The angle of inclination of the yarn is described by the non-oriented angle ϑ. (It is valid that $|\psi| = \vartheta \in \langle 0, \pi/2 \rangle$ in relation to the situation as depicted in Fig. 7.1b; one can see Eq. (3.46) also). The length x shows the "horizontal" distance between the two clamped points taken on the yarn portion between the jaws.

The gauge length h is increasing to a higher value h' as a result of movement of the "lower" jaw from a position B to a new position B'. The length of the yarn increases to a longer length l', the angle ϑ decreases to a new angle ϑ', but only the distance x stays the same[1].

---

1.   We can imagine it such that both of the jaws are fastened to solid metal rods in a tensile tester.

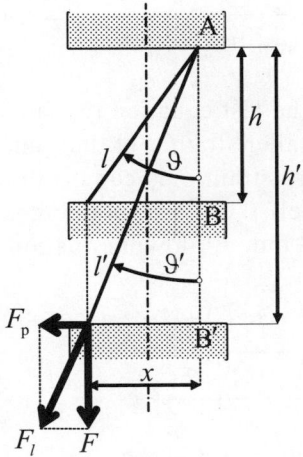

7.2 One yarn between jaws.

Let us define the relative jaw displacement as follows

$$\varepsilon = \frac{h'-h}{h} = \frac{h'}{h} - 1, \quad h' = h(1+\varepsilon), \qquad \ldots (7.1)$$

and the yarn strain as follows[2]

$$\varepsilon_l = \frac{l'-l}{l} = \frac{l'}{l} - 1, \quad l' = l(1+\varepsilon_l). \qquad \ldots (7.2)$$

We can also write the following expressions from the geometry of a yarn shown in Fig. 7.2 and from the last two equations

$$\cos \vartheta = \frac{h}{l}, \quad \cos \vartheta' = \frac{h'}{l'} = \frac{h(1+\varepsilon)}{l(1+\varepsilon_l)} = \cos \vartheta \frac{1+\varepsilon}{1+\varepsilon_l}. \qquad \ldots (7.3)$$

The well-known Pythagorean theorem is valid for the two triangles shown in Fig. 7.2. Accordingly, we can write

$$x^2 = l^2 - h^2, \quad x^2 = l'^2 - h'^2. \qquad \ldots (7.4)$$

The strain of the yarn can be derived from the previous equations as follows

$$l^2 - h^2 = l'^2 - h'^2, \quad 1 - \frac{h^2}{l^2} = \frac{l'^2}{l^2} - \frac{h'^2}{l^2} = \frac{l'^2}{l^2} - \frac{h^2}{l^2}(1+\varepsilon)^2,$$

$$1 - \cos^2 \vartheta = (1+\varepsilon_l)^2 - (1+\varepsilon)^2 \cos^2 \vartheta,$$

$$(1+\varepsilon_l)^2 = 1 - \cos^2 \vartheta + (1+\varepsilon)^2 \cos^2 \vartheta, \qquad \ldots (7.5)$$

2.　All quantities related to the yarn portion will have a superscript l.

$$\varepsilon_I = \sqrt{1+\left[\left(1+\varepsilon\right)^2-1\right]\cos^2\vartheta}-1 = \sqrt{1+\left[\varepsilon^2+2\varepsilon\right]\cos^2\vartheta}-1. \qquad \ldots (7.6)$$

It can be read from the last equation that a more oblique yarn (higher value of ϑ) displays smaller strain ε_I at the same jaw displacement ε.

Especially, if the yarn strain ε_I is equal to the yarn-breaking strain a then the yarn breaks itself. The corresponding jaw displacement is equal to the value $\varepsilon = \varepsilon^{*3}$. Then the following relation is valid from Eq. (7.5)

$$\left(1+a\right)^2 = 1-\cos^2\vartheta+\left(1+\varepsilon^*\right)^2\cos^2\vartheta,$$

$$\varepsilon^* = \sqrt{\frac{\left(1+a\right)^2-1+\cos^2\vartheta}{\cos^2\vartheta}}-1 = \sqrt{1+\frac{a^2+2a}{\cos^2\vartheta}}-1. \qquad \ldots (7.7)$$

Note: Let us note that if the angle ϑ tends to $90°$ $\left(\vartheta \to \pi/2\right)$ then the jaw displacement at the time of rupture of yarn tends to infinity ($\varepsilon^* \to \infty$).

Geometry of one oblique yarn at small deformation. Let us assume that the jaw displacement is very small. Then, according to Eq. (7.6), the yarn strain is even smaller, and then the following approximated expressions are valid[4]

$$\varepsilon^2+2\varepsilon \cong 2\varepsilon, \quad \sqrt{1+2\varepsilon\cos^2\vartheta} \cong 1+\varepsilon\cos^2\vartheta. \qquad \ldots (7.8)$$

Using such approximations in Eq. (7.6) we obtain the following relation

$$\varepsilon_I = \sqrt{1+\left[\varepsilon^2+2\varepsilon\right]\cos^2\vartheta}-1 = \sqrt{1+2\varepsilon\cos^2\vartheta}-1 = \varepsilon\cos^2\vartheta. \qquad \ldots (7.9)$$

This expression is enough good for small deformation. If the breaking strain a of the yarn is also very small then the following expression can be written from the previous expression

$$a = \varepsilon^*\cos^2\vartheta, \quad \varepsilon^* = \frac{a}{\cos^2\vartheta}. \qquad \ldots (7.10)$$

Forces on one oblique yarn in-between jaws. Let us express the force–strain relation of the yarn as follows

$$F_I = F_I\left(\varepsilon_I\right), \quad \varepsilon_I \in\left(0,\infty\right), \quad F_I\left(0\right)=0, \quad F_I\left(a\right)=P. \qquad \ldots (7.11)$$

Notes: We define this function for all values of ε_I. The force F_I is equal to zero for each non-strained yarn. The value P represents the breaking

---

3.   The quantities related to the moment of rupture will have a superscript *.
4.   These approximated expressions can be derived by using Taylor's series.

force of the yarn, i.e., the maximum force at $\varepsilon_l = a$. If the value of yarn strain ε_l is higher than a then the yarn is thought as "broken", so that it assigns a force generally smaller than P; nevertheless, we often introduce $F_l(\varepsilon_l > a)$ is equal to zero.

The force F_l is also shown in Fig. 7.2. The vector of this force assigns an angle ϑ' taken from the direction of jaw axis. The vertical component (experimentally measurable component which is parallel to the jaw axis) of this force is equal to F. Using Eqs. (7.3) and (7.11) the following expression can be written from Fig. 7.2

$$F = F_l \cos \vartheta' = F_l(\varepsilon_l) \cos \vartheta \frac{1+\varepsilon}{1+\varepsilon_l}, \qquad \ldots (7.12)$$

where ε_l is given by Eq. (7.6) as a function of ε. If the function $F_l(\varepsilon_l)$, which is specific for each yarn, is known then the (vertical) force F can be calculated as a function of the jaw displacement ε according to Eqs. (7.6) and (7.12).

If the breaking force $F_l(a) = P$ (i.e., $\varepsilon_l = a$ and $\varepsilon = \varepsilon^*$) is acting on the yarn then the value of the vertical component of the force is $F = F^*$. We call this force as "vertical rupture force". Using Eqs. (7.12), (7.11), and (7.7) we obtain the following expression for this force

$$F^* = F_l(a)\cos \vartheta \frac{1+\varepsilon^*}{1+a} = P\cos\vartheta \frac{1+\left(\sqrt{1+\dfrac{a^2+2a}{\cos^2 \vartheta}}-1\right)}{1+a} = P\cos\vartheta \frac{\sqrt{1+\dfrac{a^2+2a}{\cos^2 \vartheta}}}{1+a}$$

$$= P\frac{\sqrt{\cos^2 \vartheta + (a^2+2a+1)-1}}{1+a} = P\frac{\sqrt{(1+a)^2 - \sin^2 \vartheta}}{1+a} = P\sqrt{1-\frac{\sin^2 \vartheta}{(1+a)^2}}.$$

$$\ldots (7.13)$$

Note: Let us note that for the determination of vertical rupture force F^*, we need to know yarn-breaking force P and yarn-breaking strain a only, we do not require to know the force–strain curve of the yarn.

Simplest case of forces on oblique yarn in-between jaws. The "simplest case" of an oblique yarn fulfills the following two assumptions in addition to the four assumptions stated earlier in case of simple multi-axial textile.

5. The jaw displacement, yarn strain, and yarn-breaking strain are so small that Eqs. (7.9) and (7.10) are valid enough well.
6. The force–strain relation of the yarn is linear and it corresponds to the following expression

$$F_i(\varepsilon_l) = \frac{P}{a}\varepsilon_l \dots \varepsilon_l \le a, \left.\vphantom{\frac{P}{a}}\right\}$$
$$F_i(\varepsilon_l) = 0 \dots \varepsilon_l > a. \qquad \dots (7.14)$$

In order to have relatively easy expressions, we introduce the following general function

$$\delta(X,Y) = 1 \text{ if } X \le Y, \left.\vphantom{\frac{}{}}\right\}$$
$$\delta(X,Y) = 0 \text{ if } X > Y. \quad \text{where } X, Y \text{ are real quantities} \cdot \qquad \dots (7.15)$$

Note: Then the following expression is valid to write for the introduced function

$$\delta(CX, CY) = \delta(X,Y), \quad \text{where } C \text{ is a positive value} . \qquad \dots (7.16)$$

Equation (7.14) can be rearranged by using the function expression in Eq. (7.15) as follows

$$F_i(\varepsilon_l) = \delta(\varepsilon_l, a)\frac{P}{a}\varepsilon_l . \qquad \dots (7.17)$$

Substituting the last function in Eq. (7.12) and then using Eqs. (7.17), (7.9), (7.16), and (7.10), the vertical component of force F is expressed as follows

$$F = \delta(\varepsilon_l, a)\frac{P}{a}\varepsilon_l \cos\vartheta\frac{1+\varepsilon}{1+\varepsilon_l} = \delta(\varepsilon\cos^2\vartheta, a)\frac{P}{a}\varepsilon\cos^3\vartheta\frac{1+\varepsilon}{1+\varepsilon\cos^2\vartheta}$$

$$= \delta\left(\varepsilon, \frac{a}{\cos^2\vartheta}\right)\frac{P}{a}\varepsilon\cos^3\vartheta\frac{1+\varepsilon}{1+\varepsilon\cos^2\vartheta} = \delta(\varepsilon, \varepsilon^*)\frac{P}{a}\varepsilon\cos^3\vartheta\frac{1+\varepsilon}{1+\varepsilon\cos^2\vartheta}.$$

$$\dots (7.18)$$

Nevertheless, the following approximated expressions can be applied when the jaw displacement ε is very small

$$\frac{1}{1+\varepsilon\cos^2\vartheta} \cong 1-\varepsilon\cos^2\vartheta, \quad \varepsilon+\varepsilon^2\sin^2\vartheta-\varepsilon^3\cos^2\vartheta \cong \varepsilon. \qquad \dots (7.19)$$

Equation (7.18) can be further rearranged by using Eq. (7.19) as follows

$$F = \delta(\varepsilon, \varepsilon^*)\frac{P}{a}\cos^3\vartheta(1-\varepsilon\cos^2\vartheta)(1+\varepsilon)\varepsilon$$

$$= \delta(\varepsilon, \varepsilon^*)\frac{P}{a}\cos^3\vartheta(1+\varepsilon-\varepsilon\cos^2\vartheta-\varepsilon^2\cos^2\vartheta)\varepsilon$$

$$= \delta\left(\varepsilon, \varepsilon^*\right)\frac{P}{a}\cos^3\vartheta\left(1 + \varepsilon - \varepsilon + \varepsilon\sin^2\vartheta - \varepsilon^2\cos^2\vartheta\right)\varepsilon$$

$$= \delta\left(\varepsilon, \varepsilon^*\right)\frac{P}{a}\cos^3\vartheta\left(\varepsilon + \varepsilon^2\sin^2\vartheta - \varepsilon^3\cos^2\vartheta\right) = \delta\left(\varepsilon, \varepsilon^*\right)\frac{P}{a}\varepsilon\cos^3\vartheta.$$

$$\ldots (7.20)$$

The "vertical rupture force" F^* takes the value of force F at $\varepsilon = \varepsilon^*$, where ε^* is determined from Eq. (7.10). Then, we can write $\delta\left(\varepsilon, \varepsilon^*\right) = \delta\left(\varepsilon^*, \varepsilon^*\right) = 1$ according to the definition expressed in Eq. (7.15) and $\varepsilon\cos^2\vartheta = \varepsilon^*\cos^2\vartheta = a$ according to Eq. (7.10). Substituting these expressions into Eq. (7.20) we obtain

$$F^* = \frac{P}{a}a\cos\vartheta = P\cos\vartheta. \qquad \ldots (7.21)$$

Note: The last equation can also be derived directly from the scheme shown in Fig. 7.2. Actually, the angle ϑ' is practically equal to the angle ϑ in case of very small deformation.

Geometry of one-yarn system in-between jaws. Let us now imagine one system of yarns, fulfilling the four assumptions of a simple multi-axial textile, gripped in-between the couple of jaws A and B as shown in Fig. 7.3. The number of yarns υ per length unit (measured across the direction of yarns) characterizes the density of yarns in the system. In coherence with the textile terminology[5], let us call it "sett" of yarns.

We arrange to grip a strip of textile of width c, including the yarn system, in-between the jaws of a tensile tester. This however does not mean that all the yarns in the yarn system are gripped simultaneously by both of the jaws. The yarns near to the edge of the strip can be held by only one jaw, so that they cannot contribute to the force resulting from straining of such yarn system. As shown in Fig. 7.3, the effective width of the strip is c' and the non-effective width of the strip is δ. Then, the total width of the strip is

$$c = c' + \delta. \qquad \ldots (7.22)$$

All the yarns in the yarn system are inclined with the (non-oriented) angle ϑ taken from the vertical direction of the jaw axis. The following expression is then valid from the geometry of the yarn system as shown in Fig. 7.3

$$\tan\vartheta = \frac{\delta}{h}. \qquad \ldots (7.23)$$

---

5. In weaving technology, the traditional terms "warp sett" and "weft sett" are commonly used.

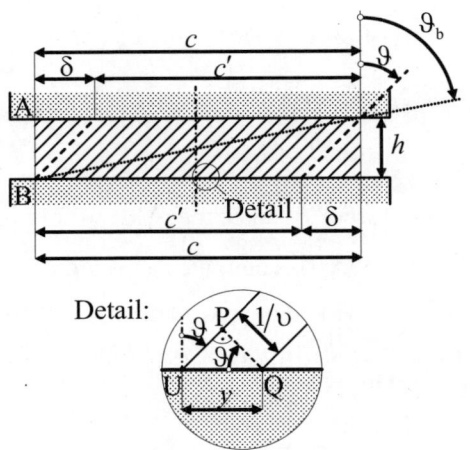

7.3 One-yarn system between jaws.

Substituting δ from Eq. (7.23) into Eq. (7.22) we obtain

$$c' = c - \delta = c - h \tan \vartheta \cdot \qquad \ldots (7.24)$$

The dotted diagonal line shown in Fig. 7.3 includes the boundary angle ϑ_b taken from the vertical direction of the jaw axis. It is shown that Eqs. (7.22), (7.23), and (7.24) are valid only when the angle $\vartheta < \vartheta_b$. If $\vartheta \geq \vartheta_b$ then $c' = 0$ and $\delta = c$, i.e., no one fiber is simultaneously gripped by both of the jaws.

The following relations are evident from Fig. 7.3

$$\tan \vartheta_b = \frac{c}{h}, \quad h = \frac{c}{\tan \vartheta_b} \cdot \qquad \ldots (7.25)$$

Note: Let us remember that the angle ϑ_b is resulting from adjustment of a tensile tester and it is not a function of yarn system.

Applying Eq. (7.25) in Eq. (7.24) we obtain the following formula

$$\left. \begin{array}{l} c' = c - \dfrac{c}{\tan \vartheta_b} \tan \vartheta = c\left(1 - \dfrac{\tan \vartheta}{\tan \vartheta_b}\right) \ldots \vartheta < \vartheta_b, \\[2mm] c' = 0 \ldots \vartheta \geq \vartheta_b. \end{array} \right\} \qquad \ldots (7.26)$$

The last expression can be rewritten as follows

$$c' = c\, M\left(\vartheta, \vartheta_b\right), \qquad \ldots (7.27)$$

where

$$M\left(\vartheta,\vartheta_{b}\right)=1-\frac{\tan\vartheta}{\tan\vartheta_{b}}...\vartheta<\vartheta_{b},\ \Bigg\}$$
$$M\left(\vartheta,\vartheta_{b}\right)=0...\vartheta\geq\vartheta_{b},$$
$$\text{especially, }M\left(0,\vartheta_{b}\right)=M\left(\vartheta,\frac{\pi}{2}\right)=1.$$

... (7.28)

Evidently, the function $M(\vartheta,\vartheta_{b})$ expresses the influence of the borders of the yarn system.

The distance y between the two gripping points of neighboring yarns is shown in Fig. 7.3. The perpendicular distance between the two neighboring yarns must be equal to the reciprocal value of the yarn sett, i.e., $1/\upsilon$. As the angle ϑ is one of the angles of the triangle UPQ[6], it is valid to write that

$$y=\frac{1/\upsilon}{\cos\vartheta}=\frac{1}{\upsilon\cos\vartheta}.$$

... (7.29)

Using Eqs. (7.27) and (7.29) the number N of gripping points in the effective width c' is obtained as follows

$$N=\frac{c'}{y}=\upsilon c\cos\vartheta\ M\left(\vartheta,\vartheta_{b}\right).$$

... (7.30)

Forces of yarn system in-between jaws. Equation (7.12) determines the vertical component F of force which is related to one oblique yarn. The N gripping points are related to N "active" yarns of the system, so that the total vertical force is $S_{\text{SYSTEM}}=FN$ and this is acting on the whole width c. Nevertheless, a further meaningful quantity is nominal (vertical) force S which is expressed by the mean vertical force per unit width of the strip. This is shown below

$$S=\frac{S_{\text{SYSTEM}}}{c}=\frac{F\,N}{c}.$$

... (7.31)

Applying Eqs. (7.12) and (7.30) into Eq. (7.31) we obtain

$$S=\left[F_{I}\left(\varepsilon_{I}\right)\cos\vartheta\,\frac{1+\varepsilon}{1+\varepsilon_{I}}\right]\frac{\left[\upsilon c\cos\vartheta\,M\left(\vartheta,\vartheta_{b}\right)\right]}{c}=\upsilon\cos^{2}\vartheta\,\frac{F_{I}\left(\varepsilon_{I}\right)\left(1+\varepsilon\right)}{1+\varepsilon_{I}}\,M\left(\vartheta,\vartheta_{b}\right),$$

... (7.32)

---

6.   The gripping line UQ of lower jaw is perpendicular to the jaw axis (dot-and-dash line); the dashed line PQ is perpendicular to the yarn line UP. Therefore, the angle UQP must be also equal to ϑ.

where Eq. (7.6) describes ε_l and Eq. (7.28) determines the function $M(\vartheta, \vartheta_b)$. If we know the input quantities, i.e., c, h, ϑ, sett υ, jaw displacement ε, and force–strain function of yarn $F_l(\varepsilon_l)$, then we can calculate the nominal force S from Eq. (7.32) by using Eqs. (7.6), (7.25) and (7.28).

We obtain the maximum of nominal force at angle $\vartheta = 0$. Then the following triplet of equations is valid from Eqs. (7.6), (7.7), and (7.28)

$$\varepsilon_l = \varepsilon, \quad \varepsilon^* = a, \quad M(\vartheta, \vartheta_b) = M(0, \vartheta_b) = 1. \qquad \ldots (7.33)$$

Applying these equalities in Eq. (7.32), we obtain

$$S_{\vartheta=0} = \upsilon F_l(\varepsilon). \qquad \ldots (7.34)$$

The nominal breaking force S^* represents the nominal force S at the moment when the vertical component of force per one yarn is $F = F^*$. In accordance with Eq. (7.31) it is valid to write that

$$S^* = \frac{F^* N}{c}. \qquad \ldots (7.35)$$

Using Eqs. (7.13) and (7.30) the nominal breaking force is derived from Eq. (7.35) as follows

$$S^* = \frac{\left[P \sqrt{1 - \dfrac{\sin^2 \vartheta}{(1+a)^2}} \right] \left[\upsilon c \cos \vartheta\, M(\vartheta, \vartheta_b) \right]}{c} = \upsilon P \cos \vartheta \sqrt{1 - \frac{\sin^2 \vartheta}{(1+a)^2}}\, M(\vartheta, \vartheta_b)$$

$$\ldots (7.36)$$

We find the maximum nominal breaking force from Eq. (7.36) at $\vartheta = 0$ and also applying the relations according to Eq. (7.33). Thus

$$S^*_{\vartheta=0} = \upsilon P. \qquad \ldots (7.37)$$

Note: This equation corresponds to Eq. (7.34), because $F_l(a) = P$ according to Eq. (7.11). Nevertheless, such a trivial equation is also evident from the logic of this matter.

Forces of simple yarn system. Equation (7.20) is valid in place of Eq. (7.12) in the earlier mentioned simplest case (small deformation and linear force–strain relation of yarns). Applying this equation together with Eq. (7.30) in Eq. (7.31), we obtain

$$S = \frac{\left[\delta\left(\varepsilon,\varepsilon^*\right)\dfrac{P}{a}\varepsilon\cos^3\vartheta\right]\left[\upsilon c\cos\vartheta\, M\left(\vartheta,\vartheta_{\mathrm{b}}\right)\right]}{c} = \delta\left(\varepsilon,\varepsilon^*\right)\frac{\upsilon P}{a}\varepsilon\cos^4\vartheta\, M\left(\vartheta,\vartheta_{\mathrm{b}}\right).$$

$$\dots (7.38)$$

We obtain the maximum of nominal force $S_{\vartheta=0}$ at angle $\vartheta = 0$, where Eq. (7.33) is valid. Applying these equalities in Eq. (7.38), we obtain

$$S_{\vartheta=0} = \delta\left(\varepsilon,a\right)\frac{\upsilon P}{a}\varepsilon. \qquad \dots (7.39)$$

Equation (7.21) is also valid in place of Eq. (7.13) in the earlier simplest case (small deformation and linear force–strain relation of yarns). Using the mentioned equation and Eq. (7.30) in Eq. (7.35) we obtain the following expression for the nominal breaking force

$$S^* = \frac{\left[P\cos\vartheta\right]\left[\upsilon c\cos\vartheta\, M\left(\vartheta,\vartheta_{\mathrm{b}}\right)\right]}{c} = \upsilon P\cos^2\vartheta\, M\left(\vartheta,\vartheta_{\mathrm{b}}\right). \qquad \dots (7.40)$$

We find the maximum nominal breaking force $S^*_{\vartheta=0}$ from the last equation at $\vartheta = 0$, i.e., also $M(\vartheta,\vartheta_{\mathrm{b}}) = 1$ according to Eq. (7.33). So we obtain $S^*_{\vartheta=0} = \upsilon P$ which is identical to the expression mentioned in Eq. (7.37).

Specific stress and specific strength of one-yarn system. Let us imagine a part of a strip of oblique yarn system, having a width equal to one, shown in Fig. 7.4a. The total length of yarns in the rectangle TUU′T′ is L. Let us "extrapolate" the yarns at the right-hand side of the scheme as shown by the dashed lines in Fig. 7.4a. It is evident that the length of yarns in the triangle TUV is same as the dashed length in the triangle T′U′V′. Therefore, the total yarn length L in the rectangle TUU′T′ is equal to the total yarn length in the parallelogram TVV′T′.

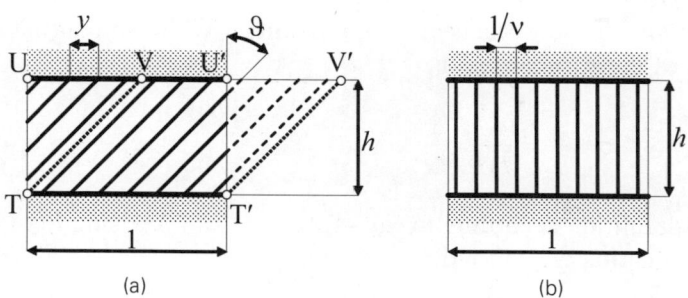

(a)   (b)

7.4 Part of yarn system of unitary width.
(a) Oblique fibers, (b) Vertically oriented fibers.

The number of yarns gripped by the unitary length TT′ and/or UU′ is $1/y$, where the distance y is given by Eq. (7.29). The length of one yarn, inclined at angle ϑ taken from the jaw axis, is $h/\cos\vartheta$. Thus the total length of yarns in the rectangle TUU′T′ or the total length of yarns in the parallelogram TVV′T′ is

$$L = \left(\frac{1}{y}\right)\left(\frac{h}{\cos\vartheta}\right) = \upsilon\cos\vartheta\,\frac{h}{\cos\vartheta} = \upsilon h\,. \qquad \ldots (7.41)$$

Note: Evidently, the total length of yarns is independent of the direction of the yarn system given by angle ϑ. Therefore, the yarns will have the same length L when they are parallel to the jaw axis (i.e. perpendicular to the gripping line of the jaws), as shown in Fig. 7.4b.

Let us denote the fineness of the yarns by the symbol T. It is then valid to write that $T = m/L$[7], where m is the mass of the yarns in the aforementioned rectangle. This relation together with Eq. (7.41) can express the mass of the yarns in the rectangle TUU′T′. This is shown below

$$m = T\,L = T\upsilon h\,. \qquad \ldots (7.42)$$

The (vertical) length of unitary strip of yarn system is equal to the gauge length h shown in Fig. 7.4. So, the fineness T_1 of such unitary strip of yarn system is

$$T_1 = \frac{m}{h} = T\upsilon = G\,, \qquad \ldots (7.43)$$

where the symbol G expresses areal mass density of yarn system.

Note: According to Eq. (7.42), the mass of the yarn lying in the rectangle TUU′T′, shown in Fig. 7.4a, is $T\upsilon h$. However, the area of the mentioned rectangle is $(1.h)$ so that the mass per unit area, i.e., areal mass density is $G = T\upsilon h/(1\cdot h) = T\upsilon$.

The nominal force S acts also on the unitary width so that the specific stress σ of the yarn system is

$$\sigma = \frac{S}{T_1} = \frac{S}{T\upsilon} = \frac{S}{G}\,. \qquad \ldots (7.44)$$

(The definition according to Eq. (1.21) was used). Using Eq. (7.32) in the last equation we can write

---

7.   See Eq. (1.3) in Chapter 1.

$$\sigma = \frac{1}{T\upsilon}\upsilon\cos^2\vartheta\frac{F_I(\varepsilon_I)(1+\varepsilon)}{1+\varepsilon_I}M(\vartheta,\vartheta_b) = \sigma_I(\varepsilon_I)\cos^2\vartheta\frac{1+\varepsilon}{1+\varepsilon_I}M(\vartheta,\vartheta_b),$$

$$... (7.45)$$

where Eq. (7.6) describes the quantity ε_I as a function of ε and ϑ, Eq. (7.28) determines the value $M(\vartheta, \vartheta_b)$, and

$$\sigma_I(\varepsilon_I) = \frac{F_I(\varepsilon_I)}{T} \qquad\qquad ... (7.46)$$

represents the specific stress of single yarn.

The maximum of specific stress of the yarn system becomes $\sigma_{\vartheta=0}$ from Eq. (7.45) at value $\vartheta = 0$, where the expressions stated in Eq. (7.33) are valid. So we can write

$$\sigma_{\vartheta=0} = \sigma_I(\varepsilon). \qquad\qquad ... (7.47)$$

The specific strength (tenacity) σ^* of the yarn system is defined similarly in Eq. (7.44). It is then valid to write

$$\sigma^* = \frac{S^*}{T_1} = \frac{S^*}{T\upsilon} = \frac{S^*}{G}. \qquad\qquad ... (7.48)$$

Using the nominal breaking force S^* according to Eq. (7.36), we obtain the relation as follows

$$\sigma^* = \frac{1}{T\upsilon}\upsilon P\cos\vartheta\sqrt{1-\frac{\sin^2\vartheta}{(1+a)^2}}M(\vartheta,\vartheta_b) = \sigma_I^*\cos\vartheta\sqrt{1-\frac{\sin^2\vartheta}{(1+a)^2}}M(\vartheta,\vartheta_b),$$

$$... (7.49)$$

where Eq. (7.28) determines the value $M(\vartheta, \vartheta_b)$, and

$$\sigma_I^* = \frac{P}{T} \qquad\qquad ... (7.50)$$

is the specific strength (tenacity) of single yarn.

The maximum specific strength (tenacity) of yarn system $\sigma_{\vartheta=0}^*$ corresponds to $\vartheta = 0$. Using $M(\vartheta,\vartheta_b) = M(0,\vartheta_b) = 1$, according to Eq. (7.33), we obtain the following relation from Eq. (7.49)

$$\sigma_{\vartheta=0}^* = \sigma_I^*. \qquad\qquad ... (7.51)$$

Note: This case corresponds to Fig. 7.4b where the previous equation is immediately obtained.

Specific stress and specific strength of yarn system for simplest case. The easier equations are valid in the earlier mentioned simplest case. Using Eqs. (7.38) and (7.50) in Eq. (7.44) we can write

$$\sigma = \frac{1}{T\upsilon}\delta\left(\varepsilon,\varepsilon^*\right)\frac{\upsilon P}{a}\varepsilon\cos^4\vartheta\, M\left(\vartheta,\vartheta_b\right) = \delta\left(\varepsilon,\varepsilon^*\right)\sigma_l^*\frac{\varepsilon}{a}\cos^4\vartheta\, M\left(\vartheta,\vartheta_b\right).$$

$$\ldots (7.52)$$

The maximum of specific stress $\sigma_{\vartheta=0}$ is obtained at $\vartheta = 0$, where Eq. (7.33) is valid. Thus

$$\sigma_{\vartheta=0} = \delta\left(\varepsilon,a\right)\sigma_l^*\frac{\varepsilon}{a}. \qquad \ldots (7.53)$$

Using the nominal breaking force S^* according to Eq. (7.40) and Eq. (7.50) in Eq. (7.48) we obtain the specific strength (tenacity) σ^* of the yarn system of the simplest case as follows

$$\sigma^* = \frac{1}{T\upsilon}\upsilon P\cos^2\vartheta\, M\left(\vartheta,\vartheta_b\right) = \sigma_l^*\cos^2\vartheta\, M\left(\vartheta,\vartheta_b\right). \qquad \ldots (7.54)$$

The maximum specific strength (tenacity) of yarn system $\sigma^*_{\vartheta=0}$ is obtained when the angle $\vartheta = 0$. Using $M(\vartheta, \vartheta_b) = 1$ according to Eq. (7.33) in this case, we obtain from Eq. (7.54) $\sigma^*_{\vartheta=0} = \sigma_l^*$, which is identical to Eq. (7.51).

Overview of equations for one system of yarns. The overview of the resulting equations describing one system of yarns is shown in Table 7.1.

Multi-axial textile between jaws. Figure 7.5 illustrates a multi-axial (tri-axial) textile. As shown, a strip of multi-axial textile of width c is gripped in-between jaws A and B of a tensile tester. The mechanical effects of single yarns are mutually independent, according to the assumption stated at the beginning of this chapter, so that we can add influences of the individual systems together so as to obtain the mechanical behavior of the whole multi-axial textile.

Forces in multi-axial textile. A multi-axial textile is created from K yarn systems. The previous equations describes each i-th system $(i = 1, 2, \ldots, K)$ but nearly all quantities – the quantities related to each i-th system – must be completed with the subscript i (e.g. $P_i, \vartheta_i, F_{l,i}\left(\varepsilon_{l,i}\right)$ etc.)[8]. The quantities common for all yarn systems are remained without

---

8. The subscript i will be "automatically" added to all quantities which relate only to the i-th system in previous equations.

Table 7.1 Overview of equations.

Independent Variable: ε.   Common Input Parameters: $P, a, \vartheta, c, h, \upsilon, T$.
Common quantities and functions:
(7.15) $\begin{aligned}\delta(X,Y)=1\cdots X\le Y,\\ \delta(X,Y)=0\cdots X>Y.\end{aligned}$
(7.25) $\tan\vartheta_b = c/h$.
(7.28) $\left.\begin{aligned}M(\vartheta,\vartheta_b)=1-\tan\vartheta/\tan\vartheta_b\ldots\vartheta<\vartheta_b,\\ M(\vartheta,\vartheta_b)=0\ldots\vartheta\ge\vartheta_b,\end{aligned}\right\}$ especially $M(0,\vartheta_b)=M\left(\vartheta,\dfrac{\pi}{2}\right)=1$.
(7.50) $\sigma_l^* = P/T$.

General Case		Simplest Case (small deformations, linear force–strain function of yarns)	
Input function: $F_l(\varepsilon_l)$.		(7.17)	$F_l(\varepsilon_l)=\delta(\varepsilon_l,a)\dfrac{P}{a}\varepsilon_l.$ (+)
(7.6)	$\varepsilon_l=\sqrt{1+\left[\varepsilon^2+2\varepsilon\right]\cos^2\vartheta}-1.$	(7.9)	$\varepsilon_l=\varepsilon\cos^2\vartheta.$
(7.7)	$\varepsilon^*=\sqrt{1+\dfrac{a^2+2a}{\cos^2\vartheta}}-1.$	(7.10)	$\varepsilon^*=\dfrac{a}{\cos^2\vartheta}.$
(7.46)	$\sigma_l(\varepsilon_l)=F_l(\varepsilon_l)/T.$	(7.17) (7.46)	$\sigma_l(\varepsilon_l)=\delta(\varepsilon_l,a)\dfrac{P}{Ta}\varepsilon_l.$ (+)
(7.32)	$S=\upsilon\cos^2\vartheta\dfrac{F_l(\varepsilon_l)(1+\varepsilon)}{1+\varepsilon_l}M(\vartheta,\vartheta_b).$	(7.38)	$S=\delta(\varepsilon,\varepsilon^*)\dfrac{\upsilon P}{a}\varepsilon\cos^4\vartheta\,M(\vartheta,\vartheta_b).$
(7.34)	$S_{\vartheta=0}=\upsilon F_l(\varepsilon).$	(7.39)	$S_{\vartheta=0}=\delta(\varepsilon,a)\dfrac{\upsilon P}{a}\varepsilon.$
(7.36)	$S^*=\upsilon P\cos\vartheta\sqrt{1-\dfrac{\sin^2\vartheta}{(1+a)^2}}M(\vartheta,\vartheta_b).$	(7.40)	$S^*=\upsilon P\cos^2\vartheta\,M(\vartheta,\vartheta_b).$
(7.37)	$S^*_{\vartheta=0}=\upsilon P.$	(7.37)	$S^*_{\vartheta=0}=\upsilon P.$
(7.50)	$\sigma_l^*=P/T$	(7.50)	$\sigma_l^*=P/T.$
(7.45)	$\sigma=\sigma_l(\varepsilon_l)\cos^2\vartheta\dfrac{1+\varepsilon}{1+\varepsilon_l}M(\vartheta,\vartheta_b).$	(7.52)	$\sigma=\delta(\varepsilon,\varepsilon^*)\sigma_l^*\dfrac{\varepsilon}{a}\cos^4\vartheta\,M(\vartheta,\vartheta_b).$
(7.47)	$\sigma_{\vartheta=0}=\sigma_l(\varepsilon).$	(7.53)	$\sigma_{\vartheta=0}=\delta(\varepsilon,a)\sigma_l^*\dfrac{\varepsilon}{a}.$
(7.49)	$\sigma^*=\sigma_l^*\cos\vartheta\sqrt{1-\dfrac{\sin^2\vartheta}{(1+a)^2}}M(\vartheta,\vartheta_b).$	(7.54)	$\sigma^*=\sigma_l^*\cos^2\vartheta\,M(\vartheta,\vartheta_b).$
(7.51)	$\sigma^*_{\vartheta=0}=\sigma_l^*.$	(7.51)	$\sigma^*_{\vartheta=0}=\sigma_l^*.$

(+) It is not necessary to calculate these expressions.

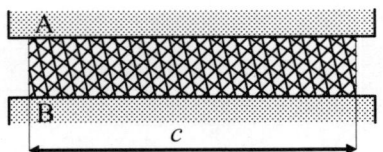

7.5 Multi-axial textile in-between jaws.

the subscript i. They are jaw displacement ε, the parameters of the adjusted tensile tester, i.e., c, h and ϑ_b, and the symbols expressed in function δ – Equation (7.15), and function M – Equation (7.28).

The nominal (vertical) force S_Σ expresses the vertical force per unitary strip of the multi-axial textile[9]. Applying Eq. (7.32) we obtain

$$S_\Sigma = \sum_{i=1}^{K} S_i = \sum_{i=1}^{K} \left\{ \upsilon_i \cos^2 \vartheta_i \, \frac{F_{l,i}\left(\varepsilon_{l,i}\right)\left(1+\varepsilon\right)}{1+\varepsilon_{l,i}} M\left(\vartheta_i, \vartheta_b\right) \right\}, \qquad \dots (7.55)$$

where, according to Eqs. (7.6) and (7.28), we use the following expressions

$$\varepsilon_{l,i} = \sqrt{1+\left[\varepsilon^2 + 2\varepsilon\right]\cos^2 \vartheta_i} - 1, \qquad \dots (7.56)$$

$$\left. \begin{array}{l} M\left(\vartheta_i, \vartheta_b\right) = 1 - \dfrac{\tan \vartheta_i}{\tan \vartheta_b} \dots \vartheta_i < \vartheta_b, \\[2mm] M\left(\vartheta_i, \vartheta_b\right) = 0 \dots \vartheta_i \geq \vartheta_b, \end{array} \right\} \text{ especially } M\left(0, \vartheta_b\right) = M\left(\vartheta_i, \frac{\pi}{2}\right) = 1.$$

$$\dots (7.57)$$

The maximum of nominal (vertical) force $S_{\Sigma, \vartheta=0}$ expresses the vertical force per unit width of the multi-axial textile at $\vartheta_i = 0$, $i = 1,2,\dots, K$. Then the following relations are valid similarly to the triplet of Eq. (7.33)

$$\varepsilon_{l,i} = \varepsilon, \quad \varepsilon_i^* = a_i, \quad M\left(\vartheta_i, \vartheta_b\right) = M\left(0, \vartheta_b\right) = 1, \quad i = 1,2,\cdots, K. \qquad \dots (7.58)$$

It is valid from Eq. (7.55)

$$S_{\Sigma, \vartheta=0} = \sum_{i=1}^{K} S_{i,\vartheta_i=0} = \sum_{i=1}^{K} \left\{ \upsilon_i F_{l,i}\left(\varepsilon\right) \right\}. \qquad \dots (7.59)$$

Note: The identical equation is obtained by summing the expression mentioned in Eq. (7.34) for all yarn systems.

---

9.   The quantities related to the whole multi-axial textile have the subscript Σ.

It is more difficult to determine the nominal breaking (vertical) force S_Σ^*, because the jaw displacement ε_i^* at the time of rupture is different for different yarn systems; actually it is valid according to Eq. (7.7)

$$\varepsilon_i^* = \sqrt{1 + \frac{a_i^2 + 2a_i}{\cos^2 \vartheta_i}} - 1. \qquad \qquad \ldots (7.60)$$

In general, we need to find out the total maximum of S_Σ corresponding to all jaw displacements ε; this value represents the nominal breaking (vertical) force S_Σ^* and the corresponding jaw displacement refers to the jaw displacement ε_Σ^* at the time of rupture of multi-axial textile.

Notes: 1. Do not forget that the yarn force–strain functions $F_{l,i}\left(\varepsilon_{l,i}\right)$ are generally different for yarns from different yarn systems, each such function is defined for all $\varepsilon_{l,i} \in \langle 0, \infty \rangle$, and functions $F_{l,i}\left(\varepsilon_{l,i}\right)$ can have positive values also when the yarn strain $\varepsilon_{l,i}$ is higher than the yarn-breaking strain a_i. (See the note mentioned below Eq. (7.11)).
2. The rupture of multi-axial textile will be studied later on by solving the expression for the specific strength (tenacity).

Forces in multi-axial textile for simplest case. The nominal (vertical) force S_Σ, expressing the vertical force per unitary strip of the multi-axial textile, is the summation of the forces according to Eq. (7.38). This can be written as follows

$$S_\Sigma = \sum_{i=1}^{K} \left\{ \delta\left(\varepsilon, \varepsilon_i^*\right) \frac{\upsilon_i P_i}{a_i} \varepsilon \cos^4 \vartheta_i \, M\left(\vartheta_i, \vartheta_b\right) \right\}. \qquad \ldots (7.61)$$

If all the systems ($i = 1, 2, \ldots, K$) assign the value $\vartheta_i = 0$ then Eq. (7.58) is valid. We can then express the maximum of nominal (vertical) force from Eq. (7.61) as follows

$$S_{\Sigma, \vartheta=0} = \sum_{i=1}^{K} \left\{ \delta\left(\varepsilon, a_i\right) \frac{\upsilon_i P_i}{a_i} \varepsilon \right\}. \qquad \ldots (7.62)$$

Note: The rupture of multi-axial textile in this simplest case will be studied later on by solving the expression for the specific strength (tenacity).

Specific stress of multi-axial textile. The specific stress of one-yarn system is determined by Eq. (7.44), which we can write in the following form

$$S_i = \sigma_i T_{1,i} = \sigma_i T_i \upsilon_i = \sigma_i G_i, \qquad \qquad \ldots (7.63)$$

where S_i is the nominal (vertical) force, acts on the unitary width of the *i*-th system and the equality

$$T_{1,i} = T_i \upsilon_i = G_i \qquad \qquad \ldots (7.64)$$

is resulting from Eq. (7.43).

Note: Let us remind that (for *i*-th yarn system) $T_{1,i}$ is the fineness of one-yarn system in the unitary strip of a multi-axial textile, T_i is the fineness of each yarn in the *i*-th system, and G_i is the areal mass density of the yarn system.

The fineness of the whole unitary strip of the multi-axial textile, shown in Fig. 7.6, is $T_\Sigma = \sum_{i=1}^{K} T_{1,i}$ and the following expression is valid according to Eq. (7.64)

$$T_\Sigma = \sum_{i=1}^{K} T_{1,i} = \sum_{i=1}^{K} (T_i \upsilon_i) = \sum_{i=1}^{K} G_i = G_\Sigma, \qquad \ldots (7.65)$$

where G_Σ means the areal mass density of the whole multi-axial textile (thicker yarns as shown in Fig. 7.6).

The total nominal (vertical) force S_Σ acting on the unitary width (of unitary strip) of the whole multi-axial textile is equal to the summation of

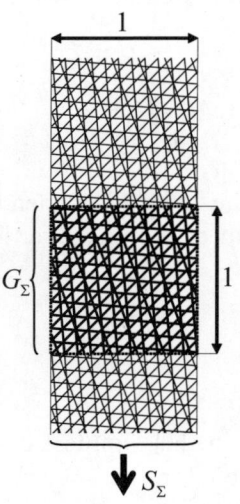

7.6 Example of unitary strip and areal unit of multi-axial textile.

the nominal (vertical) forces acting on all yarn systems. Using Eq. (7.63) it is possible to write the following expression

$$S_{\Sigma} = \sum_{i=1}^{K} S_i = \sum_{i=1}^{K} (\sigma_i T_i \upsilon_i) = \sum_{i=1}^{K} (\sigma_i G_i) . \qquad \qquad ... (7.66)$$

We can write the expression for the specific stress σ_{Σ} of the whole multi-axial textile using the definition of specific stress according to Eq. (1.21). Applying Eqs. (7.65) and (7.66) it is valid

$$\sigma_{\Sigma} = \frac{S_{\Sigma}}{T_{\Sigma}} = \frac{\sum_{i=1}^{K} (\sigma_i G_i)}{G_{\Sigma}} = \sum_{i=1}^{K} (\sigma_i g_i), \qquad \qquad ... (7.67)$$

where

$$g_i = \frac{G_i}{G_{\Sigma}}, \quad \sum_{i=1}^{K} g_i = 1 \qquad \qquad ... (7.68)$$

are the so-called mass fractions of single yarn systems.

Note: Equation (7.67) determines the specific stress σ_{Σ} of the whole multi-axial textile as the weighted arithmetical mean of the specific stresses from the individual yarn systems and the statistical weights refer to the mass fraction of the single yarn systems.

Utilizing Eq. (7.45) in Eq. (7.67) the following expression is found

$$\sigma_{\Sigma} = \sum_{i=1}^{K} \left[g_i \, \sigma_{l,i} (\varepsilon_{l,i}) \cos^2 \vartheta_i \frac{1+\varepsilon}{1+\varepsilon_{l,i}} M(\vartheta_i, \vartheta_b) \right], \qquad ... (7.69)$$

where Eq. (7.56) is used for $\varepsilon_{l,i}$ and Eq. (7.57) is used for $M(\vartheta_i, \vartheta_b)$.

The maximum of specific stress of the multi-axial textile $\sigma_{\Sigma,\vartheta=0}$ is obtained from Eq. (7.69) at $\vartheta_i = 0$, $i = 1, 2,..., K$, where the expressions mentioned in Eq. (7.58) are also valid. We can therefore write

$$\sigma_{\Sigma,\vartheta=0} = \sum_{i=1}^{K} \left[g_i \, \sigma_{l,i} (\varepsilon) \right]. \qquad \qquad ... (7.70)$$

Note: This result is in coherence with the weighted arithmetical mean of values given in Eq. (7.47).

Specific stress of multi-axial textile for simplest case. Equation (7.67) holds good quite generally. Nevertheless, applying Eq. (7.52) in Eq. (7.67) – in place of Eq. (7.45) – we obtain the following expression for the specific stress σ_{Σ} of the whole multi-axial textile for the mentioned simplest case

$$\sigma_\Sigma = \varepsilon \sum_{i=1}^{K} \left[g_i \delta(\varepsilon, \varepsilon_i^*) \frac{\sigma_{l,i}^*}{a_i} \cos^4 \vartheta_i \, M(\vartheta_i, \vartheta_b) \right]. \qquad \text{... (7.71)}$$

Further, the highest value $\sigma_{\Sigma,\vartheta\to0}$ is obtained at $\vartheta_i = 0$, $i = 1, 2, ..., K$, where Eq. (7.58) is valid. Applying these relations in Eq. (7.71) we obtain the following expression

$$\sigma_{\Sigma,\vartheta=0} = \varepsilon \sum_{i=1}^{K} \left[g_i \delta(\varepsilon, a_i) \frac{\sigma_{l,i}^*}{a_i} \right]. \qquad \text{... (7.72)}$$

Note: This result is in coherence with the weighted arithmetic mean of the values given in Eq. (7.53).

Angular utilization coefficient. An influence of the directional arrangement of the yarn systems to the utilization of the mechanical properties in the multi-axial textiles describes the angular utilization coefficient η_a as follows

$$\eta_a = \sigma_\Sigma / \sigma_{\Sigma,\vartheta=0} \qquad \text{... (7.73)}$$

where $\sigma_{\Sigma,\vartheta=0} > 0$. This utilization coefficient generally varies with the jaw displacement ε when Eqs. (7.69) and (7.70) are used in the definition expressed in Eq. (7.73). On the other hand, we may use Eqs. (7.71) and (7.72) if the simplest case can be assumed. Further, if the jaw displacement is smaller than each values a_i, i.e., all values $\delta(\varepsilon, a_i) = 1$ according to Eq. (7.15), then the angular utilization coefficient

$\eta_a = \sum_{i=1}^{K} \left[g_i \frac{\sigma_{l,i}^*}{a_i} \cos^4 \vartheta_i \, M(\vartheta_i, \vartheta_b) \right] \Big/ \sum_{i=1}^{K} \left[g_i \frac{\sigma_{l,i}^*}{a_i} \right]$ is independent of the jaw

displacement ε.

Active and passive groups of yarn systems. The areal mass density of each yarn system G_i and the total areal mass density G_Σ of the whole multi-axial textile can be evaluated by using Eqs. (7.64) and (7.65). The border angle ϑ_b can be determined by using Eq. (7.25).

Let us now divide all yarn systems creating a multi-axial textile into two groups.

(a) The first group contains the yarn systems whose angles are given by $\vartheta_i < \vartheta_b$, i.e., $M(\vartheta_i, \vartheta_b) > 0$ according to Eq. (7.28). We call this group as the active group of yarn systems in the multi-axial textile – in short "active group"– because such yarn systems are actively contributing to the forces and stresses of the multi-axial textile. The total areal mass density of this active group of yarn systems is

$$G_{A,\Sigma} = \sum_{\substack{i=1,2,\cdots K, \\ \vartheta_i < \vartheta_b}} G_i \qquad . \qquad \qquad \ldots (7.74)$$

The number of systems in the active group is called K_A.

(b) The second group of yarn systems whose angles are given by $\vartheta_i \geq \vartheta_b$, i.e., $M(\vartheta_i, \vartheta_b) = 0$ according to Eq. (7.28). We call this group as the passive group of yarn systems in the multi-axial textile – in short "passive group"– because such yarn systems cannot contribute to the forces and stresses of the multi-axial textile. The total areal mass density of this passive group is

$$G_{P,\Sigma} = \sum_{\substack{i=1,2,\cdots K, \\ \vartheta_i \geq \vartheta_b}} G_i \qquad . \qquad \qquad \ldots (7.75)$$

The number of systems in the passive group of yarn systems is called K_P.

The following expression is valid from the last two equations and Eq. (7.65)

$$G_\Sigma = \sum_{i=1}^{K} G_i = \sum_{\substack{i=1,2,\cdots K, \\ \vartheta_i < \vartheta_b}} G_i + \sum_{\substack{i=1,2,\cdots K, \\ \vartheta_i \geq \vartheta_b}} G_i = G_{A,\Sigma} + G_{P,\Sigma} \qquad . \qquad \ldots (7.76)$$

It is also valid

$$K = K_A + K_P. \qquad \qquad \ldots (7.77)$$

It is evident that only the active group of yarn systems determines the mechanical behavior (including strength) of the multi-axial textile.

Specific strength (tenacity) of multi-axial textile. The problem of specific strength (and/or breaking force) of the multi-axial textile can be solved by means of active group of yarn systems only. Quite generally, the solution follows the commentary mentioned after Eq. (7.60). We must find out the total maximum of the specific stress corresponding to all values of jaw displacement. Such a maximum represents the specific strength (tenacity) and the corresponding value of jaw displacement refers to the jaw displacement at the time of rupture of the multi-axial textile.

Nevertheless, the force–strain relation $F_{l,i}(\varepsilon_{l,i})$ of yarn from each i-th yarn system is often equal to zero when its strain $\varepsilon_{l,i}$ is higher than the breaking strain of the yarn a_i. Such a function fulfills – besides Eq. (7.11) – the mentioned assumptions; see the scheme shown in Fig. 7.7. It is therefore valid to write that

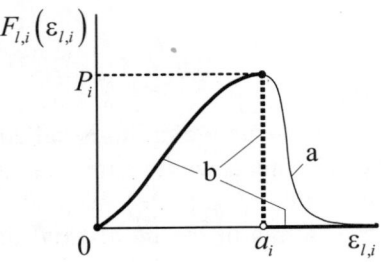

7.7 Scheme of force–strain function $F_{l,i}(\varepsilon_{l,i})$ of yarn.

a...general function, b...function $F_{l,i}(\varepsilon_{l,i} > a_i) = 0$.

$$\left.\begin{array}{l} F_{l,i}\left(\varepsilon_{l,i} \le a_i\right)\ldots\text{increasing function,}\quad F_{l,i}(0) = 0,\quad F_{l,i}(a_i) = P_i, \\ F_{l,i}\left(\varepsilon_{l,i} > a_i\right) = 0, \end{array}\right\} i = 1, 2, \cdots K.$$

$$\ldots (7.78)$$

Note: The force–strain function of the multi-axial textile for the simplest case, determined by Eq. (7.14), is a type of the function $F_{l,i}(\varepsilon_{l,i})$ according to Eq. (7.78).

Note: If $\varepsilon_{l,i} > a_i$, i.e., also $\varepsilon_i > \varepsilon_i^*$ according to Eq. (7.7) or Eq. (7.10), then all the forces and the strengths of the *i*-th system are equal to zero, because all yarns are broken.

Let us first study the active group of yarn systems only. (We can imagine it as "a part of multi-axial textile" where all the yarn systems are mechanically active). We can calculate the jaw displacement ε_i^* at the time of rupture (breaking strain of yarn system) according to Eq. (7.7) or Eq. (7.10) (also in Table 7.1) for each yarn system of active group. Then let us rename the values of the subscripts *i* so that it is valid $\varepsilon_{i-1}^* \le \varepsilon_i^*$, $i = 1, 2, \ldots, K_A$, , where $\varepsilon_0^* = 0$. (Compare it with the introductory part of Section 6.3). After renaming, Eq. (7.74) takes the following form

$$G_{A,\Sigma} = \sum_{i=1}^{K_A} G_i . \qquad\qquad \ldots (7.79)$$

Further, let us define the mass fractions of the individual yarn systems in the active group ("a part of multi-axial textile") analogically to Eq. (7.68)

$$g_{A,i} = \frac{G_i}{G_{A,\Sigma}}, \quad \sum_{i=1}^{K_A} g_{A,i} = 1 . \qquad\qquad \ldots (7.80)$$

We can calculate the specific stress σ_i as a function of jaw displacement ε, specific strength σ_i^* and the corresponding jaw displacement ε_i^* at break according to equations mentioned together in Table 7.1.

Note: Do not forget that: (1) We must add the corresponding subscript i to each quantity related to the yarn system of the active group. (2) The functions $F_{l,i}(\varepsilon_{l,i})$ still satisfy Eq. (7.78).

We can also calculate the total areal mass density $G_{A,\Sigma}$ by means of Eq. (7.79) and the mass fraction $g_{A,i}$ of the yarn systems according to Eq. (7.80).

Independent to the differences in the real geometry let us think that (imaginary) "parallel fiber bundles" have the same mechanical behavior than the yarn systems in the active group. Then the specific strength of the active group can be solved by using the tools described for the blended bundles in Section 6.3. The present initial quantities and the corresponding quantities of the blended bundle are shown in the first part of Table 7.2. By making these substitutions and applying the method described in Section 6.3, we can find

(1) Specific stress $\sigma_{A,\Sigma}(\varepsilon)$ of active group of yarn systems as a function of jaw displacement ε,
(2) specific strength $\sigma_{A,\Sigma}^*$ of active group of yarn systems,
(3) minimum specific strength $\sigma_{A,\Sigma,\min}^*$ of active group of yarn systems, and
(4) mass fractions $g_{A,i,\min}$ corresponding to the minimum specific strength.

These quantities are shown in the second part of Table 7.2.

The passive group does not contribute to the forces, but it contributes to increase the areal mass density of the multi-axial textile. The specific stress and/or strength of the active group of yarn systems is always a force divided by the areal mass density $G_{A,\Sigma}$ of this active group. (See, for example, Eq. (7.44)). However, the whole multi-axial textile has the total areal mass density $G_\Sigma \geq G_{A,\Sigma}$ – Equation (7.76). So, the specific stresses and strengths of the active group must be multiplied by the ratio $G_{A,\Sigma}/G_\Sigma$ in order to obtain the corresponding values of the whole multi-axial textile. Thus

$$\sigma_\Sigma = \sigma_{A,\Sigma} \frac{G_{A,\Sigma}}{G_\Sigma}, \tag{7.81}$$

$$\sigma_\Sigma^* = \sigma_{A,\Sigma}^* \frac{G_{A,\Sigma}}{G_\Sigma}, \tag{7.82}$$

$$\sigma_{\Sigma,\min}^* = \sigma_{A,\Sigma,\min}^* \frac{G_{A,\Sigma}}{G_\Sigma}. \tag{7.83}$$

Table 7.2 Comparison of quantities of multi-axial textile and multi-component parallel fiber bundle

Active group of yarn systems in multi-axial textile		Multi-componential parallel fiber bundle according to Section 6.3	
Initial quantity	Symbol	Initial quantity	Symbol
Subscript of yarn system	i	Subscript of component	i
Number of yarn systems	K_A	Number of components	K
Mass fraction of yarn system	$g_{A,i}$	Mass fraction in bundle	g_i
Strain of each yarn system	ε	Strain of bundle	ε
Specific stress of yarn system	σ_i	Specific stress of fiber	$\sigma_i(\varepsilon)$
Specific strength of yarn system	σ_i^*	Specific strength of fiber	σ_i^*
Breaking jaw displacement of yarn system	ε_i^*	Breaking strain of fiber	a_i
Evaluated quantities according to the tools mentioned in Section 6.3			
Specific stress of active group	$\sigma_{A,\Sigma}$	Bundle specific stress	$\sigma_b(\varepsilon)$
Specific strength of active group	$\sigma_{A,\Sigma}^*$	Bundle specific strength	σ_b^*
Minimum specific strength of active group	$\sigma_{A,\Sigma,min}^*$	Minimum bundle specific strength	$\sigma_{b,min}^*$
Mass fractions in active group corresponding to minimum specific strength	$g_{A,i,min}$	Mass fraction in bundle corresponding to minimum bundle specific strength	$g_{i,min}$

Note: Equation (7.81) produced the same results as Eq. (7.69) and/or Eq. (7.71).

Similarly, the mass fractions $g_{A,i}$ and $g_{A,i,min}$ can be recalculated to mass fractions related to the whole multi-axial textile as follows

$$g_i = g_{A,i}\frac{G_{A,\Sigma}}{G_\Sigma}, \quad g_{i,min} = g_{A,i,min}\frac{G_{A,\Sigma}}{G_\Sigma}. \qquad \ldots (7.84)$$

Evidently, the summation $\sum_{i=1}^{K_A} g_i = \sum_{i=1}^{K_A} g_{i,min} = G_{A,\Sigma}/G_\Sigma = 1 - G_{P,\Sigma}/G_\Sigma$,

where the ratio $G_{P,\Sigma}/G_\Sigma$ is the areal mass density of overall yarn systems creating the passive group of yarn system. (The mass relations of the passive group of yarn systems do not play any role).

7.2   Regular multi-axial textiles

A multi-axial textile would be called regular multi-axial textile if the following two assumptions are valid:

1. The yarn systems creating a multi-axial textile are distinguished by directions only.
2. The directions of yarn systems are distributed regularly.

First assumption. According to the first assumption the angle ϑ_i and the quantities determined by means of angle ϑ_i must have the subscript i. The other quantities, common for all yarn systems, will be written now without this subscript. Table 7.3 reports about the symbols of common function and quantities.

Table 7.3 Common input symbols.

Input quantity or function	General symbol	Common symbol by regular textiles
Fineness of one yarn	T_i	T
Sett of yarns	υ_i	υ
Force–strain relation of the yarn	$F_{l,i}(\varepsilon_{l,i})$	$F_l(\varepsilon_{l,i})$ [+]
Breaking force of the yarn	P_i	P
Breaking strain of the yarn	a_i	a

(+) The argument $\varepsilon_{l,i}$ of common function F_l is different for different yarn systems; *see* Eq. (7.93) preliminarily.

Further, according to Eq. (7.64), the areal mass density of each yarn system is $G = T\upsilon$; according to Eq. (7.65), the areal mass density of the multi-axial textile is $G_\Sigma = \sum_{i=1}^{K} G = KG$; and according to Eq. (7.68), the mass fraction of each yarn system is

$$g = \frac{G}{G_\Sigma} = \frac{G}{KG} = \frac{1}{K} . \qquad \qquad \dots (7.85)$$

The specific stress of single yarn, generally determined in accordance with Eq. (7.46) by expression $\sigma_{l,i}(\varepsilon_{l,i}) = F_{l,i}(\varepsilon_{l,i})/T_i$ takes the following expression now

$$\sigma_l(\varepsilon_{l,i}) = F_l(\varepsilon_{l,i})/T . \qquad \qquad \dots (7.86)$$

The specific strength (tenacity) of single yarn, generally determined in accordance with Eq. (7.50) by expression $\sigma_{l,i}^* = P_i/T_i$ is now expressed as follows

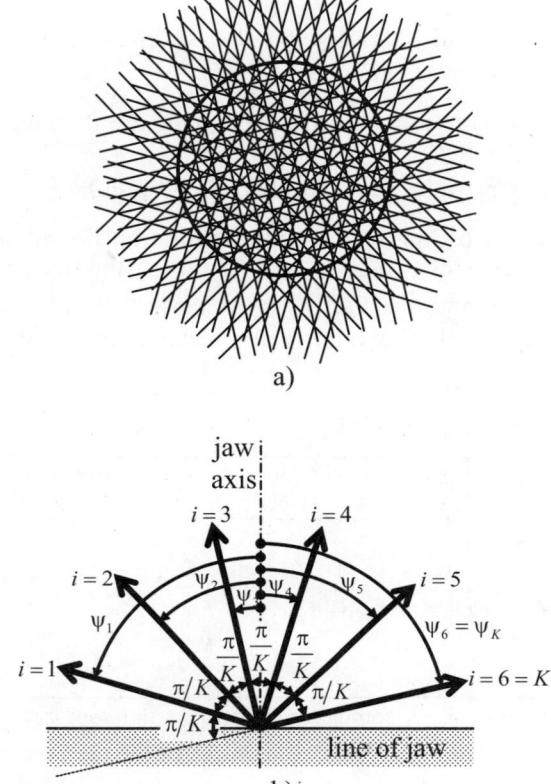

a)

b)

7.8 Example of angle distribution in a regular multi-axial textile.

(a) Multi-axial textile ($K = 6$) in the circle;
(b) Directional vectors of yarn systems.

$$\sigma_l^* = P/T .\qquad \qquad \qquad \text{... (7.87)}$$

This is a common quantity valid for all yarn systems.

Second assumption. The second assumption is illustrated in Fig. 7.8. An example of a regular multi-axial textile, containing $K = 6$ yarn systems, is shown inside a circle in Fig. 7.8a. The corresponding directional vectors of the yarn systems are shown by thick arrows in Fig. 7.8b. The oriented angle ψ_1 determines the direction of the first system. Similarly, the oriented angle ψ_2 determines the direction of the second system. Likewise, the oriented angle ψ_K determines the direction of the last, that is, K-th system.

Note: In contrary to the previous chapter we now use oriented angles $\psi_i \in (-\pi/2, \pi/2 \rangle$. In the previous chapter, the non-oriented angle ϑ_i is given by

$$|\psi_i| = \vartheta_i \in \langle 0, \pi/2 \rangle. \qquad \dots (7.88)$$

It is evident from Fig. 7.8b that the angular difference between the neighboring systems is constant and is equal to the value π/K. The angle ψ_K of the last K-th system must lie in the interval

$$\psi_K \in \left(\frac{\pi}{2} - \frac{\pi}{K}, \frac{\pi}{2} \right), \qquad \dots (7.89)$$

as shown in Fig. 7.8b, and the following equation is valid for each of angle ψ_i

$$\psi_i = \psi_K - (K - i) \frac{\pi}{K} = \psi_K - \pi + \frac{i}{K} \pi, \quad i = 1, 2, \cdots, K . \qquad \dots (7.90)$$

So, if we know the angle ψ_K of the last yarn system then we can calculate each of angle ψ_i according to Eq. (7.90).

The equations in Section 7.1 are written in terms of the non-oriented angles ϑ_i in the form of goniometrical functions of $\cos\vartheta_i$, $\sin^2\vartheta_i$ and $\tan\vartheta_i$. Now, the following equalities are valid according to Eq. (7.88)

$$\cos\vartheta_i = \cos\psi_i, \quad \sin^2\vartheta_i = \sin^2\psi_i, \quad \tan\vartheta_i = \tan|\psi_i|. \qquad \dots (7.91)$$

Applying the symbols mentioned in Table 7.3 and equations from (7.85) to (7.88), and (7.91), we can obtain a set of equations for the regular multi-axial textiles from the previous chapter.

Forces in regular multi-axial textile. The nominal (vertical) force S_Σ follows Eq. (7.55) and takes the following expression

$$S_\Sigma = \upsilon(1 + \varepsilon) \sum_{i=1}^{K} \left\{ \cos^2 \psi_i \frac{F_l(\varepsilon_{l,i})}{1 + \varepsilon_{l,i}} M(|\psi_i|, \vartheta_b) \right\}, \qquad \dots (7.92)$$

where according to Eqs. (7.56) and (7.57) we obtain

$$\varepsilon_{l,i} = \sqrt{1 + \left[\varepsilon^2 + 2\varepsilon \right] \cos^2 \psi_i} - 1, \qquad \dots (7.93)$$

$$\left. \begin{array}{l} M(|\psi_i|, \vartheta_b) = 1 - \dfrac{\tan|\psi_i|}{\tan\vartheta_b} \dots |\psi_i| < \vartheta_b, \\[2mm] M(|\psi_i|, \vartheta_b) = 0 \dots |\psi_i| \geq \vartheta_b, \end{array} \right\} \text{ especially, } M(0, \vartheta_b) = M\left(|\psi_i|, \frac{\pi}{2}\right) = 1.$$

$$\dots (7.94)$$

The maximum of nominal (vertical) force $S_{\Sigma,\vartheta=0}$ follows Eq. (7.59) and takes the following expression

$$S_{\Sigma,\vartheta=0} = \upsilon \sum_{i=1}^{K} F_i(\varepsilon) = \upsilon K\, F_l(\varepsilon).$$ ... (7.95)

The jaw displacement ε_i^* at the time of rupture of the i-th yarn system follows Eq. (7.60) and takes the following expression

$$\varepsilon_i^* = \sqrt{1 + \frac{a^2 + 2a}{\cos^2 \psi_i}} - 1.$$ ... (7.96)

Forces in regular multi-axial textile for simplest case. The nominal (vertical) force S_Σ follows Eq. (7.61) in this case and takes the following expression

$$S_\Sigma = \frac{\upsilon P}{a} \varepsilon \sum_{i=1}^{K} \left\{ \delta(\varepsilon, \varepsilon_i^*) \cos^4 \psi_i\, M(|\psi_i|, \vartheta_b) \right\}$$ ... (7.97)

and the maximum of nominal (vertical) force $S_{\Sigma,\vartheta=0}$ follows Eq. (7.62) and takes the following expression

$$S_{\Sigma,\vartheta=0} = \delta(\varepsilon, a) \frac{\upsilon P}{a} \varepsilon \sum_{i=1}^{K} 1 = K \frac{\upsilon P}{a} \varepsilon\, \delta(\varepsilon, a).$$ ... (7.98)

Specific stress of regular multi-axial textile. The specific stress σ_Σ follows Eq. (7.69) in this case and then we obtain

$$
\begin{aligned}
\sigma_\Sigma &= g\,(1+\varepsilon) \sum_{i=1}^{K} \left[\cos^2 \psi_i\, \frac{\sigma_l(\varepsilon_{l,i})}{1+\varepsilon_{l,i}} M(|\psi_i|, \vartheta_b) \right] \\
&= \frac{(1+\varepsilon)}{K} \sum_{i=1}^{K} \left[\cos^2 \psi_i\, \frac{\sigma_l(\varepsilon_{l,i})}{1+\varepsilon_{l,i}} M(|\psi_i|, \vartheta_b) \right]
\end{aligned}
$$ ... (7.99)

and the maximum specific stress $\sigma_{\Sigma,\vartheta=0}$ follows Eq. (7.70) and we get

$$\sigma_{\Sigma,\vartheta=0} = g\,\sigma_l(\varepsilon) \sum_{i=1}^{K} 1 = \frac{1}{K} \sigma_l(\varepsilon) K = \sigma_l(\varepsilon).$$ ... (7.100)

Specific stress of regular multi-axial textile for simplest case. In the simplest case, the specific stress σ_Σ follows Eq. (7.71) and takes the following expression

$$\sigma_{\Sigma} = g\frac{\sigma_l^*}{a}\varepsilon\sum_{i=1}^{K}\left[\delta\left(\varepsilon,\varepsilon_i^*\right)\cos^4\psi_i\,M\left(\left|\psi_i\right|,\vartheta_b\right)\right]$$

$$= \frac{\sigma_l^*}{Ka}\varepsilon\sum_{i=1}^{K}\left[\delta\left(\varepsilon,\varepsilon_i^*\right)\cos^4\psi_i\,M\left(\left|\psi_i\right|,\vartheta_b\right)\right]. \qquad \dots (7.101)$$

The maximum specific stress $\sigma_{\Sigma,\vartheta=0}$ follows Eq. (7.72) and takes the following expression

$$\sigma_{\Sigma,\vartheta=0} = g\frac{\sigma_l^*}{a}\varepsilon\delta\left(\varepsilon,a\right)\sum_{i=1}^{K}\left[1\right] = \frac{\sigma_l^*}{Ka}\varepsilon\delta\left(\varepsilon,a\right)K = \frac{\sigma_l^*}{a}\varepsilon\delta\left(\varepsilon,a\right). \qquad \dots (7.102)$$

Angular utilization. The angular utilization coefficient is defined by Eq. (7.73) as the ratio $\eta_a = \sigma_{\Sigma}/\sigma_{\Sigma,\vartheta=0}$. Using Eqs. (7.99) and (7.100) we obtain the following expression

$$\eta_a = \frac{(1+\varepsilon)}{K\sigma_l(\varepsilon)}\sum_{i=1}^{K}\left[\cos^2\psi_i\,\frac{\sigma_l\left(\varepsilon_{l,i}\right)}{1+\varepsilon_{l,i}}M\left(\left|\psi_i\right|,\vartheta_b\right)\right], \qquad \dots (7.103)$$

where $\sigma_l(\varepsilon) > 0$. Especially, the angular utilization in the simplest case follows Eqs. (7.101) and (7.102). Then, it is valid to write that

$$\eta_a = \frac{\dfrac{\sigma_l^*}{Ka}\varepsilon\sum_{i=1}^{K}\left[\delta\left(\varepsilon,\varepsilon_i^*\right)\cos^4\psi_i\,M\left(\left|\psi_i\right|,\vartheta_b\right)\right]}{\dfrac{\sigma_l^*}{a}\varepsilon\delta\left(\varepsilon,a\right)}$$

$$= \frac{1}{K\delta\left(\varepsilon,a\right)}\sum_{i=1}^{K}\left[\delta\left(\varepsilon,\varepsilon_i^*\right)\cos^4\psi_i\,M\left(\left|\psi_i\right|,\vartheta_b\right)\right], \qquad \dots (7.104)$$

where $\varepsilon \le a$.

Note: In accordance with the commentary stated below Eq. (7.73), this angular utilization is independent of the jaw displacement ε.

Special alternative to the simplest case of regular multi-axial textile. We often use regular textiles prepared from a very few expensive fibers or yarns, which have roughly linear force–strain relation (i.e. corresponding to our "simplest case" – glass, kevlar, etc.) in different types of technical textiles. Nevertheless, these structures are not primarily developed for application in a tensile testing machine, but for use in specific technical applications, where

(a) All yarns are fixed (sewn, glued, etc.) in the structure of the product; the free ends of yarns do not exist.

(b) The applications do not demand high deformation of the yarns that the breakage of the yarns would occur. It is assumed that all yarns will be strained without breakage during applications.

We will call such a simplest case of regular multi-axial textile as "special alternative" in short.

The assumption (a) can be interpreted with a view to in an (imaginary) tensile testing machine as a case shown in Fig. 7.9. Here the gauge length is much smaller than the width of multi-axial textile under the jaws, $h \ll c$. Then the angle ϑ_b approaches to its value $\pi/2$, then the value $\tan\vartheta_b \to \infty$ and the value

$$M\left(\vartheta_i, \vartheta_b\right) = M\left(\left|\psi_i\right|, \vartheta_b\right) \to 1 \qquad \ldots (7.105)$$

according to Eq. (7.57). (The "free" ends of the yarns near the edge of the jaws can be neglected).

If the jaw displacement $\varepsilon \leq \varepsilon_i^* = \sqrt{1 + \left(a^2 + 2a\right)/\cos^2\psi_i} - 1$ Eq. (7.96) is valid for each yarn system and then the assumption (b) is also valid.

Note: Evidently, this inequality is always valid, when $\varepsilon \leq a$.

Moreover, if $\varepsilon \leq \varepsilon_i^*$ then

$$\delta\left(\varepsilon, \varepsilon_i^*\right) = 1. \qquad \ldots (7.106)$$

This accords to Eq. (7.15).

Let us substitute the expressions mentioned in Eqs. (7.105), (7.106), (7.90) in Eq. (7.104) and we obtain the following expression for angular utilization in the case of special alternative to the simplest case of regular multi-axial textile

$$\eta_a = \frac{1}{K}\sum_{i=1}^{K}\cos^4\psi_i = \frac{1}{K}\sum_{i=1}^{K}\cos^4\left(\psi_K - \pi + \frac{i}{K}\pi\right). \qquad \ldots (7.107)$$

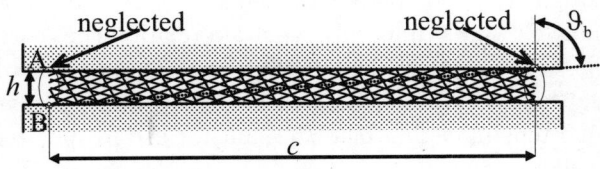

7.9 Neglecting margins.

Rearrangement of last expression for angular utilization. Applying the

known   formulas $\cos(\alpha - \pi) = -\cos\alpha$, $\cos^2\alpha = \dfrac{1}{2} + \dfrac{1}{2}\cos(2\alpha)$,   and

$\cos(\alpha + \beta) = \cos\alpha\cos\beta - \sin\alpha\sin\beta$, we can write the following expressions

$$\cos^4\left(\psi_K - \pi + \frac{i}{K}\pi\right) = \left[-\cos\left(\psi_K + \frac{i}{K}\pi\right)\right]^4$$

$$= \cos^4\left(\psi_K + \frac{i}{K}\pi\right) = \left[\cos^2\left(\psi_K + \frac{i}{K}\pi\right)\right]^2$$

$$= \left[\frac{1}{2} + \frac{1}{2}\cos\left(2\psi_K + \frac{i}{K}2\pi\right)\right]^2$$

$$= \frac{1}{4} + \frac{1}{2}\cos\left(2\psi_K + \frac{i}{K}2\pi\right) + \frac{1}{4}\cos^2\left(2\psi_K + \frac{i}{K}2\pi\right)$$

$$= \frac{1}{4} + \frac{1}{2}\cos\left(2\psi_K + \frac{i}{K}2\pi\right) + \frac{1}{4}\left[\frac{1}{2} + \frac{1}{2}\cos\left(4\psi_K + \frac{i}{K}4\pi\right)\right]$$

$$= \frac{3}{8} + \frac{1}{2}\cos\left(2\psi_K + \frac{i}{K}2\pi\right) + \frac{1}{8}\cos\left(4\psi_K + \frac{i}{K}4\pi\right)$$

$$= \frac{3}{8} + \frac{1}{2}\left[\cos(2\psi_K)\cos\left(\frac{i}{K}2\pi\right) - \sin(2\psi_K)\sin\left(\frac{i}{K}2\pi\right)\right]$$

$$+ \frac{1}{8}\left[\cos(4\psi_K)\cos\left(\frac{i}{K}4\pi\right) - \sin(4\psi_K)\sin\left(\frac{i}{K}4\pi\right)\right]$$

$$= \frac{3}{8} + \frac{1}{2}\cos(2\psi_K)\cos\left(\frac{i}{K}2\pi\right) - \frac{1}{2}\sin(2\psi_K)\sin\left(\frac{i}{K}2\pi\right)$$

$$+ \frac{1}{8}\cos(4\psi_K)\cos\left(\frac{i}{K}4\pi\right) - \frac{1}{8}\sin(4\psi_K)\sin\left(\frac{i}{K}4\pi\right).$$

$$\text{... (7.108)}$$

Substituting Eq. (7.108) in Eq. (7.107) we obtain the angular utilization in the case of special alternative to the simplest case of regular multi-axial textile in the form as follows

$$\eta_a = \frac{3}{8} + \frac{1}{2K}\cos(2\psi_K)\sum_{i=1}^{K}\cos\left(\frac{i}{K}2\pi\right) - \frac{1}{2K}\sin(2\psi_K)\sum_{i=1}^{K}\sin\left(\frac{i}{K}2\pi\right)$$

$$+ \frac{1}{8K}\cos(4\psi_K)\sum_{i=1}^{K}\cos\left(\frac{i}{K}4\pi\right) - \frac{1}{8K}\sin(4\psi_K)\sum_{i=1}^{K}\sin\left(\frac{i}{K}4\pi\right).$$

$$\text{... (7.109)}$$

Note: We used $(1/K)\sum_{i=1}^{K}(3/8) = (1/K)K(3/8) = 3/8$.

There are four sums in Eq. (7.109). However, they can be solved analytically as shown below.

Evaluation of sums $\sum_{i=1}^{K}\cos\left(\dfrac{i}{K}2\pi\right)$ *and* $\sum_{i=1}^{K}\sin\left(\dfrac{i}{K}2\pi\right)$. Let us define the following complex numbers

$$w_i = \cos\left(\frac{i}{K}2\pi\right) + j\sin\left(\frac{i}{K}2\pi\right), \quad i = 1,2,\cdots,K, \qquad \ldots (7.110)$$

where j is the imaginary number ($j^2 = -1$). Especially, the first complex number ($i = 1$) is

$$w_1 = \cos\left(\frac{2\pi}{K}\right) + j\sin\left(\frac{2\pi}{K}\right). \qquad \ldots (7.111)$$

In accordance with the well-known Abraham de Moivre's theorem[10] we can write

$$\cos\left(\frac{i}{K}2\pi\right) + j\sin\left(\frac{i}{K}2\pi\right) = \left[\cos\left(\frac{2\pi}{K}\right) + j\sin\left(\frac{2\pi}{K}\right)\right]^{i}, \qquad \ldots (7.112)$$

$$w_i = w_1^{i}.$$

The progression $\{w_i\}$ of complex numbers therefore follows geometrical progression, where the initial value as well as the quotient is equal to w_1. The sum of s_K of first K members of such progression[11] is

$s_K = \sum_{i=1}^{K} w_i = w_1\dfrac{1-w_1^{K}}{1-w_1}$. Using Eqs. (7.110), (7.111) and (7.112) in the last expression we obtain

$$s_K = \sum_{i=1}^{K} w_i = w_1\frac{1-w_1^{K}}{1-w_1} = w_1\frac{1-w_K}{1-w_1} = w_1\frac{1-\cos\left(\dfrac{K}{K}2\pi\right) - j\sin\left(\dfrac{K}{K}2\pi\right)}{1-\cos(2\pi/K) + j\sin(2\pi/K)}$$

$$= w_1\frac{1-\cos(2\pi) - j\sin(2\pi)}{1-\cos\left(\dfrac{2\pi}{K}\right) + j\sin\left(\dfrac{2\pi}{K}\right)}. \qquad \ldots (7.113)$$

---

10. Generally, it is valid that $\cos(i\alpha) + j\sin(i\alpha) = (\cos\alpha + j\sin\alpha)^{i}$; this is known as Moivre's theorem.

11. Generally, the sum of the first K members of a geometrical progression $\{a_i\}$ is $a_1(1-q^{K})/(1-q)$, where q is the quotient of this geometrical progression.

The denominator of the last quotient is evidently different from zero for each $K \geq 2$ (two or more yarn systems). On the other hand, the numerator is evidently equal to zero so that the sum $s_K = 0$ and the following relations are valid

$$0 = s_K = \sum_{i=1}^{K} w_i = \sum_{i=1}^{K} \left[\cos\left(\frac{i}{K} 2\pi\right) + j \sin\left(\frac{i}{K} 2\pi\right) \right]$$

$$= \sum_{i=1}^{K} \cos\left(\frac{i}{K} 2\pi\right) + j \sum_{i=1}^{K} \sin\left(\frac{i}{K} 2\pi\right). \qquad \ldots (7.114)$$

A complex number is equal zero when the real part and the imaginary part are equal to zero. Thus

$$\sum_{i=1}^{K} \cos\left(\frac{i}{K} 2\pi\right) = 0, \quad \sum_{i=1}^{K} \sin\left(\frac{i}{K} 2\pi\right) = 0. \qquad \ldots (7.115)$$

Evaluation of sums $\sum_{i=1}^{K} \cos\left(\frac{i}{K} 4\pi\right)$ *and* $\sum_{i=1}^{K} \sin\left(\frac{i}{K} 4\pi\right)$. Let us define the following complex numbers

$$v_i = \cos\left(\frac{i}{K} 4\pi\right) + j \sin\left(\frac{i}{K} 4\pi\right), \quad i = 1, 2, \cdots, K \qquad \ldots (7.116)$$

$$v_1 = \cos\left(\frac{4\pi}{K}\right) + j \sin\left(\frac{4\pi}{K}\right). \qquad \ldots (7.117)$$

In analogy to Eq. (7.112) it is also valid to write the following expression

$$\cos\left(\frac{i}{K} 4\pi\right) + j \sin\left(\frac{i}{K} 4\pi\right) = \left[\cos\left(\frac{4\pi}{K}\right) + j \sin\left(\frac{4\pi}{K}\right) \right]^{i}. \qquad \ldots (7.118)$$

$$v_i = v_1^i.$$

The sum of the first K members of the geometrical progression $\{v_i\}$ is

$$s_K' = \sum_{i=1}^{K} v_i = v_1 \frac{1 - v_1^K}{1 - v_1} = v_1 \frac{1 - v_K}{1 - v_1} = v_1 \frac{1 - \cos\left(\frac{K}{K} 4\pi\right) - j \sin\left(\frac{K}{K} 4\pi\right)}{1 - \cos\left(4\pi/K\right) + j \sin\left(4\pi/K\right)}$$

$$= v_1 \frac{1 - \cos\left(4\pi\right) - j \sin\left(4\pi\right)}{1 - \cos\left(\frac{4\pi}{K}\right) + j \sin\left(\frac{4\pi}{K}\right)}. \qquad \ldots (7.119)$$

The numerator of the last quotient is also equal to zero as in the previous case. But, the denominator is different from zero for each $K \geq 3$. Then,

$$
\begin{aligned}
0 = s'_K = \sum_{i=1}^{K} v_i &= \sum_{i=1}^{K} \left[\cos\left(\frac{i}{K}4\pi\right) + j\sin\left(\frac{i}{K}4\pi\right) \right] \\
&= \sum_{i=1}^{K} \cos\left(\frac{i}{K}4\pi\right) + j\sum_{i=1}^{K} \sin\left(\frac{i}{K}4\pi\right),
\end{aligned}
$$

$$
\sum_{i=1}^{K} \cos\left(\frac{i}{K}4\pi\right) = 0, \quad \sum_{i=1}^{K} \sin\left(\frac{i}{K}4\pi\right) = 0, \quad K \geq 3. \qquad \text{... (7.120)}
$$

However, the denominator of the quotient expressed in Eq. (7.119) is equal to zero for $K = 2$ so that we obtain an indeterminate expression for this equation. Especially, for $K = 2$, we need to write directly

$$
\begin{aligned}
s'_2 = \sum_{i=1}^{2} v_i &= \sum_{i=1}^{2} \left[\cos\left(\frac{i}{2}4\pi\right) + j\sin\left(\frac{i}{2}4\pi\right) \right] \\
&= \cos(2\pi) + j\sin(2\pi) + \cos(4\pi) + j\sin(4\pi) = 2 + j0.
\end{aligned} \qquad \text{... (7.121)}
$$

Then the following expressions are valid especially for $K = 2$

$$
\begin{aligned}
2 + j0 = s'_2 = \sum_{i=1}^{2} v_i &= \sum_{i=1}^{2} \left[\cos\left(\frac{i}{2}4\pi\right) + j\sin\left(\frac{i}{2}4\pi\right) \right] \\
&= \sum_{i=1}^{2} \cos\left(\frac{i}{2}4\pi\right) + j\sum_{i=1}^{K} \sin\left(\frac{i}{2}4\pi\right),
\end{aligned}
$$

$$
\sum_{i=1}^{2} \cos\left(\frac{i}{2}4\pi\right) = 2, \quad \sum_{i=1}^{2} \sin\left(\frac{i}{2}4\pi\right) = 0, \quad K = 2. \qquad \text{... (7.122)}
$$

Summarily, we can write the following expressions from Eqs. (7.115), (7.120), and (7.122)

$$
\left.
\begin{aligned}
&\sum_{i=1}^{K} \cos\left(\frac{i}{K}2\pi\right) = 0, \quad \sum_{i=1}^{K} \sin\left(\frac{i}{K}2\pi\right) = 0, \quad \sum_{i=1}^{K} \sin\left(\frac{i}{K}4\pi\right) = 0, \\
&\sum_{i=1}^{K} \cos\left(\frac{i}{K}4\pi\right) = 2 ... K = 2, \quad \sum_{i=1}^{K} \cos\left(\frac{i}{K}4\pi\right) = 0 ... K \geq 3.
\end{aligned}
\right\}
$$

$$
\text{... (7.123)}
$$

Angular utilization coefficient of special alternative. Substituting the expressions mentioned in Eq. (7.123) in Eq. (7.109) we obtain the following expressions

For $K = 2$:

$$\eta_a = \frac{3}{8} + \frac{1}{8 \cdot 2} \cos(4\psi_2) \cdot 2 = \frac{3}{8} + \frac{1}{8} \cos(4\psi_2)$$

$$= \frac{3}{8} + \frac{1}{8} \left[\cos^2(2\psi_2) - \sin^2(2\psi_2) \right]$$

$$= \frac{3}{8} + \frac{1}{8} \left[\cos^2(2\psi_2) - 1 + \cos^2(2\psi_2) \right] = \frac{1}{4} + \frac{1}{4} \cos^2(2\psi_2). \qquad \text{... (7.124)}$$

For $K \geq 3$:

$$\eta_a = \frac{3}{8}. \qquad \text{... (7.125)}$$

The last two equations characterize the mechanical behavior of the special alternative to the simplest case of regular multi-axial textile in relation to the direction of the forces (direction of imaginary jaw axis). If the number of systems is $K \geq 3$ then – according to Eq. (7.125) – the angular utilization η_a takes a constant value which is equal to 3/8. This is independent of the angle ψ_K of the last yarn system. Such a multi-axial textile is modularly isotropic (that is, same in all directions).

In opposite to them, the mechanical behavior of a regular bi-axial textile ($K = 2$) depends significantly on the angle $\psi_K = \psi_2$ between the system that takes the force and the second yarn system, as shown in Eq. (7.124) and displayed in Fig. 7.10. If we are straining the bi-axial textile diagonally ($\psi_2 = \pi/4 = 45°$) then the angular utilization is $\eta_a = 0.25$, that is, only one half of the value $\eta_a = 0.5$ by straining along the first or the second yarn system; see Fig. 7.10. We, therefore, need to apply only half force in the diagonal direction.

Note: The structure of the square woven fabric is a little similar to our bi-axial textile and we empirically know that the diagonal straining of such a fabric is much easier than the straining of it along the warp or the weft direction.

Based on our information, a group of specialists from NASA derived some results like previous equations while developing special parachutes during the APOLLO program[12]. The specialists observed that the traditional

---

12. Many years ago, Mr. Vladimír Svatý, who is the originator of the principle and construction of air-jet looms, passed this information to one of authors of this book.

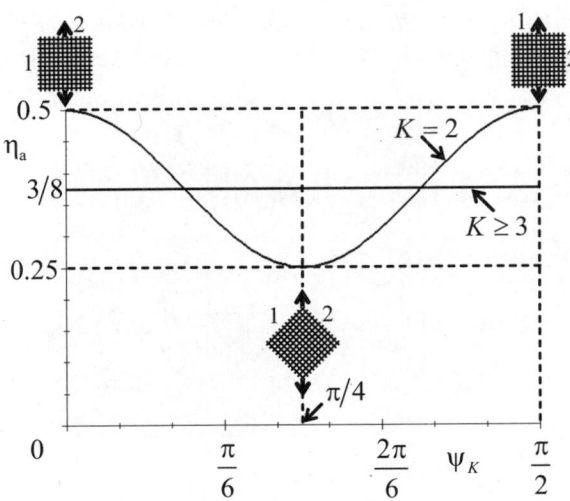

7.10 Angular utilization coefficient of special alternative according to Eqs. (7.124) and (7.125).

woven fabrics developed too high stress concentration which finally led to the destruction of the parachutes during usage. This encouraged them to initiate the development of a weaving machine for the production of three-axial woven fabric and the parachutes prepared from the three-axial woven fabric were then found as fully successful.

The regular multi-axial textiles are often used also as reinforcement in textile composites and/or similar products where the mechanical isotropy is required. The regular four-axial textile ($\psi_1 = -45°$, $\psi_2 = 0°$, $\psi_3 = 45°$, $\psi_4 = 90°$) is most frequently used for such usage, because the longitudinal and the transversal directions (0° and 90°) can be technologically realized more easily than the other two directions. Similarly, in a three-axial textile, the longitudinal direction $\psi_2 = 0°$ is technologically easy to realize, but the other two directions ($\psi_1 = -60°$, $\psi_3 = 60°$) are difficult to realize.

7.3 Planar bundle with a continuous distribution of directions

The linear textiles (fibers and yarns) do have a finite number of directions as discussed in the previous chapters. However, the products created from continuously distributed directions of suitable linear textiles – most frequently fibers– are also often used (for example, fibrous webs required for preparing non-woven textiles, etc.). Therefore, in spite of the previous chapters, we call the linear textiles which are creating products that are solved in this chapter as "fibers".

Simple planar bundle. Let us think of a simple planar bundle that satisfies the following assumptions.

1. All fibers are enough (infinitely) long and straight.
2. All fibers show identical properties.
3. The fibers do not mutually influence one another.
4. The fibers have continuously distributed directions and this distribution is the same at every place of the planar bundle (assumption of homogeneity).

Note: Try to compare this set of assumptions with the definition of simple multi-axial textiles as mentioned in Section 7.1.

Basic idea of solution. Let us imagine a multi-axial textile as described in the previous chapters which is created from a very high number K of systems so that the individual values g_i of the mass fractions [Eq. (7.68)] are very small. Such a multi-axial textile is approaching to a planar yarn and/or fiber bundle made up of fibers showing continuously distributed directions. So, we can perceive that each planar bundle as a multi-axial textile composed of infinite number of systems ($K \to \infty$), which are oriented to all directions and have very small mass fractions. The angular distribution of such fibers was studied in detail in Chapter 3.

Mass fraction. Let us imagine the strip width c of a planar bundle situated in-between jaws A and B of (real or imaginary) a tensile testing machine as shown in Fig. 7.11. The (mean) number of fibers present in the unitary width of jaw B (marked by symbol o in Fig. 7.11) was called υ in Section 3.5 and according to Eq. (3.56) it is valid that $\upsilon = (G/t)k_n$, where G is the areal mass density of the whole planar bundle and t is the fineness of the fibers. The quantity k_n is generally expressed according to Eq. (3.18) as

follows $k_n = \int_0^{\pi/2} \cos\vartheta\, u(\vartheta)\,\mathrm{d}\vartheta$, where $u(\vartheta)$, $\vartheta \in \langle 0, \pi/2\rangle$ is the probability density function of non-oriented angle ϑ of fibers present in the whole

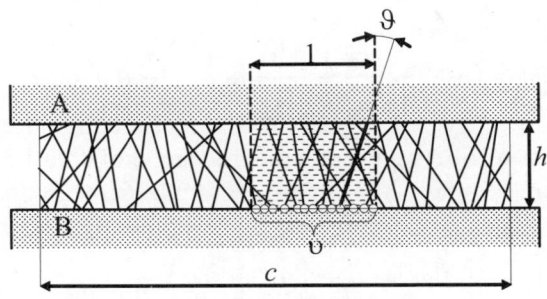

7.11 Number of gripped fibers in unitary width of jaw.

planar bundle. (The angle ϑ is measured from the vertical jaw axis – see this angle made by one general fiber in Fig. 7.11).

The horizontal gripping line of jaw B can be considered as a "sectional line", too. The probability density function of direction of fibers protruding from the gripping line of jaw B ("sectional line"), was called $u^*(\vartheta)$ in Chapter 3 and it was derived in Eq. (3.20) that $u^*(\vartheta) = \cos\vartheta\, u(\vartheta)/k_n$. Thus, the relative frequency of fibers protruding from the gripping line of jaw B and having an angle ϑ is $u^*(\vartheta)d\vartheta$. The number of such fibers, going out from the unit width of jaw B, is very small and it then takes the following expression

$$d\upsilon = \upsilon u^*(\vartheta)\, d\vartheta. \qquad \qquad \dots (7.126)$$

The length of a general fiber between jaws is evidently $h/\cos\vartheta$, where h is gauge length – see Fig. 7.11. The mass of such fiber is $(h/\cos\vartheta)s\rho$, where s is fiber cross-sectional area and ρ is fiber mass density. The mass of fibers, having angle ϑ and protruding from the unitary width of jaw B, is very small and it then takes the following expression

$$dm_h = \frac{h}{\cos\vartheta}s\rho\, d\upsilon = \frac{h}{\cos\vartheta}s\rho\,\upsilon u^*(\vartheta)d\vartheta = \upsilon\frac{hs\rho}{\cos\vartheta}u^*(\vartheta)d\vartheta. \quad \dots (7.127)$$

Note: Initially some fibers occupying the unitary width of jaw B as shown in Fig. 7.11 are partly lying outside the horizontal dashed rectangle of area $1\cdot h$. However, other fibers with the same angle ϑ situated outside the unitary length are lying partly inside the mentioned rectangle. Because of the assumption of homogeneity we can think that both the masses of fibers are the same. So, the mass of fibers dm_h represents the complete mass of the fibers and/or fiber portions, having angle ϑ and lying inside the horizontally dashed rectangle of area $1\cdot h$.

After substitution of $u^*(\vartheta)$ according to Eq. (3.20) and $t = s\rho$ using Eq. (1.5) in Eq. (7.127) the following expression is obtained

$$dm_h = \upsilon\frac{h}{\cos\vartheta}t\frac{\cos\vartheta\, u(\vartheta)}{k_n}d\vartheta = \upsilon\frac{ht}{k_n}u(\vartheta)d\vartheta. \qquad \dots (7.128)$$

The total mass of fibers present in the rectangle of area $1\cdot h$ as shown in Fig. 7.11 is then

$$m_h = \int_{\vartheta=0}^{\vartheta=\pi/2} dm_h = \upsilon\frac{ht}{k_n}\int_0^{\pi/2} u(\vartheta)d\vartheta = \upsilon\frac{ht}{k_n}. \qquad \dots (7.129)$$

Note: The areal mass density of the planar bundle is then $G = m_h/(1 \cdot h) = \upsilon t/k_n$. From this relation we obtain $\upsilon = (G/t)k_n$, which is identical to the expression mentioned in Eq. (3.56).

The mass fraction of fibers having angle ϑ is expressed by $dg = dm_h/m_h$, which is obviously very small. This can be expressed by using Eqs. (7.128) and (7.129) as follows

$$dg = \frac{dm_h}{m_h} = \frac{\upsilon \dfrac{ht}{k_n} u(\vartheta) d\vartheta}{\upsilon \dfrac{ht}{k_n}} = u(\vartheta) d\vartheta \cdot \qquad \ldots (7.130)$$

Specific stress of simple planar bundle. The specific stress of multi-axial textiles is expressed in general by Eq. (7.69). In order to apply our basic idea of solution to this, we must make the following changes:

- We use the general angle ϑ in place of ϑ_i.
- We use the general fiber strain ε_l according to Eq. (7.6) in place of $\varepsilon_{l,i}$.
- We use the general specific stress in fiber $\sigma_l(\varepsilon_l)$, defined by Eq. (7.46), in place of $\sigma_{l,i}(\varepsilon_{l,i})$.
- We use the general form of the function $M(\vartheta, \vartheta_b)$ – influence of borders or margins of the jaws – according to Eq. (7.28) in place of $M(\vartheta_i, \vartheta_b)$.
- We use the mass fraction dg according to Eq. (7.130) in place of g_i.
- Finally, we use the definite integral $\int_{\vartheta=0}^{\vartheta=\pi/2}$ in place of $\sum_{i=1}^{K}$.

Then the specific stress σ_Σ of the planar bundle at a jaw displacement ε can be expressed by using Eq. (7.69) as follows

$$\sigma_\Sigma = \int_{\vartheta=0}^{\vartheta=\pi/2} dg\, \sigma_l(\varepsilon_l) \cos^2 \vartheta \frac{1+\varepsilon}{1+\varepsilon_l} M(\vartheta, \vartheta_b) =$$

$$= \int_0^{\pi/2} u(\vartheta) \sigma_l(\varepsilon_l) \cos^2 \vartheta \frac{1+\varepsilon}{1+\varepsilon_l} M(\vartheta, \vartheta_b) d\vartheta, \qquad \ldots (7.131)$$

where ε_l is given by Eq. (7.6).

The maximum of specific stress $\sigma_{\Sigma, \vartheta=0}$ can be expressed by using Eq. (7.70) as follows

$$\sigma_{\Sigma,\vartheta=0} = \int_{\vartheta=0}^{\vartheta=\pi/2} dg\,\sigma_l(\varepsilon) = \sigma_l(\varepsilon) \int_0^{\pi/2} u(\vartheta)d\vartheta = \sigma_l(\varepsilon). \quad \dots (7.132)$$

Note: This case represents a bundle of parallel and identical fibers so that this trivial result is logically evident.

Specific stress of simple planar bundle for the simplest case. The simplest case was first introduced by means of Eqs. from (7.14) to (7.19); in short, it assumes that the small deformations and linearity of force–strain relation of fibers are valid. Then, we must make the following more changes in Eq. (7.71):

- We use the fiber specific strength (tenacity) σ_i^* in place of $\sigma_{l,i}^*$.
- We use the fiber specific strain a in place of a_i.
- We use the general jaw displacement ε^* by break of fiber having angle ϑ, defined by Eq. (7.10), in place of ε_i^*.
- We use the general form of the function $\delta(\varepsilon, \varepsilon^*)$, defined by Eq. (7.15), in place of $\delta(\varepsilon, \varepsilon_i^*)$.

In this case, the specific stress σ_Σ of our planar bundle at a jaw displacement ε can be expressed by using Eq. (7.71) as follows

$$\sigma_\Sigma = \varepsilon \int_{\vartheta=0}^{\vartheta=\pi/2} dg\,\delta(\varepsilon,\varepsilon^*)\frac{\sigma_l^*}{a}\cos^4\vartheta\,M(\vartheta,\vartheta_b)$$

$$= \varepsilon\frac{\sigma_l^*}{a}\int_0^{\pi/2} u(\vartheta)\,\delta(\varepsilon,\varepsilon^*)\cos^4\vartheta\,M(\vartheta,\vartheta_b)\,d\vartheta \qquad \dots (7.133)$$

and the maximum of specific stress $\sigma_{\Sigma,\vartheta=0}$ can be expressed by using Eq. (7.72) as follows

$$\sigma_{\Sigma,\vartheta=0} = \varepsilon \int_{\vartheta=0}^{\vartheta=\pi/2} dg\,\delta(\varepsilon,a)\frac{\sigma_l^*}{a} = \delta(\varepsilon,a)\frac{\sigma_l^*}{a}\varepsilon\int_0^{\pi/2} u(\vartheta)d\vartheta = \delta(\varepsilon,a)\frac{\sigma_l^*}{a}\varepsilon \quad \dots (7.134)$$

Angular utilization coefficient. The angular utilization coefficient is defined according to Eq. (7.73). If Eqs. (7.131) and (7.132) – more general case – are substituted to Eq. (7.73) then the following expression is obtained

$$\eta_a = \frac{\sigma_\Sigma}{\sigma_{\Sigma,\vartheta=0}} = \frac{1}{\sigma_l(\varepsilon)}\int_0^{\pi/2} u(\vartheta)\sigma_l(\varepsilon_l)\cos^2\vartheta\frac{1+\varepsilon}{1+\varepsilon_l}M(\vartheta,\vartheta_b)\,d\vartheta, \quad \sigma_l(\varepsilon)>0,$$

$$\dots (7.135)$$

where ε_l is given by Eq. (7.6).

However, if Eqs. (7.133) and (7.134) – simplest case – are substituted to Eq. (7.73) then the following expression is obtained

$$\eta_a = \frac{\sigma_\Sigma}{\sigma_{\Sigma,\vartheta=0}} = \frac{\varepsilon\dfrac{\sigma_l^*}{a}\displaystyle\int_0^{\pi/2} u(\vartheta)\,\delta(\varepsilon,\varepsilon^*)\cos^4\vartheta\,M(\vartheta,\vartheta_b)\,d\vartheta}{\delta(\varepsilon,a)\dfrac{\sigma_l^*}{a}\varepsilon}$$

... (7.136)

$$= \frac{1}{\delta(\varepsilon,a)}\int_0^{\pi/2} u(\vartheta)\,\delta(\varepsilon,\varepsilon^*)\cos^4\vartheta\,M(\vartheta,\vartheta_b)\,d\vartheta,\quad \varepsilon\le a.$$

Special alternative to simple planar bundle. In analogy to the previous chapter let us assume that

(a) All fibers are fixed (sewn, glued, etc.) in the structure of the product; the free ends of fibers do not exist at all. It is then valid to write that $M(\vartheta,\vartheta_b) = 1$.

(b) The applications do not demand high deformation of fibers that the breakage of the yarns would occur. It is assumed that all fibers will be strained without breakage during applications. Then it is valid to write that $\varepsilon \le a$ so that it is also valid that $\delta(\varepsilon, a) = 1$ and surely it is valid that $\delta(\varepsilon, \varepsilon^*) = 1$[13] in case of the simplest planar bundle.

This version we will call "special alternative to simplest planar bundle" in short.

In this case, Eq. (7.135) can be written as follows

$$\eta_a = \frac{1}{\sigma_l(\varepsilon)}\int_0^{\pi/2} u(\vartheta)\,\sigma_l(\varepsilon_l)\cos^2\vartheta\,\frac{1+\varepsilon}{1+\varepsilon_l}\,d\vartheta,\qquad \text{... (7.137)}$$

where ε_l is given by Eq. (7.6), and Eq. (7.136) – simplest case – can be written by

$$\eta_a = \int_0^{\pi/2} u(\vartheta)\cos^4\vartheta\,d\vartheta.\qquad \text{... (7.138)}$$

Let us illustrate the last Eq. (7.138) of angular utilization coefficient with the help of two examples shown below.

Example 7.1 – Isotropic orientation. The directional distribution of fibers in the case of isotropic orientation is given by a constant value of probability density function $u(\vartheta) = 2/\pi$ according to Eq. (3.53). Then the following expression is obtained from Eq. (7.138)

---

13. Do not forget that it is valid to write $\varepsilon^* \ge a$ according to Eq. (7.10).

$$\eta_a = \frac{2}{\pi} \int_0^{\pi/2} \cos^4 \vartheta \, d\vartheta .$$

... (7.139)

However, it is valid[14]

$$\cos^4 \vartheta = \left[\cos^2 \vartheta\right]^2 = \left[\frac{1}{2} + \frac{1}{2}\cos(2\vartheta)\right]^2 = \frac{1}{4} + \frac{1}{2}\cos(2\vartheta) + \frac{1}{4}\cos^2(2\vartheta)$$

$$= \frac{1}{4} + \frac{1}{2}\cos(2\vartheta) + \frac{1}{4}\left[\frac{1}{2} + \frac{1}{2}\cos(4\vartheta)\right] = \frac{3}{8} + \frac{1}{2}\cos(2\vartheta) + \frac{1}{8}\cos(4\vartheta),$$

... (7.140)

so that the angular utilization according to Eq. (7.139) is possible to rearrange as follows

$$\eta_a = \int_0^{\pi/2} \frac{2}{\pi}\left[\frac{3}{8} + \frac{1}{2}\cos(2\vartheta) + \frac{1}{8}\cos(4\vartheta)\right] d\vartheta$$

$$= \frac{2}{\pi}\left\{\int_0^{\pi/2} \frac{3}{8} d\vartheta + \int_0^{\pi/2} \frac{1}{2}\cos(2\vartheta) \, d\vartheta + \int_0^{\pi/2} \frac{1}{8}\cos(4\vartheta) \, d\vartheta\right\}$$

$$= \frac{2}{\pi}\left\{\frac{3}{8}[\vartheta]_0^{\pi/2} + \frac{1}{2}\left[\frac{1}{2}\sin(2\vartheta)\right]_0^{\pi/2} + \frac{1}{8}\left[\frac{1}{4}\sin(4\vartheta)\right]_0^{\pi/2}\right\}$$ ... (7.141)

$$= \frac{2}{\pi}\left\{\frac{\pi}{2} + \frac{1}{4}0 + \frac{1}{32}0\right\} = \frac{3}{8}.$$

This result is identical with Eq. (7.125).

Note: The regular multi-axial textile in special alternative to the simplest case has this value of angular utilization coefficient η_a when any number of yarn systems $K \geq 3$, according to Eq. (7.125). It means that the value 3/8 still remains the same also if the number of yarn systems increase to a very high value that is $K \to \infty$. Then, such a multi-axial textile is more close to the isotropic structure discussed in this example.

Example 7.2 – Orientation according to the model distribution. The model of planar distribution of fiber directions (having one preferential direction) was derived in Chapter 3. Then the probability density function $u(\vartheta)$ of non-oriented angle ϑ is described by Eq. (3.49). Using this distribution in Eq. (7.138) we obtain

$$\eta_a = \int_0^{\pi/2} \left[\frac{1}{\pi}\frac{C}{C^2 - \left(C^2 - 1\right)\cos^2\left(\vartheta + \alpha\right)} + \frac{1}{\pi}\frac{C}{C^2 - \left(C^2 - 1\right)\cos^2\left(\vartheta - \alpha\right)}\right]\cos^4 \vartheta \, d\vartheta,$$

... (7.142)

14. The formula $\cos^2 \alpha = \frac{1}{2} + \frac{1}{2}\cos(2\alpha)$ is used.

where C is the measure of preference of a given direction and α is the angle between the preferential direction and the direction of vertical jaw axis.

The integral expressed in Eq. (7.142) is possible to solve analytically. This is derived in Appendix 5[15] where Eq. (7.142) can be rearranged according to Eq. (A5.17) as follows

$$\eta_a = \frac{C}{2(C+1)^2}\left[(2C+1)\cos^4\alpha + 6\cos^2\alpha\sin^2\alpha + \frac{(C+2)}{C}\sin^4\alpha\right]. \quad \dots (7.143)$$

The value of parameter $C = 1$ corresponds to the isotropic orientation of fibers in a planar bundle. Thus

$$\eta_a = \frac{1}{8}\left[3\cos^4\alpha + 6\cos^2\alpha\sin^2\alpha + 3\sin^4\alpha\right]$$

$$= \frac{3}{8}\left[\cos^4\alpha + 2\cos^2\alpha\sin^2\alpha + \sin^4\alpha\right] = \frac{3}{8}\left[\cos^2\alpha + \sin^2\alpha\right]^2 = \frac{3}{8},$$

$$\dots (7.144)$$

which is identical to Eq. (7.141), as expected. On the other hand, if the value $C \to \infty$ then the orientation of fibers is limited to parallel fiber bundle and the angular utilization coefficient according to Eq. (7.143) is expressed by the following form

$$\eta_a = \lim_{C\to\infty}\frac{C}{2(C+1)^2}\left[(2C+1)\cos^4\alpha + 6\cos^2\alpha\sin^2\alpha + \frac{(C+2)}{C}\sin^4\alpha\right]$$

$$= \lim_{C\to\infty}\left[\frac{C(2C+1)}{2(C+1)^2}\cos^4\alpha + \frac{6C}{2(C+1)^2}\cos^2\alpha\sin^2\alpha + \frac{(C+2)}{2(C+1)^2}\sin^4\alpha\right]$$

$$= \lim_{C\to\infty}\left[\frac{\left(2+\frac{1}{C}\right)}{2\left(1+\frac{1}{C}\right)^2}\cos^4\alpha + \frac{\frac{6}{C}}{2\left(1+\frac{1}{C}\right)^2}\cos^2\alpha\sin^2\alpha + \frac{\left(\frac{1}{C}+\frac{2}{C^2}\right)}{2\left(1+\frac{1}{C}\right)^2}\sin^4\alpha\right]$$

$$= \cos^4\alpha. \quad \dots (7.145)$$

(The result of the last equation can be derived also directly from the geometry of the oblique parallel fiber bundle as shown in Fig. 7.12).

The graphical interpretation of the resulting Eq. (7.143) is shown in Fig. 7.13.

---

15. A more general solution considering the influence of functions $\delta(\varepsilon,\varepsilon^*)$ and $M(\vartheta,\vartheta_b)$, i.e., an analytical solution of Eq. (7.136) is reported in Reference [20].

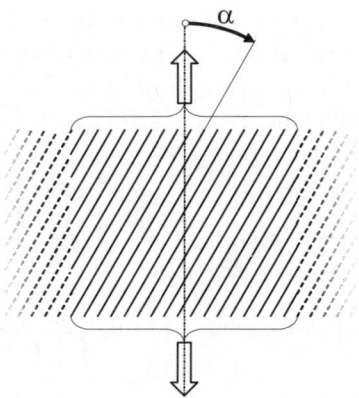

7.12 Oblique parallel fiber bundle.

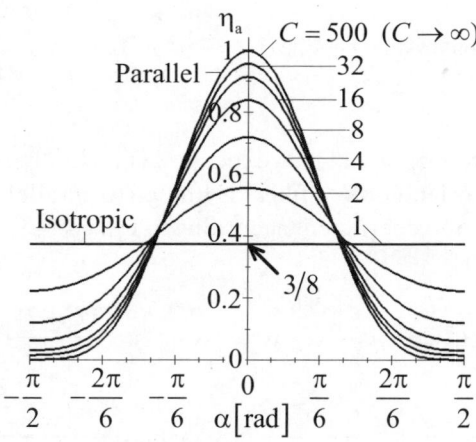

7.13 Angular utilization coefficient in special alternative.

Note: It is evident from Fig. 7.13 that the maximum value of the angular utilization coefficient η_a is obtained if the direction vertical jaw axis corresponds to the preferential direction of fibers, i.e. $\alpha = 0$. On the other hand, the minimum value of the angular utilization coefficient η_a is obtained if the direction of the vertical jaw axis is perpendicular to the preferential direction of fibers, i.e. $\alpha = \pm\pi/2$. This phenomenon is often used during the testing of fiber orientation of non-woven textiles. The strength of a non-woven textile, say produced from a carded web, is measured in longitudinal (preferential direction) and transversal directions and the ratio of both the values is then used as an empirical characteristic of fiber orientation.

7.4   References

1. Dow, N., and Tranfield, G. (1969). Preliminary investigations o flexibility of weaving triaxial fabrics, *Textile Research Journal*, **40**, 986–998.

2. Skelton, J. (1971). Triaxially woven fabrics: Their structures and properties, *Textile Research Journal*, **41**, 637–647.

3. Sugun, B. S., and Rao, R. M. V. G. K. (2000). Mechanical behaviour of woven and multiaxial fabric composites, *Journal of Reinforced Plastics and Composites*, **19**, 743–753.

4. Pastore, C. M. (2000). Opportunities and challenges for textile reinforced composites, *Mechanics of Composite Materials*, **36**, 97–116.

5. Araujo, M., Lima, M., and Costa, N. (2001). New weaving concept for multiaxial fabrics, *Proceedings of the 1st Autex Conference*, Portugal, June 26–29, 2001.

6. Cybulska, M., and Frontczak-Wasiak, I. (2002). Modelling and properties of multiaxial woven structures, *Proceedings of the 2nd Autex Conference*, Belgium, 2002.

7. Wang, Y. (2002). Mechanical properties of stiched multiaxial fabric reinforced composites from manual layup process, *Applied Composite Materials*, **9**, 81–97.

8. Jiao, W. H., and Chen, N. L. (2004). Performance advantages of biaxial warp knitted fabrics used as coated substrates, *Journal of Donghua University*, **30**, 91–104.

9. Frontezak-Wasiak, I., and Snycerski, M. (2005). Characteristics of multi-axial woven structures, *Fibers and Textiles in Eastern Europe*, **13**, 27–33.

10. Baozhong, S., Hong, H., and Bohong, G. (2005). Compressive behavior of multi-axial multi-layer warp knitted (MMWK) fabric composite at various strain rates, *Composite Structures*, **78**, 84–90.

11. Robinson, P., Iannucci, L., and Oakeshott, J. L. (2007). Development of a representative unit cell model for bi-axial NCF composites, *Journal of Composite Materials*, **41**, 801–835.

12. Luo, Y., and Hong, H. (2008). Mechanical properties of PVC coated bi-axial warp knitted fabric with and without initial cracks under multi-axial tensile loads, *Composite Structures*, **89**, 536–542.

13. Truong, T. C., Ivanov, D. S., Klimshin, D. V., Lomov, S. V., and Verpoest, I. (2008). Carbon composites based on multi-axial multi-ply stitched preforms, Part 7: Mechanical properties and damage observations in composites with sheared reinforcement, *Composites Part A: Applied Science and Manufacturing*, **39**, 1380–1393.

14. Hong, H., and Ying, X. (2008). Tearing properties of coated multi-axial warp knitted fabric, *Autex Research Journal*, **8**, 13–16.

15. Luo, Y., Hong, H., and Fangueiro, R. (2008). Tensile and tearing properties of bi-axial warp knitted coated fabrics, *Autex Research Journal*, **8**, 17–20.

16. Luo, Y., Hong, H., and Fangueiro, R. (2008). Tensile and tearing properties of PVC coated bi-axial warp knitted fabrics under bi-axial loads, *Indian Journal of Fiber and Textile Research*, **33**, 146–150.

17. Beil, N. B., and Roberts, W. W. Jr. (2009). Modeling and computer simulation of the compressional behavior of fiber assemblies, Part I: Energy-absorption capability of multi-axial warp-knitted FRP tubes, *Journal of Crashworthiness*,**14**, 407–418.

18. Tomohiko, S., Asami, N., and Hiroyuki, H. (2009). Effect of CF/GF fiber hybrid on impact properties of multi-axial warp knitted fabric composite materials, *Composites Part A: Applied Science and Manufacturing*, **40**, 1982–1990.

19. Delisee, C., Pierre-Jacques, L., and Vautrin, A. (2010). Characterization of 3D morphology and microcracks in composites reinforced by multi-axial multi-ply stitched preforms, *Composites Part A: Applied Science and Manufacturing*, **41**, 653–662.

20. Neckář, B. (2001). *Morphology and Structural Mechanics of General Fibrous Assemblies*, Technical University of Liberec, 1st edn. 1998 and 2nd edn. 2001 (Czech).

Appendix 1

Evaluation of the integral $\int_0^{\pi/2} \cos\vartheta\, u(\vartheta)\,d\vartheta$ for fiber orientation

Let us consider the integral $k_n = \int_0^{\pi/2} \cos\vartheta\, u(\vartheta)\,d\vartheta$, where the probability density function $u(\vartheta)$ is described by Eq. (3.49). By substituting and rearranging, we find

$$
k_n = \int_0^{\pi/2} \cos\vartheta \left[\frac{1}{\pi}\frac{C}{C^2 - \left(C^2-1\right)\cos^2\left(-\vartheta-\alpha\right)} + \frac{1}{\pi}\frac{C}{C^2 - \left(C^2-1\right)\cos^2\left(\vartheta-\alpha\right)} \right] d\vartheta
$$

$$
= \frac{C}{\pi}\left[\int_0^{\pi/2} \frac{\cos\left(-\vartheta\right)d\vartheta}{C^2 - \left(C^2-1\right)\cos^2\left(-\vartheta-\alpha\right)} + \int_0^{\pi/2} \frac{\cos\vartheta\,d\vartheta}{C^2 - \left(C^2-1\right)\cos^2\left(\vartheta-\alpha\right)} \right]
$$

$$
\vartheta = -\gamma, \quad d\vartheta = -d\gamma
$$

$$
= \frac{C}{\pi}\left[-\int_0^{-\pi/2} \frac{\cos\gamma\,d\gamma}{C^2 - \left(C^2-1\right)\cos^2\left(\gamma-\alpha\right)} + \int_0^{\pi/2} \frac{\cos\vartheta\,d\vartheta}{C^2 - \left(C^2-1\right)\cos^2\left(\vartheta-\alpha\right)} \right].
$$

$$
\ldots \text{(A1.1)}
$$

(We use $\cos\vartheta = \cos(-\vartheta)$).

The integral variable in both integrations is renamed to x, we thus obtain

$$
k_n = \frac{C}{\pi}\left[\int_{-\pi/2}^{0} \frac{\cos x\,dx}{C^2 - \left(C^2-1\right)\cos^2\left(x-\alpha\right)} + \int_0^{\pi/2} \frac{\cos x\,dx}{C^2 - \left(C^2-1\right)\cos^2\left(x-\alpha\right)} \right]
$$

$$
= \frac{C}{\pi}\int_{-\pi/2}^{\pi/2} \frac{\cos x\,dx}{C^2 - \left(C^2-1\right)\cos^2\left(x-\alpha\right)} = \frac{C}{\pi}\int_{-\pi/2}^{\pi/2} \frac{\cos\left[\left(x-\alpha\right)+\alpha\right]dx}{C^2 - \left(C^2-1\right)\cos^2\left(x-\alpha\right)}
$$

$$
= \frac{C}{\pi}\int_{-\pi/2}^{\pi/2} \frac{\cos\left(x-\alpha\right)\cos\alpha - \sin\left(x-\alpha\right)\sin\alpha}{C^2 - \left(C^2-1\right)\cos^2\left(x-\alpha\right)}\,dx
$$

$$= \frac{C \cos \alpha}{\pi} \int_{-\pi/2}^{\pi/2} \frac{\cos(x-\alpha)}{C^2 - (C^2-1)\left[1 - \sin^2(x-\alpha)\right]} dx$$

$$- \frac{C \sin \alpha}{\pi} \int_{-\pi/2}^{\pi/2} \frac{\sin(x-\alpha)}{C^2 - (C^2-1)\cos^2(x-\alpha)} dx$$

$$= \frac{C \cos \alpha}{\pi} \int_{-\pi/2}^{\pi/2} \frac{\cos(x-\alpha)}{1 + (C^2-1)\sin^2(x-\alpha)} dx - \frac{C \sin \alpha}{\pi} \int_{-\pi/2}^{\pi/2} \frac{\sin(x-\alpha)}{C^2 - (C^2-1)\cos^2(x-\alpha)} dx.$$

... (A1.2)

We solve the above integration by applying the rule of substitution. We apply the following substitutions in the first integral expression

$$\sin(x-\alpha) = \frac{y}{\sqrt{C^2-1}}, \quad \cos(x-\alpha)\, dx = \frac{dy}{\sqrt{C^2-1}},$$
... (A1.3)

and in the second integral expression, we apply the following substitutions

$$\cos(x-\alpha) = \frac{Cz}{\sqrt{C^2-1}}, \quad -\sin(x-\alpha)\, dx = \frac{C\, dz}{\sqrt{C^2-1}}.$$
... (A1.4)

Thus, we find

$$k_n = \frac{C \cos \alpha}{\pi\sqrt{C^2-1}} \int_{\sqrt{C^2-1}\sin\left(-\frac{\pi}{2}-\alpha\right)}^{\sqrt{C^2-1}\sin\left(\frac{\pi}{2}-\alpha\right)} \frac{dy}{1+y^2} + \frac{C^2 \sin \alpha}{\pi\sqrt{C^2-1}} \int_{\frac{\sqrt{C^2-1}}{C}\cos\left(-\frac{\pi}{2}-\alpha\right)}^{\frac{\sqrt{C^2-1}}{C}\cos\left(\frac{\pi}{2}-\alpha\right)} \frac{dz}{C^2 - C^2 z^2}$$

$$= \frac{C \cos \alpha}{\pi\sqrt{C^2-1}} \int_{\sqrt{C^2-1}\sin\left(-\frac{\pi}{2}-\alpha\right)}^{\sqrt{C^2-1}\sin\left(\frac{\pi}{2}-\alpha\right)} \frac{dy}{1+y^2} + \frac{\sin \alpha}{\pi\sqrt{C^2-1}} \int_{\frac{\sqrt{C^2-1}}{C}\cos\left(-\frac{\pi}{2}-\alpha\right)}^{\frac{\sqrt{C^2-1}}{C}\cos\left(\frac{\pi}{2}-\alpha\right)} \frac{dz}{1 - z^2}.$$

... (A1.5)

The previous expressions are well-known integrals, which can be solved as follows

$$k_n = \frac{C \cos \alpha}{\pi\sqrt{C^2-1}} \left\{\arctan y\right\}_{\sqrt{C^2-1}\sin\left(-\frac{\pi}{2}-\alpha\right)}^{\sqrt{C^2-1}\sin\left(\frac{\pi}{2}-\alpha\right)} + \frac{\sin \alpha}{\pi\sqrt{C^2-1}} \left\{\frac{1}{2}\ln\left|\frac{z+1}{z-1}\right|\right\}_{\frac{\sqrt{C^2-1}}{C}\cos\left(-\frac{\pi}{2}-\alpha\right)}^{\frac{\sqrt{C^2-1}}{C}\cos\left(\frac{\pi}{2}-\alpha\right)},$$

$$k_n = \frac{C\cos\alpha}{\pi\sqrt{C^2-1}}\left\{\arctan\left[\sqrt{C^2-1}\sin\left(\frac{\pi}{2}-\alpha\right)\right] - \arctan\left[\sqrt{C^2-1}\sin\left(-\frac{\pi}{2}-\alpha\right)\right]\right\}$$

$$+ \frac{\sin\alpha}{\pi\sqrt{C^2-1}}\left\{\frac{1}{2}\ln\left|\frac{\frac{\sqrt{C^2-1}}{C}\cos\left(\frac{\pi}{2}-\alpha\right)+1}{\frac{\sqrt{C^2-1}}{C}\cos\left(\frac{\pi}{2}-\alpha\right)-1}\right| - \frac{1}{2}\ln\left|\frac{\frac{\sqrt{C^2-1}}{C}\cos\left(-\frac{\pi}{2}-\alpha\right)+1}{\frac{\sqrt{C^2-1}}{C}\cos\left(-\frac{\pi}{2}-\alpha\right)-1}\right|\right\}.$$

$$\dots \text{(A1.6)}$$

By rearranging, we find

$$k_n = \frac{C\cos\alpha}{\pi\sqrt{C^2-1}}\left\{\arctan\left[\sqrt{C^2-1}\sin\left(\frac{\pi}{2}-\alpha\right)\right] + \arctan\left[\sqrt{C^2-1}\sin\left(\frac{\pi}{2}-\alpha\right)\right]\right\}$$

$$+ \frac{\sin\alpha}{2\pi\sqrt{C^2-1}}\left\{\ln\left|\frac{\sqrt{C^2-1}\cos\left(\frac{\pi}{2}-\alpha\right)+C}{\sqrt{C^2-1}\cos\left(\frac{\pi}{2}-\alpha\right)-C}\right| - \ln\left|\frac{-\sqrt{C^2-1}\cos\left(\frac{\pi}{2}-\alpha\right)+C}{-\sqrt{C^2-1}\cos\left(\frac{\pi}{2}-\alpha\right)-C}\right|\right\}$$

$$= \frac{2C\cos\alpha}{\pi\sqrt{C^2-1}}\arctan\left[\sqrt{C^2-1}\sin\left(\frac{\pi}{2}-\alpha\right)\right]$$

$$+ \frac{\sin\alpha}{2\pi\sqrt{C^2-1}}\ln\left|\frac{\left[\sqrt{C^2-1}\cos\left(\frac{\pi}{2}-\alpha\right)+C\right]\left[-\sqrt{C^2-1}\cos\left(\frac{\pi}{2}-\alpha\right)-C\right]}{\left[\sqrt{C^2-1}\cos\left(\frac{\pi}{2}-\alpha\right)-C\right]\left[-\sqrt{C^2-1}\cos\left(\frac{\pi}{2}-\alpha\right)+C\right]}\right|.$$

$$\dots \text{(A1.7)}$$

(We use $\sin(\varphi+\pi) = -\sin\varphi$, $\cos(\varphi+\pi) = -\cos\varphi$, $\arctan(-u) = -\arctan u$).
Furthermore,

$$k_n = \frac{2C\cos\alpha}{\pi\sqrt{C^2-1}}\arctan\left[\sqrt{C^2-1}\sin\left(\frac{\pi}{2}-\alpha\right)\right]$$

$$+ \frac{\sin\alpha}{2\pi\sqrt{C^2-1}}\ln\left|\frac{\left[\sqrt{C^2-1}\cos\left(\frac{\pi}{2}-\alpha\right)+C\right]\left[\sqrt{C^2-1}\cos\left(\frac{\pi}{2}-\alpha\right)+C\right]}{\left[\sqrt{C^2-1}\cos\left(\frac{\pi}{2}-\alpha\right)-C\right]\left[\sqrt{C^2-1}\cos\left(\frac{\pi}{2}-\alpha\right)-C\right]}\right|$$

$$= \frac{2C\cos\alpha}{\pi\sqrt{C^2-1}}\arctan\left[\sqrt{C^2-1}\sin\left(\frac{\pi}{2}-\alpha\right)\right] + \frac{\sin\alpha}{2\pi\sqrt{C^2-1}}\ln\left|\frac{\sqrt{C^2-1}\cos\left(\frac{\pi}{2}-\alpha\right)+C}{\sqrt{C^2-1}\cos\left(\frac{\pi}{2}-\alpha\right)-C}\right|^2.$$

$$\dots \text{(A1.8)}$$

From the previous equation, the coefficient k_n takes the following form

$$k_n = \frac{2C\cos\alpha}{\pi\sqrt{C^2-1}}\arctan\left[\sqrt{C^2-1}\cos\alpha\right] + \frac{\sin\alpha}{\pi\sqrt{C^2-1}}\ln\left|\frac{\sqrt{C^2-1}\sin\alpha+C}{\sqrt{C^2-1}\sin\alpha-C}\right|.$$

$$\dots \text{(A1.9)}$$

(We apply $\cos\left(\frac{\pi}{2}-\alpha\right) = \sin\alpha$ and $\sin\left(\frac{\pi}{2}-\alpha\right) = \cos\alpha$).

In case of $\alpha = 0$, and from Eq. (A1.9), the following expression is found

$$k_n = \frac{2C\arctan\left(\sqrt{C^2-1}\right)}{\pi\sqrt{C^2-1}}.$$

$$\dots \text{(A1.10)}$$

Moreover, if $C = 1$, then

$$k_n = \lim_{C\to 1}\frac{2C\arctan\left(\sqrt{C^2-1}\right)}{\pi\sqrt{C^2-1}} = \frac{2}{\pi}.$$

$$\dots \text{(A1.11)}$$

If $\alpha = \pi/2$ (or $\alpha = -\pi/2$), we find the following expression from Eq. (A1.9)

$$k_n = \frac{1}{\pi\sqrt{C^2-1}}\ln\left|\frac{\sqrt{C^2-1}+C}{\sqrt{C^2-1}-C}\right|.$$

$$\dots \text{(A1.12)}$$

Note: We can also obtain Eq. (A1.12) from the limit of Eq. (A1.11) as $C \to 1$.

Finally, we introduce the integral of k_n as $C \to 1$ (isotropic orientation in plane). From Eq. (A1.9), we find

$$k_n = \lim_{C\to\infty}\left\{\frac{2\cos\alpha}{\pi\sqrt{1-\frac{1}{C^2}}}\arctan\left[\sqrt{C^2-1}\cos\alpha\right] + \frac{\sin\alpha}{\pi\sqrt{C^2-1}}\ln\left|\frac{\sqrt{1-\frac{1}{C^2}}\sin\alpha+1}{\sqrt{1-\frac{1}{C^2}}\sin\alpha-1}\right|\right\}.$$

$$k_n = \frac{2\cos\alpha}{\pi}\frac{\pi}{2}+0\cdot\ln\left|\frac{\sin\alpha+1}{\sin\alpha-1}\right| = \cos\alpha.$$

$$\dots \text{(A1.13)}$$

Binomial expansion. The well-known binomial expansion is usually formulated as follows

$$(a \pm b)^n = \sum_{k=0}^{n} (\pm 1)^k \binom{n}{k} a^{n-k} b^k, \quad a,b \ldots \text{real numbers}, \quad n = 1,2,\cdots. \quad \ldots \text{(A2.1)}$$

A special form of this is obtained if the sign is positive and $b = 1$ as mentioned below

$$(a+1)^n = \sum_{k=0}^{n} \binom{n}{k} a^{n-k}, \quad a \ldots \text{real numbers}, \quad n = 1,2,\cdots. \qquad \ldots \text{(A2.2)}$$

The last expression is generalized for $n = 0$. It is then valid to write that

$$(a+1)^n = \binom{n}{0} a^n + \binom{n}{1} a^{n-1} + \ldots + \binom{n}{n-1} a + 1, \quad a \ldots \text{real numbers}, \quad n = 0,1,2,\cdots.$$

$$\ldots \text{(A2.3)}$$

Note: The last expression shows the combination numbers, which are popularly known as the so-called binomial coefficients. We may remind that it is valid to write the following expressions

$$\binom{n}{k} = \frac{n!}{(n-k)!k!}, \quad 0! = 1, \quad \binom{n}{0} = \frac{n!}{n!0!} = 1, \quad \binom{0}{0} = \frac{0!}{0!0!} = 1. \quad \ldots \text{(A2.4)}$$

The following expression is valid to write from Eq. (A2.1) considering the negative sign, natural numbers n, and the equality $a = b = 1$

$$0 = (1-1)^n = \sum_{k=0}^{n} (-1)^k \binom{n}{k} 1^{n-k} 1^k = \sum_{k=0}^{n} (-1)^k \binom{n}{k}, \quad n = 1,2\cdots. \qquad \ldots \text{(A2.5)}$$

Function $(e^x - 1)^n$. We can write the following expression from Eq. (A2.1) considering $a = e^x$, $b = 1$, and the negative sign as follows

$$\left(e^x -1\right)^n = \sum_{k=0}^{n}(-1)^k \binom{n}{k} e^{(n-k)x} 1^k = \sum_{k=0}^{n}(-1)^k \binom{n}{k} e^{(n-k)x}, \quad n=1,2\cdots \cdots \quad (A2.6)$$

By applying Eqs. (A2.1) and (A2.5), Eq. (A2.6) can be written as follows

$$\left(e^x -1\right)^n = \sum_{k=0}^{n}\left[(-1)^k \binom{n}{k} e^{(n-k)x}\right] - \overbrace{\sum_{k=0}^{n}\left[(-1)^k \binom{n}{k}\right]}^{=0} = \sum_{k=0}^{n}\left[(-1)^k \binom{n}{k}\left(e^{(n-k)x} -1\right)\right]$$

$$= \sum_{k=0}^{n-1}\left[(-1)^k \binom{n}{k}\left(e^{(n-k)x} -1\right)\right] + \overbrace{(-1)^n \binom{n}{n}\left(e^{(n-n)x} -1\right)}^{=0}$$

$$= \sum_{k=0}^{n-1}\left[(-1)^k \binom{n}{k}\left(e^{(n-k)x} -1\right)\right].$$

$$\cdots (A2.7)$$

According to the expansion of Taylor series, we find the following expression

$$e^{(n-k)x} -1 = \frac{(n-k)x}{1!} + \frac{(n-k)^2 x^2}{2!} + \frac{(n-k)^3 x^3}{3!} + \cdots = \sum_{i=1}^{\infty}\frac{(n-k)^i x^i}{i!} \quad \cdots (A2.8)$$

By substituting Eq. (A2.8) into Eq. (A2.7), the following expression is obtained

$$\left(e^x -1\right)^n = \sum_{k=0}^{n-1}\left[(-1)^k \binom{n}{k}\left(e^{(n-k)x} -1\right)\right] = \sum_{k=0}^{n-1}\left[(-1)^k \binom{n}{k}\sum_{i=1}^{\infty}\frac{(n-k)^i x^i}{i!}\right]$$

$$= \sum_{i=1}^{\infty}\left\{\frac{x^i}{i!}\sum_{k=0}^{n-1}\left[(-1)^k \binom{n}{k}(n-k)^i\right]\right\}, \quad n=1,2\cdots.$$

$$\cdots (A2.9)$$

Function S_n^i. We apply the following summation symbol in the previous expression

$$S_n^i = \frac{1}{n!}\sum_{k=0}^{n-1}\left[(-1)^k \binom{n}{k}(n-k)^i\right], \quad n=1,2,\cdots, \quad i=1,2,\cdots. \qquad \cdots (A2.10)$$

Now, Eq. (A2.9) can be written as follows

$$\left(e^x - 1\right)^n = \sum_{i=1}^{\infty}\left\{\frac{x^i}{i!}n!\,S_n^i\right\}. \qquad \ldots \text{(A2.11)}$$

We introduce a new summation index u as mentioned below

$$u = n - k, \ (k = n - u). \qquad \ldots \text{(A2.12)}$$

Now we get the following expression for S_n^i from Eq. (A2.10)

$$S_n^i = \frac{1}{n!}\sum_{u=n}^{1}\left[(-1)^{n-u}\binom{n}{n-u}u^i\right] = \frac{(-1)^n}{n!}\sum_{u=1}^{n}\left[\left(\frac{1}{-1}\right)^u\binom{n}{u}u^i\right]$$

$$= \frac{(-1)^n}{n!}\sum_{u=1}^{n}\left[(-1)^u\binom{n}{u}u^i\right]. \qquad \ldots \text{(A2.13)}$$

Function Q_n^i. The summation in the last expression will be denoted by the symbol

$$Q_n^i = \sum_{u=1}^{n}\left[(-1)^u\binom{n}{u}u^i\right], \quad i = 1,2,\cdots, \quad n = 1,2,\cdots. \qquad \ldots \text{(A2.14)}$$

Then the following expression is valid for the variable S_n^i

$$S_n^i = \frac{(-1)^n}{n!}Q_n^i. \qquad \ldots \text{(A2.15)}$$

Properties of function Q_n^i. For $n = 1$, Q_n^i can be expressed directly from Eq. (A2.14)

$$Q_1^i = \sum_{u=1}^{1}\left[(-1)^u\binom{n}{u}u^i\right] = (-1)^1\binom{1}{1}1^i = -1, \quad i = 1,2,\cdots. \qquad \ldots \text{(A2.16)}$$

For $n = 2, 3, \ldots$ Eq. (A2.14) should be reformulated in the following manner

$$Q_n^i = \sum_{u=1}^{n}\left[(-1)^u\frac{n!}{(n-u)!\,u!}u^i\right] = \sum_{u=1}^{n}\left[(-1)^u\frac{(n-1)!}{([n-1]-[u-1])!(u-1)!}\frac{n}{u}u^i\right]$$

$$= n\sum_{u=1}^{n}\left[(-1)^u\binom{n-1}{u-1}u^{i-1}\right] = n\sum_{u=1}^{n}\left[(-1)^u\binom{n-1}{u-1}u^{i-1}\right].$$

$$\ldots \text{(A2.17)}$$

Again, we introduce a new summation index $v = u - 1$ and write that

$$Q_n^i = n \sum_{v=0}^{n-1} \left[(-1)^{v+1} \binom{n-1}{v} (v+1)^{i-1} \right] = -n \sum_{v=0}^{n-1} \left[(-1)^v \binom{n-1}{v} (v+1)^{i-1} \right]$$

$$= -n \sum_{u=0}^{n-1} \left[(-1)^u \binom{n-1}{u} (u+1)^{i-1} \right], \quad i = 1, 2, \cdots, \quad n = 2, 3, \cdots.$$

...(A2.18)

For $i = 1$, Q_n^i can be calculated directly from Eqs. (A2.18) and (A2.5) as follows

$$Q_{n>1}^1 = -n \sum_{u=0}^{n-1} \left[(-1)^u \binom{n-1}{u} (u+1)^{1-1} \right] = -n \overbrace{\sum_{u=0}^{n-1} \left[(-1)^u \binom{n-1}{u} \right]}^{=0} = 0, \quad n = 2, 3, \cdots.$$

... (A2.19)

For $i = 2, 3, \ldots$ and $n = 2, 3, \ldots$ we rearrange Eq. (A2.18) by applying Eq. (A2.3)

$$Q_n^i = -n \sum_{u=0}^{n-1} \left[(-1)^u \binom{n-1}{u} \left\{ \binom{i-1}{0} u^{i-1} + \binom{i-1}{1} u^{i-2} + \cdots + \binom{i-1}{i-2} u + 1 \right\} \right]$$

$$= -n \binom{i-1}{0} \sum_{u=0}^{n-1} \left[(-1)^u \binom{n-1}{u} u^{i-1} \right] - n \binom{i-1}{1} \sum_{u=0}^{n-1} \left[(-1)^u \binom{n-1}{u} u^{i-2} \right]$$

$$\cdots - n \binom{i-1}{i-2} \sum_{u=0}^{n-1} \left[(-1)^u \binom{n-1}{u} u \right] - n \sum_{u=0}^{n-1} \left[(-1)^u \binom{n-1}{u} \right].$$

... (A2.20)

According to Eq. (A2.5), the last summation in the pervious expression is equal to zero. For all other summations, the addition components are equal to zero for $u = 0$. By applying Eq. (A2.14), we find

$$Q_n^i = -n \binom{i-1}{0} \sum_{u=1}^{n-1} \left[(-1)^u \binom{n-1}{u} u^{i-1} \right] - n \binom{i-1}{1} \sum_{u=1}^{n-1} \left[(-1)^u \binom{n-1}{u} u^{i-2} \right] - \cdots$$

$$\cdots - n \binom{i-1}{i-2} \sum_{u=1}^{n-1} \left[(-1)^u \binom{n-1}{u} u \right] - n \cdot 0 =$$

$$= -n \binom{i-1}{0} Q_{n-1}^{i-1} - n \binom{i-1}{1} Q_{n-1}^{i-2} - \cdots - n \binom{i-1}{i-2} Q_{n-1}^1, \quad i = 2, 3, \cdots, n = 2, 3, \cdots.$$

... (A2.21)

It is obvious that the last equation enables us to reduce the subscript of Q_n^i by one unit.

The following statement is valid

$$Q_n^i = 0, \quad i = 1, 2, \cdots, \quad n = i+1, i+2, \cdots. \qquad \cdots (A2.22)$$

Proof (complete mathematical induction method):

a) For the first values $i = 1$ and $n = 2, 3, \ldots$ the validity of the statement is directly obtained from Eq. (A2.19).

b) We assume that the statement expressed by Eq. (A2.22) is valid for all higher indices but less than given $i > 1$. For a given i and arbitrary $n > i$, we can express Q_n^i by means of Eq. (A2.21). The quantities $Q_{n-1}^{i-1}, Q_{n-1}^{i-2}, \cdots, Q_{n-1}^1$ on the right-hand side have superscript lesser than i and the subscripts are greater than the superscripts. According to the assumption, each of these quantities is equal to zero. Therefore, it is valid that $Q_n^i = 0$. Thus, the proof is derived.

Equations (A2.21) and (A2.22) allow us to determine the value of Q_n^n for $i = n = 2, 3, 4, \ldots$

$$\left.\begin{aligned} Q_2^2 &= -2\binom{1}{0}Q_1^1, \quad (i = n = 2), \\[2mm] Q_n^n &= -n\binom{n-1}{0}Q_{n-1}^{n-1} - n\binom{n-1}{1}\overset{=0}{\overbrace{Q_{n-1}^{n-2}}} - \cdots \\[2mm] &\quad \cdots - n\binom{n-1}{n-2}\overset{=0}{\overbrace{Q_{n-1}^1}}, \quad i = n = 3, 4, \cdots, \end{aligned}\right\} \quad Q_n^n = (-1)\, n\, Q_{n-1}^{n-1}, \quad i = n = 2, 3, \cdots$$

$$\cdots (A2.23)$$

By repeating the above procedure and substituting Eq. (A2.16), we find the following expression for $n = 2, 3, \ldots$

$$Q_n^n = (-1)\, n\, Q_{n-1}^{n-1} = (-1)^2\, n(n-1)\, Q_{n-2}^{n-2} = \cdots = (-1)^{n-1}\overset{=n!}{\overbrace{n(n-1)\cdots(2)}}\overset{=-1}{\overbrace{Q_1^1}} = (-1)^n\, n!$$

$$\cdots (A2.24)$$

It is valid $Q_1^1 = -1$ from the Eq. (A2.16) by $i = 1$ so that we can extend the previous equation as follows

$$Q_n^n = (-1)^n\, n!, \quad n = 1, 2, \cdots. \qquad \cdots (A2.25)$$

If we substitute at first Eq. (A2.22), then Eq. (A2.25), and finally Eq. (A2.16) into Eq. (A2.15), we find

$$S_{n>i}^i = \frac{(-1)^n}{n!} \overset{=0}{\overline{Q_{n>i}^i}} = 0, \qquad i = 1, 2, \cdots, \quad n = i+1, i+2, \cdots \qquad \ldots \text{(A2.26)}$$

$$S_n^n = \frac{(-1)^n}{n!} Q_n^n = \frac{(-1)^n}{n!} (-1)^n n! = 1, \qquad n = 1, 2, \cdots. \qquad \ldots \text{(A2.27)}$$

$$S_{n=1}^i = \frac{(-1)^1}{1!} \overset{=-1}{\overline{Q_1^i}} = 1, \quad i = 1, 2, \cdots, \quad n = 1. \qquad \ldots \text{(A2.28)}$$

Function ξ_{n+1}^{i-n} and its properties. We define ξ_{n+1}^{i-n} in the following manner for $n = 1, 2, \ldots,$, $i = n, n+1, \ldots$

$$\left. \begin{aligned} \xi_{n+1}^{i-n} &= 1, \quad n = 1 \\ \xi_{n+1}^{i-n} &= \sum_{t=0}^{i-n} \left[n^t \xi_n^{i-n-t} \right], \quad n = 2, 3, \cdots, \end{aligned} \right\} \quad i = n, n+1, \cdots \qquad \ldots \text{(A2.29)}$$

We recognize that the following result is obtained for $i = n$ from the definition

$$\xi_{n+1}^0 = 1, n = 1 \quad \text{and} \quad \xi_{n+1}^0 = \sum_{t=0}^{0} \left[n^t \xi_n^{-n-t} \right] = n^0 \xi_n^0 = \xi_n^0, n = 2, 3, \cdots \ldots \text{(A2.30)}$$

Here, it is valid to write that

$$\xi_{n+1}^0 = 1, \quad n = 1, 2, \cdots. \qquad \ldots \text{(A2.31)}$$

(The proof for the validity of the complete mathematical induction method is evident from Eq. (A2.30)).

In the following text, we shall prove the validity of the following statement

$$\xi_{n+1}^{i-n} = S_n^i, \quad n = 1, 2, \cdots, \quad i = n, n+1, \cdots. \qquad \ldots \text{(A2.32)}$$

Proof (complete mathematical induction method):

a) For $n = 1$, the statement stated in Eq. (A2.32) takes the form $\xi_{1+1}^{i-1} = S_1^i$, $i = 1, 2, \cdots$. According to the definition expressed in Eq. (A2.29) $\xi_{1+1}^{i-1} = 1$ and according to Eq. (A2.28) $S_1^i = 1$ for all $i = 1, 2, \ldots$. Expression (A2.32) is then valid for $n = 1$.

b) For $n = 2, 3, \ldots$ and $i = n, n+1, \ldots$ the second expression in Eq. (A2.29) is valid. This can be expanded as follows

$$\xi_{n+1}^{i-n} = \sum_{t=0}^{i-n}\left[n^t\xi_n^{i-n-t}\right] = n^0\xi_n^{i-n} + n^1\xi_n^{i-n-1} + \cdots + n^{i-n}\xi_n^0$$

$$= n^0\xi_{(n-1)+1}^{(i-1)-(n-1)} + n^1\xi_{(n-1)+1}^{(i-2)-(n-1)} + \cdots + n^{i-n}\xi_{(n-1)+1}^{(n-1)-(n-1)}. \qquad \ldots (A2.33)$$

We assume that the function ξ on the right-hand side of the above equation satisfies the statement expressed in Eq. (A2.32). (The value $n-1$ is used with a sense to n, the values $i-1$, $i-2$ etc. are used with a sense to i). Then, we can express Eq. (A2.33) in the following form

$$\xi_{n+1}^{i-n} = n^0 S_{n-1}^{i-1} + n^1 S_{n-1}^{i-2} + \cdots + n^{i-n} S_{n-1}^{n-1}. \qquad \ldots (A2.34)$$

By applying Eq. (A2.15) and then Eq. (A2.14) into the last equation, we find

$$\xi_{n+1}^{i-n} = \frac{(-1)^{n-1}}{(n-1)!}\left\{n^0 Q_{n-1}^{i-1} + n^1 Q_{n-1}^{i-2} + \cdots + n^{i-n} Q_{n-1}^{n-1}\right\} = \frac{(-1)^{n-1}}{(n-1)!}\left\{n^0 \sum_{u=1}^{n-1}\left[(-1)^u\binom{n-1}{u}u^{i-1}\right]\right.$$

$$\left. + n^1 \sum_{u=1}^{n-1}\left[(-1)^u\binom{n-1}{u}u^{i-2}\right] + \cdots + n^{i-n}\sum_{u=1}^{n-1}\left[(-1)^u\binom{n-1}{u}u^{n-1}\right]\right\}$$

$$= \frac{(-1)^{n-1}}{(n-1)!}\sum_{u=1}^{n-1}\left[(-1)^u\binom{n-1}{u}\left(u^{i-1}+nu^{i-2}+\cdots+n^{i-n}u^{n-1}\right)\right].$$

$$\ldots (A2.35)$$

It is evident from the above equation that a geometrical series is expressed within the square brackets. The first element of this series is u^{i-1}, the quotient takes a value n/u, and the number of elements in this series is $i-n+1$. Therefore, the summation is

$$u^{i-1} + nu^{i-2} + \cdots + n^{i-n}u^{n-1} = u^{i-1}\frac{\left(n/u\right)^{i-n+1}-1}{n/u-1} = u^{i-1}\frac{\left(n^{i-n+1}-u^{i-n+1}\right)u}{u^{i-n+1}\left(n-u\right)}$$

$$= \frac{1}{n-u}u^{n-1}\left(n^{i-n+1}-u^{i-n+1}\right) = \frac{n^i}{n-u}\left(\frac{u^{n-1}}{n^{n-1}}-\frac{u^i}{n^i}\right).$$

$$\ldots (A2.36)$$

By applying Eq. (A2.36) into Eq. (A2.35), we find

$$\xi_{n+1}^{i-n} = \frac{(-1)^{n-1}}{(n-1)!}\sum_{u=1}^{n-1}\left[(-1)^u\binom{n-1}{u}\frac{n^i}{n-u}\left(\overbrace{\frac{u^{n-1}}{n^{n-1}}}^{b}-\overbrace{\frac{u^i}{n^i}}^{a}\right)\right]$$

$$= \underbrace{\frac{(-1)^{n-1}}{(n-1)!}\sum_{u=1}^{n-1}\left[(-1)^{u+1}\binom{n-1}{u}\frac{u^i}{n-u}\right]}_{A} - \underbrace{\frac{(-1)^{n-1}}{(n-1)!}\sum_{u=1}^{n-1}\left[(-1)^{u+1}\binom{n-1}{u}\frac{n^{i-n+1}}{n-u}u^{n-1}\right]}_{B}.$$

$$\ldots (A2.37)$$

(It is shown that component 'a' created element A and component 'b' created element B). Rearranging the first element A and applying Eqs. (A2.14) and (A2.15), we can write the following expression

$$A = \frac{(-1)^{n-1}}{(n-1)!}\sum_{u=1}^{n-1}\left[(-1)^{u+1}\frac{(n-1)!}{(n-1-u)!u!}\frac{u^i}{n-u}\right] = \frac{(-1)^{n-1}}{(n-1)!n}\sum_{u=1}^{n-1}\left[(-1)^{u+1}\frac{n!}{(n-u)!u!}u^i\right]$$

$$= \frac{(-1)^n}{n!}\sum_{u=1}^{n-1}\left[(-1)^u\binom{n}{u}u^i\right] = \underbrace{\frac{(-1)^n}{n!}\sum_{u=1}^{n}\left[(-1)^u\binom{n}{u}u^i\right]}_{=Q_n^i} - \frac{(-1)^n}{n!}(-1)^n\binom{n}{n}n^i = S_n^i - \frac{n^i}{n!}.$$

$$\text{... (A2.38)}$$

Now, we rearrange the second element B of the right-hand side of Eq. (A2.37). Applying Eqs. (A2.14) and (A2.22), we find

$$B = \frac{(-1)^{n-1}}{(n-1)!}\frac{n^i}{n^{n-1}n}\sum_{u=1}^{n-1}\left[(-1)^{u+1}\frac{(n-1)!}{(n-1-u)!u!}\frac{n}{(n-u)}u^{n-1}\right]$$

$$= \frac{n^i}{n^{n-1}}\frac{(-1)^n}{n!}\sum_{u=1}^{n-1}\left[(-1)^u\binom{n}{u}u^{n-1}\right]$$

$$= \frac{n^i}{n^{n-1}}\frac{(-1)^n}{n!}\overbrace{\sum_{u=1}^{n}\left[(-1)^u\binom{n}{u}u^{n-1}\right]}^{Q_n^{n-1}=0} - \frac{n^i}{n^{n-1}}\frac{(-1)^n}{n!}(-1)^n\binom{n}{n}n^{n-1} = -\frac{n^i}{n!}.$$

$$\text{... (A2.39)}$$

By applying Eqs. (A2.38) and (A2.39) into Eq. (A2.37), the following expression is obtained

$$\xi_{n+1}^{i-n} = \left(S_n^i - \frac{n^i}{n!}\right) - \left(-\frac{n^i}{n!}\right) = S_n^i. \qquad \text{... (A2.40)}$$

This is identical to the previous statement expressed in Eq. (A2.32). Therefore, we can say that the proof is derived.

Alternative expression for function $(e^x - 1)^n$. By substituting Eqs. (A2.26) and (A2.32) into Eq. (A2.11), we find the following expression

$$\left.\begin{array}{l}\left(e^x-1\right)^1 = \displaystyle\sum_{i=1}^{\infty}\left\{\frac{x^i}{i!}1!\,\xi_{1+1}^{i-1}\right\}, \quad n=1 \\[4mm] \left(e^x-1\right)^n = \displaystyle\sum_{i=1}^{n-1}\left\{\frac{x^i}{i!}n!\,\overset{=0}{S_n^i}\right\} + \sum_{i=n}^{\infty}\left\{\frac{x^i}{i!}n!\,S_n^i\right\} = \sum_{i=n}^{\infty}\left\{\frac{x^i}{i!}n!\,\xi_{n+1}^{i-n}\right\}, \\[4mm] \hspace{8cm} n=2,3,\cdots\end{array}\right\}\left(e^x-1\right)^n = \sum_{i=n}^{\infty}\left\{\frac{x^i}{i!}n!\,\xi_{n+1}^{i-n}\right\},$$

$$n=1,2,\cdots. $$

$$\text{... (A2.41)}$$

Appendix 3
Useful terms and quantities in mechanics

Structural mechanics. Often a force acts on a fibrous assembly and the assembly reacts due to its deformation. This category of behavior is studied in mechanics. There exist minimum two types of tools for solving such problems at the present time – continuum mechanics and structural mechanics.

The continuum mechanics interprets an investigated object as the mechanical continuum. We imagine that the "smallest part" of such an object is elemental (infinitesimal), we determine the parameters of the general element, and then we derive the behaviors of the whole object, usually by using the principle of integration. This "tool" is relatively very universal and it appears to be very effective for objects composed of a huge number of particles such as building materials, metal bodies, etc.

On the other hand, the structural mechanics[1] deals with the specific structure of the investigated object. Based on the geometrical model of structure (often simplified) we determine the mechanical rules, which are valid among finite elements (fibers, etc.) of this body and on this basis we derive the behaviors of the whole object. Evidently, this method of study must use different approaches for different types of fibrous assemblies. Such methodology is not too universal, but, on the other hand, it can respect the individual character of the investigated object more accurately.

Note: The structural approach ("part by part") is used also to solve traditional constructions created according to the designed projects in mechanical engineering and civil engineering. But, these structures are usually relatively simple –they are made together from a few pieces of finite parts with deterministic geometry. In opposite to them, the fibrous assemblies are usually created from hundred to million of fibers whose geometry and mechanical behaviors often possess significantly random character. Therefore, they usually require more sophisticated ways to deal with them[2].

---

1. The term "structural mechanics" of fibrous assemblies was probably coined by Hearle et al. [1].
2. Pan et al. [2] understands the mechanics of fibrous assemblies as a part of "Fiber Material Science" and this branch belongs to the so-called "Soft Matter Physics", established by Pierre-Gilles de Gennes (Nobel award in 1991) [3].

Forces. The basic term in mechanics is the vector quantity of force $\boldsymbol{F}$. If the vector of the force directs outside of our object we usually speak about tensile force, but, if it acts in the opposite direction then we prefer the term compressive force. (Remember, a compressive force can be interpreted as tensile force, but with opposite sign.) If the vector of the force is perpendicular to the tangential plan (at the point of application) we shall speak about normal force (or normal pressure force), but if this vector lies in the mentioned tangential plan we shall speak about tangential force. (Remember, each general force can be decomposed to normal and tangential components.)

Our fibrous object is found to be broken at some value of (normal) tensile force, which we call as breaking force. We understand the breaking force as the maximum force, which can be carried by our fibrous object.

Stresses. Usually a force F acts on some planar area s. In physics, the force related to area is known as stress σ'

$$\sigma' = F/s. \qquad \qquad \ldots (A3.1)$$

In the textile branch, we often use the (normal) force F related to fineness t, which is identical to the so-called specific stress in mechanics according to Equation (1.21), $\sigma = F/t = \sigma'/\rho$, where ρ is the fiber density.

A force can be related to the area at the beginning of the non-deformed body. Then, we speak about engineering (nominal) stress. The same force can be related also to the final area, i.e., deformed area, of the body. Then, we speak about the so-called Cauchy's (real) stress.

Note: For the adjectives for the forces such as, tensile, pressure, normal, tangential, and breaking, we shall use different types of stresses or specific stresses analogically. For example, we will think about breaking stress and call this quantity strength. We will also speak about specific breaking stress and call this quantity specific strength or alternatively tenacity.

Table A3.1 describes some of the common terms that are frequently used.

Deformations. A tensile force results into deformation to the stressed fiber object and the starting length l is extended by elongation Δl. The relative elongation is described as follows

$$\varepsilon = \Delta l/l, \qquad \qquad \ldots (A3.2)$$

where the symbol ε denotes strain.

At break, we call the corresponding elongation as the breaking elongation Δl^* and the corresponding strain as the breaking strain or the breaking extension a.

Table A3.1 Commonly used terms.

State	Type of behavior	Term of quantity	Physical dimensions	Examples of symbols		
				Chapter 1	Chapter 5	Chapter 6
Before rupture	Action of force	Force(+)	[N]	F	F	F
		Engineering Stress(+)	[Pa]	σ^*	σ^*	σ'
		Cauchy's Stress(+)		–	σ	–
		Engineering Specific Stress(+)	[N tex⁻¹]	σ	–	σ
		Cauchy's Specific Stress(+)		–	–	–
		Engineering Pressure	[Pa]	–	$p, -\sigma^*$	–
		Cauchy's Pressure		–	$-\sigma$	–
	Deformation	Elongation	[mm]	–	$\Delta l, \lambda$	
		Strain	[1]	–	ε	ε
At rupture	Action of force	Breaking Force(+)	[N]	–	–	F^*, P, P
		(Engineering) Strength(+)	[Pa]	–	–	σ'^*
		(Engineering) Specific Strength(+), or Tenacity(+)	[N tex⁻¹]	–	–	σ^*
	Deformation	Breaking Elongation	[mm]	–	–	Δl^*
		Breaking Strain(+), eventually Extension(+)	[1]	–	–	A

(+) It is used also with suitable adjective, e.g. tensile, compression, normal, tangential, etc.

References

1. Hearle, J. W. S., Grosberg, P., and Backer, S. (1969). *Structural Mechanics of Fibers, Yarns, and Fabrics*, vol. 1, Wiley Interscience, New York.
2. Pan, N., He, J.-H., and Yu, J. (2007). Fibrous materials as soft matter, *Textile Research Journal*, **77**(4), 205–213.
3. Gennes, P.-G.d. (1997). Soft Matter: Nobel Lecture, December 9, 1991, in "Nobel Lectures, Physics," vol. 1991–1995, World Scientific Publishing, Singapore.

Derivative of deformation energy $dE(\delta,\xi)/d\mu$

Function $\Phi(\mu)$. Using Eq. (5.64) the following expression is valid to write for the derivative of deformation energy $E(\delta,\ \xi)$ with respect to the packing density μ

$$\frac{dE(\delta,\xi)}{d\mu} = \frac{k_F V}{q\pi d^2} \int_{-\pi/2}^{\pi/2} \frac{d}{d\mu}\left\{\frac{1-h_0/\delta_0}{\left[(h_0/\delta_0)\delta - \xi\gamma d\right]^2}\right\} f(\psi_1)\,d\psi_1 \,. \qquad \dots \text{(A4.1)}$$

Let us designate the expression mentioned within the curly brackets by the symbol $\Phi(\mu)$ as follows

$$\Phi(\mu) = \frac{1-h_0/\delta_0}{\left[(h_0/\delta_0)\delta - \xi\gamma d\right]^2}\,. \qquad \dots \text{(A4.2)}$$

This function expresses packing density implicitly against two variables δ and ξ. The relation between δ and μ is shown in Eq. (5.55) and the relation between ξ and μ is mentioned in Eq. (5.57). The following equation is therefore valid

$$\frac{d\Phi(\mu)}{d\mu} = \frac{\partial\Phi(\mu)}{\partial\delta}\frac{d\delta}{d\mu} + \frac{\partial\Phi(\mu)}{\partial\xi}\frac{d\xi}{d\mu}\,. \qquad \dots \text{(A4.3)}$$

Partial derivatives. It follows from Eq. (A4.2) that

$$\frac{\partial\Phi(\mu)}{\partial\delta} = \frac{\partial}{\partial\delta}\left\{\frac{1-h_0/\delta_0}{\left[(h_0/\delta_0)\delta - \xi\gamma d\right]^2}\right\} = (1-h_0/\delta_0)\frac{(-2)(h_0/\delta_0)}{\left[(h_0/\delta_0)\delta - \xi\gamma d\right]^3}\,.$$

$$\dots \text{(A4.4)}$$

From Eq. (5.55) we obtain

$$\frac{d\delta}{d\mu} = \frac{d}{d\mu}\left[\frac{\gamma d}{1-e^{-\frac{8\mu\gamma}{\pi}J(\psi_1)}}\right] = \gamma d\frac{(-1)\left[-e^{-\frac{8\mu\gamma}{\pi}J(\psi_1)}\right]\left[-\frac{8\gamma}{\pi}J(\psi_1)\right]}{\left[1-e^{-\frac{8\mu\gamma}{\pi}J(\psi_1)}\right]^2}$$

$$= \frac{-1}{\gamma d} \frac{(\gamma d)^2}{\left[1 - e^{-\frac{8\mu\gamma}{\pi}J(\psi_1)}\right]^2} e^{-\frac{8\mu\gamma}{\pi}J(\psi_1)} \frac{8\gamma}{\pi} J(\psi_1) = \frac{-8}{\pi d} J(\psi_1)\delta^2 \left(1 - \frac{\gamma d}{\delta}\right).$$

$$\ldots (A4.5)$$

So, from the last two equations it is valid to write that

$$\frac{\partial \Phi(\mu)}{\partial \delta} \frac{d\delta}{d\mu} = (1 - h_0/\delta_0) \frac{(-2)(h_0/\delta_0)}{\left[(h_0/\delta_0)\delta - \xi\gamma d\right]^3} \frac{-8}{\pi d} J(\psi_1)\delta^2 \left(1 - \frac{\gamma d}{\delta}\right)$$

$$= \frac{16 J(\psi_1)}{\pi d} \frac{(1 - h_0/\delta_0)}{(h_0/\delta_0)^2} \frac{(h_0/\delta_0)^3}{\left[(h_0/\delta_0) - \xi\frac{\gamma d}{\delta}\right]^3 \delta} \left(1 - \frac{\gamma d}{\delta}\right)$$

$$\ldots (A4.6)$$

$$= \frac{16 J(\psi_1)}{\pi d^2} \frac{(1 - h_0/\delta_0)}{(h_0/\delta_0)^2} \frac{1 - \frac{\gamma d}{\delta}}{\left(1 - \xi\frac{\gamma d}{\delta}\frac{\delta_0}{h_0}\right)^3} \frac{d}{\delta}.$$

The following expression is evident from Eq. (A4.2)

$$\frac{\partial \Phi(\mu)}{\partial \xi} = \frac{\partial}{\partial \xi} \left\{ \frac{1 - h_0/\delta_0}{\left[(h_0/\delta_0)\delta - \xi\gamma d\right]^2} \right\} = (1 - h_0/\delta_0) \frac{(-2)(-\gamma d)}{\left[(h_0/\delta_0)\delta - \xi\gamma d\right]^3}$$

$$= 2 \frac{(1 - h_0/\delta_0)\gamma d}{\delta^3 (h_0/\delta_0)^3 \left(1 - \xi\frac{\gamma d}{\delta}\frac{\delta_0}{h_0}\right)^3} = \frac{2}{d^2} \frac{1 - h_0/\delta_0}{(h_0/\delta_0)^2} \frac{1}{\delta} \frac{h_0}{\delta_0} \frac{\frac{\gamma d}{\delta}}{\left(1 - \xi\frac{\gamma d}{\delta}\frac{\delta_0}{h_0}\right)^3} \frac{d}{\delta},$$

$$\ldots (A4.7)$$

so that

$$\frac{\partial \Phi(\mu)}{\partial \xi} \frac{d\xi}{d\mu} = 2 \frac{(1 - h_0/\delta_0)\gamma d}{\delta^3 (h_0/\delta_0)^3 \left(1 - \xi\frac{\gamma d}{\delta}\frac{\delta_0}{h_0}\right)^3}$$

$$= \frac{2}{d^2} \frac{1 - h_0/\delta_0}{(h_0/\delta_0)^2} \frac{1}{\delta} \frac{h_0}{\delta_0} \frac{\frac{\gamma d}{\delta}}{\left(1 - \xi\frac{\gamma d}{\delta}\frac{\delta_0}{h_0}\right)^3} \frac{d}{\delta} \frac{d\xi}{d\mu}.$$

$$\ldots (A4.8)$$

Using Eqs. (A3.6) and (A3.8) in Eq. (A3.3), we obtain

$$\frac{d\Phi(\mu)}{d\mu} = \frac{16J(\psi_1)}{\pi d^2} \frac{(1-h_0/\delta_0)}{(h_0/\delta_0)^2} \frac{1-\dfrac{\gamma d}{\delta}}{\left(1-\xi\dfrac{\gamma d}{\delta}\dfrac{\delta_0}{h_0}\right)^3} \frac{d}{\delta} + \frac{2}{d^2} \frac{1-h_0/\delta_0}{(h_0/\delta_0)^2} \frac{1}{\dfrac{\delta}{d}\dfrac{h_0}{\delta_0}} \frac{\dfrac{\gamma d}{\delta}}{\left(1-\xi\dfrac{\gamma d}{\delta}\dfrac{\delta_0}{h_0}\right)^3} \frac{d}{\delta}\frac{d\xi}{d\mu}$$

$$= \frac{2}{d^2} \frac{(1-h_0/\delta_0)}{(h_0/\delta_0)^2} \frac{d}{\delta} \frac{1}{\left(1-\xi\dfrac{\gamma d}{\delta}\dfrac{\delta_0}{h_0}\right)^3} \left[\frac{8J(\psi_1)}{\pi}\left(1-\frac{\gamma d}{\delta}\right) + \frac{1}{\dfrac{\delta}{d}\dfrac{h_0}{\delta_0}}\frac{\gamma d}{\delta}\frac{d\xi}{d\mu}\right]$$

$$= \frac{16J(\psi_1)}{\pi d^2} \frac{(1-h_0/\delta_0)}{(h_0/\delta_0)^2} \frac{d}{\delta} \frac{1}{\left(1-\xi\dfrac{\gamma d}{\delta}\dfrac{\delta_0}{h_0}\right)^3} \left[\left(1-\frac{\gamma d}{\delta}\right) + \frac{\pi}{8J(\psi_1)}\frac{1}{\dfrac{\delta}{d}\dfrac{h_0}{\delta_0}}\frac{\gamma d}{\delta}\frac{d\xi}{d\mu}\right]$$

$$= \frac{16J(\psi_1)}{\pi d^2} \frac{(1-h_0/\delta_0)}{(h_0/\delta_0)^2} \frac{d}{\delta} \frac{1-\dfrac{\gamma d}{\delta}\left(1-\dfrac{\pi}{8J(\psi_1)}\dfrac{1}{\dfrac{\delta}{d}\dfrac{h_0}{\delta_0}}\dfrac{d\xi}{d\mu}\right)}{\left(1-\xi\dfrac{\gamma d}{\delta}\dfrac{\delta_0}{h_0}\right)^3}.$$

$$\ldots (A4.9)$$

Derivative of deformation energy. Applying Eqs. (A4.2) and (A4.9) into Eq. (A4.1), we can write

$$\frac{dE(\delta,\xi)}{d\mu} = \frac{k_F V}{q\pi d^2} \int_{-\pi/2}^{\pi/2} \frac{d\Phi(\mu)}{d\mu} f(\psi_1) d\psi_1$$

$$= \frac{k_F V}{q\pi d^2} \int_{-\pi/2}^{\pi/2} \left\{ \frac{16J(\psi_1)}{\pi d^2} \frac{(1-h_0/\delta_0)}{(h_0/\delta_0)^2} \frac{d}{\delta} \frac{1-\dfrac{\gamma d}{\delta}\left(1-\dfrac{\pi}{8J(\psi_1)}\dfrac{1}{\dfrac{\delta}{d}\dfrac{h_0}{\delta_0}}\dfrac{d\xi}{d\mu}\right)}{\left(1-\xi\dfrac{\gamma d}{\delta}\dfrac{\delta_0}{h_0}\right)^3} \right\} f(\psi_1) d\psi_1$$

$$\frac{dE(\delta,\xi)}{d\mu} = \frac{16k_F V}{q\pi^2 d^4} \int_{-\pi/2}^{\pi/2} \left\{ J(\psi_1) \frac{(1-h_0/\delta_0)}{(h_0/\delta_0)^2} \frac{d}{\delta} \frac{1-\dfrac{\gamma d}{\delta}\left(1-\dfrac{\pi}{8J(\psi_1)}\dfrac{1}{\dfrac{\delta}{d}\dfrac{h_0}{\delta_0}}\dfrac{d\xi}{d\mu}\right)}{\left(1-\xi\dfrac{\gamma d}{\delta}\dfrac{\delta_0}{h_0}\right)^3} \right\} f(\psi_1) d\psi_1.$$

$$\ldots (A4.10)$$

Angular utilization coefficient of special alternative to simple planar bundle

Introductory relation. At first, let us rearrange Eq. (7.142) as follows

$$\eta_a = \int_0^{\pi/2} \left[\frac{1}{\pi} \frac{C}{C^2 - (C^2-1)\cos^2(\vartheta+\alpha)} + \frac{1}{\pi} \frac{C}{C^2 - (C^2-1)\cos^2(\vartheta-\alpha)} \right] \cos^4\vartheta\, d\vartheta$$

$$= \int_0^{\pi/2} \frac{1}{\pi} \frac{C\cos^4\vartheta\, d\vartheta}{C^2 - (C^2-1)\cos^2(\vartheta+\alpha)} + \int_0^{\pi/2} \frac{1}{\pi} \frac{C\cos^4\vartheta\, d\vartheta}{C^2 - (C^2-1)\cos^2(\vartheta-\alpha)}$$

(Substitution: $x = \vartheta + \alpha$, $dx = d\vartheta$) (Substitution: $y = -\vartheta + \alpha$, $dy = -d\vartheta$)

$$= \int_\alpha^{\alpha+\pi/2} \frac{1}{\pi} \frac{C\cos^4(x-\alpha)\, dx}{C^2 - (C^2-1)\cos^2 x} + \int_\alpha^{\alpha-\pi/2} \frac{1}{\pi} \frac{C\cos^4(-y+\alpha)(-dy)}{C^2 - (C^2-1)\cos^2(-y)}$$

$$= \int_\alpha^{\alpha+\pi/2} \frac{1}{\pi} \frac{C\cos^4(x-\alpha)\, dx}{C^2 - (C^2-1)\cos^2 x} \cdot - \int_\alpha^{\alpha-\pi/2} \frac{1}{\pi} \frac{C\cos^4(y-\alpha)\, dy}{C^2 - (C^2-1)\cos^2 y}$$

$$= \int_\alpha^{\alpha+\pi/2} \frac{1}{\pi} \frac{C\cos^4(x-\alpha)\, dx}{C^2 - (C^2-1)\cos^2 x} + \int_{\alpha-\pi/2}^{\alpha} \frac{1}{\pi} \frac{C\cos^4(y-\alpha)\, dy}{C^2 - (C^2-1)\cos^2 y}.$$

$$\dots \text{(A5.1)}$$

We rename the integrating variables in both the integrals by the symbol ψ. Thus

$$\eta_a = \int_\alpha^{\alpha+\pi/2} \frac{1}{\pi} \frac{C\cos^4(\psi-\alpha)\, d\psi}{C^2 - (C^2-1)\cos^2\psi} + \int_{\alpha-\pi/2}^{\alpha} \frac{1}{\pi} \frac{C\cos^4(\psi-\alpha)\, d\psi}{C^2 - (C^2-1)\cos^2\psi}$$

$$= \int_{\alpha-\pi/2}^{\alpha+\pi/2} \frac{1}{\pi} \frac{C\cos^4(\psi-\alpha)\, d\psi}{C^2 - (C^2-1)\cos^2\psi}. \qquad \dots \text{(A5.2)}$$

Because the integral function is periodic with a period π and the difference between the lower and upper limits is also equal to π, we can write

$$\eta_a = \int_{\alpha-\pi/2}^{\alpha+\pi/2} \frac{1}{\pi} \frac{C\cos^4(\psi-\alpha)\,d\psi}{C^2-(C^2-1)\cos^2\psi} = \int_{-\pi/2}^{\pi/2} \frac{1}{\pi} \frac{C\cos^4(\psi-\alpha)\,d\psi}{C^2-(C^2-1)\cos^2\psi}. \quad \ldots (A5.3)$$

The expression $\cos^4(\psi-\alpha)$ as mentioned in the numerator of the last expression can be rearranged[1] as follows

$$\cos^4(\psi-\alpha)=(\cos\psi\cos\alpha+\sin\psi\sin\alpha)^4 = \cos^4\psi\cos^4\alpha$$
$$+4\cos^3\psi\cos^3\alpha\sin\psi\sin\alpha$$
$$+6\cos^2\psi\cos^2\alpha\sin^2\psi\sin^2\alpha$$
$$+4\cos\psi\cos\alpha\sin^3\psi\sin^3\alpha+\sin^4\psi\sin^4\alpha \quad \ldots (A5.4)$$
$$= \cos^4\alpha\left(\cos^4\psi\right)$$
$$+4\cos^3\alpha\sin\alpha\left(\cos^3\psi\sin\psi\right)$$
$$+6\cos^2\alpha\sin^2\alpha\left(\cos^2\psi\sin^2\psi\right)$$
$$+4\cos\alpha\sin^3\alpha\left(\cos\psi\sin^3\psi\right)$$
$$+\left(\sin^4\psi\right)\sin^4\alpha.$$

The next expression can be obtained after substituting Eq. (A5.4) to Eq. (A5.3)

$$\eta_a = \frac{C}{\pi}\cos^4\alpha \int_{-\pi/2}^{\pi/2} \frac{\cos^4\psi\,d\psi}{C^2-(C^2-1)\cos^2\psi}$$
$$+\frac{C}{\pi}4\cos^3\alpha\sin\alpha \int_{-\pi/2}^{\pi/2} \frac{\cos^3\psi\sin\psi\,d\psi}{C^2-(C^2-1)\cos^2\psi}$$
$$+\frac{C}{\pi}6\cos^2\alpha\sin^2\alpha \int_{-\pi/2}^{\pi/2} \frac{\cos^2\psi\sin^2\psi\,d\psi}{C^2-(C^2-1)\cos^2\psi}$$
$$+\frac{C}{\pi}4\cos\alpha\sin^3\alpha \int_{-\pi/2}^{\pi/2} \frac{\cos\psi\sin^3\psi\,d\psi}{C^2-(C^2-1)\cos^2\psi} \quad \ldots (A5.5)$$
$$+\frac{C}{\pi}\sin^4\alpha \int_{-\pi/2}^{\pi/2} \frac{\sin^4\psi\,d\psi}{C^2-(C^2-1)\cos^2\psi}.$$

The following equalities can be used in further derivations

$$C^2-(C^2-1)\cos^2\psi = (C^2-1)\sin^2\psi+1 = C^2\sin^2\psi+\cos^2\psi. \quad \ldots (A5.6)$$

---

1. Here the well-known binomial theorem is used.

Partial integrals. It is necessary to prepare some partial integrals for the solution of five definite integrals stated in Eq. (A5.5). We use the following symbols in the next expressions:

- The non-defined integrals have the symbol I with a numerical subscript (I_1, I_2, etc.); the final constant of integration is not written.

- The symbol $\left[I\right]_{-\pi/2}^{\pi/2}$ indicates a definite integral in relation to an indefinite integral I with lower limit $-\pi/2$ and upper limit $\pi/2$.

- The symbol $\left[f(\psi)\right]_{-\pi/2}^{\pi/2}$ of a function $f(\psi)$ represents the difference $f(\pi/2) - f(-\pi/2)$.

Then the following relations are valid.

$$I_1 = \int \frac{d\psi}{C^2 - (C^2-1)\cos^2\psi} = \int \frac{d\psi}{C^2\sin^2\psi + \cos^2\psi} = \int \frac{1}{C^2\tan^2\psi + 1}\frac{d\psi}{\cos^2\psi}$$

(Substitution: $\tan\psi = x$, $d\psi/\cos^2\psi = dx$)

$$= \int \frac{dx}{C^2 x^2 + 1} = \frac{1}{C}\int \frac{dt}{t^2+1} = \frac{1}{C}\arctan t = \frac{1}{C}\arctan(Cx) = \frac{1}{C}\arctan(C\tan\psi).$$

(Substitution: $t = Cx$, $dt = Cdx$.)

... (A5.7a)

$$\left[I_1\right]_{-\pi/2}^{\pi/2} = \lim_{\psi\to\pi/2}\left[\frac{1}{C}\arctan(C\tan\psi)\right] - \lim_{\psi\to-\pi/2}\left[\frac{1}{C}\arctan(C\tan\psi)\right]$$

$$= \frac{\pi}{2C} - \left(-\frac{\pi}{2C}\right) = \frac{\pi}{C}.$$

... (A5.7b)

$$I_2 = \int \frac{\cos^2\psi\, d\psi}{C^2 - (C^2-1)\cos^2\psi} = \int \frac{\cos^2\psi\, d\psi}{C^2\sin^2\psi + \cos^2\psi}$$

$$= \int \frac{(C^2-1)\cos^2\psi\, d\psi}{(C^2-1)(C^2\sin^2\psi + \cos^2\psi)} = \int \frac{C^2(1-\sin^2\psi) - \cos^2\psi}{(C^2-1)(C^2\sin^2\psi + \cos^2\psi)}\, d\psi$$

$$= \int \frac{C^2 - (C^2\sin^2\psi + \cos^2\psi)}{(C^2-1)(C^2\sin^2\psi + \cos^2\psi)}\, d\psi$$

$$= \frac{C^2}{C^2-1}\int \frac{d\psi}{C^2\sin^2\psi + \cos^2\psi} - \frac{1}{C^2-1}\int d\psi = \frac{C^2}{C^2-1}I_1 - \frac{\psi}{C^2-1}.$$

... (A5.8a)

$$\left[I_2\right]_{-\pi/2}^{\pi/2} = \frac{C^2}{C^2-1}\left[I_1\right]_{-\pi/2}^{\pi/2} - \left[\frac{\psi}{C^2-1}\right]_{-\pi/2}^{\pi/2} = \frac{C^2}{C^2-1}\left[I_1\right]_{-\pi/2}^{\pi/2} - \left[\frac{\frac{\pi}{2}}{C^2-1}\right] + \left[\frac{-\frac{\pi}{2}}{C^2-1}\right]$$

$$= \frac{C^2}{C^2-1}\left[I_1\right]_{-\pi/2}^{\pi/2} - \frac{\pi}{C^2-1} = \frac{C^2}{C^2-1}\frac{\pi}{C} - \frac{\pi}{C^2-1} = \pi\frac{C-1}{C^2-1} = \frac{\pi}{C+1}.$$

$$\ldots \text{(A5.8b)}$$

$$I_3 = \int\frac{\cos\psi\,\sin\psi\,d\psi}{C^2 - \left(C^2-1\right)\cos^2\psi}$$

$$= \frac{1}{C^2-1}\int\frac{\cos\psi\,\sin\psi\,d\psi}{\dfrac{C^2}{C^2-1} - \cos^2\psi} = \frac{1}{C^2-1}\frac{1}{2}\int\frac{dt}{t} = \frac{1}{2\left(C^2-1\right)}\ln|t|$$

$$\text{(Substitution: } \frac{C^2}{C^2-1} - \cos^2\psi = t,\ \cos\psi\,\sin\psi\,d\psi = \frac{dt}{2}.\text{)}$$

$$= \frac{1}{2\left(C^2-1\right)}\ln\left(\frac{C^2}{C^2-1} - \cos^2\psi\right).$$

$$\ldots \text{(A5.9a)}[2]$$

$$\left[I_3\right]_{-\pi/2}^{\pi/2} = \left[\frac{1}{2\left(C^2-1\right)}\ln\left(\frac{C^2}{C^2-1} - \cos^2\psi\right)\right]_{-\pi/2}^{\pi/2}$$

$$= \frac{1}{2\left(C^2-1\right)}\left[\ln\left(\frac{C^2}{C^2-1} - \cos^2\frac{\pi}{2}\right) - \ln\left(\frac{C^2}{C^2-1} - \cos^2\frac{-\pi}{2}\right)\right]$$

$$= \frac{1}{2\left(C^2-1\right)}\left[\ln\left(\frac{C^2}{C^2-1}\right) - \ln\left(\frac{C^2}{C^2-1}\right)\right] = 0.$$

$$\ldots \text{(A5.9b)}$$

$$I_4 = \int\frac{\cos^3\psi\,\sin\psi\,d\psi}{C^2 - \left(C^2-1\right)\cos^2\psi} = \frac{1}{C^2-1}\int\frac{\cos\psi\,\sin\psi}{\dfrac{C^2}{C^2-1} - \cos^2\psi}\cos^2\psi\,d\psi$$

$$= \frac{1}{C^2-1}\int\frac{\cos\psi\,\sin\psi}{\dfrac{C^2}{C^2-1} - \cos^2\psi}\left[\frac{C^2}{C^2-1} - \left(\frac{C^2}{C^2-1} - \cos^2\psi\right)\right]d\psi$$

---

2. Because $C > 1$ it must be valid that $t > 0$ so that a symbol for an absolute value is not necessary.

$$= \frac{C^2}{C^2-1} \int \frac{\cos\psi \sin\psi \, d\psi}{C^2-\left(C^2-1\right)\cos^2\psi} - \frac{1}{C^2-1}\int \cos\psi \sin\psi \, d\psi$$

$$= \frac{C^2}{C^2-1}I_3 + \frac{1}{2\left(C^2-1\right)}\int\left(-2\cos\psi\sin\psi\right)d\psi = \frac{C^2}{C^2-1}I_3 + \frac{\cos^2\psi}{2\left(C^2-1\right)}.$$

$$\ldots \text{(A5.10a)}$$

$$\left[I_4\right]_{-\pi/2}^{\pi/2} = \frac{C^2}{C^2-1}\left[I_3\right]_{-\pi/2}^{\pi/2} + \left[\frac{\cos^2\psi}{2\left(C^2-1\right)}\right]_{-\pi/2}^{\pi/2}$$

$$= \frac{C^2}{C^2-1}\left[I_3\right]_{-\pi/2}^{\pi/2} + \left[\frac{\cos^2\dfrac{\pi}{2}}{2\left(C^2-1\right)}\right] - \left[\frac{\cos^2\dfrac{-\pi}{2}}{2\left(C^2-1\right)}\right] = \frac{C^2}{C^2-1}\left[I_3\right]_{-\pi/2}^{\pi/2}$$

$$= \frac{C^2}{C^2-1}0 = 0.$$

$$\ldots \text{(A5.10b)}$$

$$I_5 = \int \frac{\cos\psi \sin^3\psi \, d\psi}{C^2-\left(C^2-1\right)\cos^2\psi} = \int \frac{\left(1-\cos^2\psi\right)\sin\psi\cos\psi \, d\psi}{C^2-\left(C^2-1\right)\cos^2\psi}$$

$$= \int \frac{\sin\psi\cos\psi \, d\psi}{C^2-\left(C^2-1\right)\cos^2\psi} - \int \frac{\sin\psi\cos^3\psi \, d\psi}{C^2-\left(C^2-1\right)\cos^2\psi} = I_3 - I_4. \quad \ldots \text{(A5.11a)}$$

$$\left[I_5\right]_{-\pi/2}^{\pi/2} = \left[I_3\right]_{-\pi/2}^{\pi/2} + \left[I_4\right]_{-\pi/2}^{\pi/2} = 0-0 = 0. \qquad \ldots \text{(A5.11b)}$$

$$I_6 = \int \frac{\cos^2\psi \sin^2\psi \, d\psi}{C^2-\left(C^2-1\right)\cos^2\psi} = \frac{1}{C^2-1}\int \frac{\left(C^2-1\right)\cos^2\psi\sin^2\psi \, d\psi}{C^2\sin^2\psi+\cos^2\psi}$$

$$= \frac{1}{C^2-1}\int \frac{\cos^2\psi\left(C^2\sin^2\psi-\sin^2\psi\right)d\psi}{C^2\sin^2\psi+\cos^2\psi}$$

$$= \frac{1}{C^2-1}\int \frac{\cos^2\psi\left(C^2\sin^2\psi-1+\cos^2\psi\right)d\psi}{C^2\sin^2\psi+\cos^2\psi}$$

$$= \frac{1}{C^2-1}\int \frac{\cos^2\psi\left(C^2\sin^2\psi+\cos^2\psi\right)-\cos^2\psi}{C^2\sin^2\psi+\cos^2\psi}d\psi \qquad \ldots \text{(A5.12)}$$

$$= \frac{1}{C^2-1}\int \cos^2\psi \, d\psi - \frac{1}{C^2-1}\int \frac{\cos^2\psi}{C^2\sin^2\psi+\cos^2\psi}d\psi.$$

Nevertheless, it is valid to write that

$$\int \cos^2 \psi \, d\psi = \sin \psi \cos \psi + \int \sin^2 \psi \, d\psi = \sin \psi \cos \psi + \int \left(1 - \cos^2 \psi\right) d\psi$$

$$\left(\begin{array}{l} \text{Integration by parts: } u' = \cos \psi, \quad v = \cos \psi, \\ \qquad\qquad\qquad\quad u = \sin \psi, \quad v' = -\sin \psi. \end{array}\right)$$

$$= \sin \psi \cos \psi + \int d\psi - \int \cos^2 \psi \, d\psi$$

$$= \sin \psi \cos \psi + \psi - \int \cos^2 \psi \, d\psi,$$

$$2 \int \cos^2 \psi \, d\psi = \sin \psi \cos \psi + \psi, \qquad \int \cos^2 \psi \, d\psi = \frac{\sin \psi \cos \psi}{2} + \frac{\psi}{2}.$$
$$\ldots (A5.13)$$

Substituting the expressions mentioned in Eqs. (A5.8b) and (A5.13) to Eq. (A5.12), we find

$$I_6 = \frac{\sin \psi \cos \psi}{2(C^2 - 1)} + \frac{\psi}{2(C^2 - 1)} - \frac{1}{C^2 - 1} I_2. \qquad \ldots (A5.14a)$$

$$\left[I_6\right]_{-\pi/2}^{\pi/2} = \left[\frac{\sin \psi \cos \psi}{2(C^2 - 1)} + \frac{\psi}{2(C^2 - 1)}\right]_{-\pi/2}^{\pi/2} - \frac{1}{C^2 - 1}\left[I_2\right]_{-\pi/2}^{\pi/2}$$

$$= \left[\frac{\sin \dfrac{\pi}{2} \cos \dfrac{\pi}{2}}{2(C^2 - 1)} + \frac{\dfrac{\pi}{2}}{2(C^2 - 1)}\right] - \left[\frac{\sin \dfrac{-\pi}{2} \cos \dfrac{-\pi}{2}}{2(C^2 - 1)} + \frac{\dfrac{-\pi}{2}}{2(C^2 - 1)}\right]$$

$$- \frac{1}{C^2 - 1}\left[I_2\right]_{-\pi/2}^{\pi/2} = \frac{\pi}{2(C^2 - 1)} - \frac{1}{C^2 - 1}\left[I_2\right]_{-\pi/2}^{\pi/2}$$

$$= \frac{\pi}{2(C^2 - 1)} - \frac{1}{C^2 - 1}\frac{\pi}{C + 1} = \frac{\pi}{2(C^2 - 1)}\left[1 - \frac{2}{C + 1}\right]$$

$$= \frac{\pi}{2(C^2 - 1)}\frac{(C - 1)}{(C + 1)} = \frac{\pi}{2(C + 1)^2}.$$

$$\ldots (A5.14b)$$

Further

$$I_7 = \int \frac{\cos^4 \psi \, d\psi}{C^2 - (C^2-1)\cos^2 \psi} = \int \frac{\cos^4 \psi \, d\psi}{C^2 \sin^2 \psi + \cos^2 \psi} =$$

$$= \int \frac{\cos^2 \psi (1-\sin^2 \psi) \, d\psi}{C^2 \sin^2 \psi + \cos^2 \psi} \qquad \qquad \dots \text{(A5.15a)}$$

$$= \int \frac{\cos^2 \psi \, d\psi}{C^2 \sin^2 \psi + \cos^2 \psi} - \int \frac{\cos^2 \psi \sin^2 \psi \, d\psi}{C^2 \sin^2 \psi + \cos^2 \psi} = I_2 - I_6.$$

$$[I_7]_{-\pi/2}^{\pi/2} = [I_2]_{-\pi/2}^{\pi/2} - [I_6]_{-\pi/2}^{\pi/2} = \frac{\pi}{C+1} - \frac{\pi}{2(C+1)^2} = \pi \frac{2(C+1)-1}{2(C+1)^2} = \frac{\pi(2C+1)}{2(C+1)^2}.$$

$$\dots \text{(A5.15b)}$$

$$I_8 = \int \frac{\sin^4 \psi \, d\psi}{C^2 - (C^2-1)\cos^2 \psi} = \int \frac{(1-\cos^2 \psi)^2 \, d\psi}{C^2 \sin^2 \psi + \cos^2 \psi} = \int \frac{(1-2\cos^2 \psi + \cos^4 \psi) \, d\psi}{C^2 \sin^2 \psi + \cos^2 \psi}$$

$$= \int \frac{d\psi}{C^2 \sin^2 \psi + \cos^2 \psi} - 2\int \frac{\cos^2 \psi \, d\psi}{C^2 \sin^2 \psi + \cos^2 \psi} + \int \frac{\cos^4 \psi \, d\psi}{C^2 \sin^2 \psi + \cos^2 \psi}$$

$$= I_1 - 2I_2 + I_7.$$

$$\dots \text{(A5.16a)}$$

$$[I_8]_{-\pi/2}^{\pi/2} = [I_1]_{-\pi/2}^{\pi/2} - 2[I_2]_{-\pi/2}^{\pi/2} + [I_7]_{-\pi/2}^{\pi/2} = \frac{\pi}{C} - 2\frac{\pi}{C+1} + \frac{\pi(2C+1)}{2(C+1)^2} =$$

$$= \pi \frac{2(C+1)^2 - 4C(C+1) + C(2C+1)}{2C(C+1)^2}$$

$$= \pi \frac{2C^2 + 4C + 2 - 4C^2 - 4C + 2C^2 + C}{2C(C+1)^2} = \frac{\pi(C+2)}{2C(C+1)^2}.$$

$$\dots \text{(A5.16b)}$$

Angular utilization coefficient. Equations (A5.10b) and (A5.11b), and equations from (A5.14b) to (A5.16b) determine five integrals as mentioned in Eq. (A5.5). So, we can rearrange the angular utilization coefficient as follows

$$\eta_a = \frac{C}{\pi}\cos^4 \alpha [I_7]_{-\pi/2}^{\pi/2} + \frac{C}{\pi}4\cos^3 \alpha \sin \alpha [I_4]_{-\pi/2}^{\pi/2} + \frac{C}{\pi}6\cos^2 \alpha \sin^2 \alpha [I_6]_{-\pi/2}^{\pi/2}$$

$$+ \frac{C}{\pi}4\cos \alpha \sin^3 \alpha [I_5]_{-\pi/2}^{\pi/2} + \frac{C}{\pi}\sin^4 \alpha [I_8]_{-\pi/2}^{\pi/2}$$

$$= \frac{C}{\pi} \cos^4 \alpha \frac{\pi(2C+1)}{2(C+1)^2} + \frac{C}{\pi} 4\cos^3 \alpha \sin \alpha \cdot 0 + \frac{C}{\pi} 6\cos^2 \alpha \sin^2 \alpha \frac{\pi}{2(C+1)^2}$$

$$+ \frac{C}{\pi} 4\cos \alpha \sin^3 \alpha \cdot 0 + \frac{C}{\pi} \sin^4 \alpha \frac{\pi(C+2)}{2C(C+1)^2}$$

$$= \frac{C}{\pi} \cos^4 \alpha \frac{\pi(2C+1)}{2(C+1)^2} + \frac{C}{\pi} 6\cos^2 \alpha \sin^2 \alpha \frac{\pi}{2(C+1)^2} + \frac{C}{\pi} \sin^4 \alpha \frac{\pi(C+2)}{2C(C+1)^2}$$

$$= \frac{C}{2(C+1)^2} \left[(2C+1)\cos^4 \alpha + 6\cos^2 \alpha \sin^2 \alpha + \frac{(C+2)}{C} \sin^4 \alpha \right].$$

$$\ldots \text{(A5.17)}$$

Index